Rx752

A HISTORY OF PHYSICS
in its Elementary Branches (through 1925): Including the Evolution of Physical Laboratories

By Florian Cajori, Ph.D.
*Late Professor of the History of Mathematics
in the University of California*

Revised and Enlarged Edition

DOVER PUBLICATIONS, INC.
NEW YORK

This new Dover edition, first published in 1962, is an unabridged and unaltered republication of the last revised (1929) edition of the work originally published by the Macmillan Company.

Standard Book Number: 486-20970-9
Library of Congress Catalog Card Number: 62-3998

Manufactured in the United States of America
Dover Publications, Inc.
180 Varick Street
New York, N. Y. 10014

PREFACE TO THE REVISED EDITION

SINCE the first appearance of this History, many things have happened in the development of physics. To young students of science the discovery of radioactivity and the introduction of the electron are not happenings of their own time, but are events of the past fully as much as are Galileo's experiments on falling bodies and Newton's law of gravitation. For this reason it is desirable to present to the younger students the historic outline which to the older generation is part and parcel of its own intellectual life and experience.

The task of describing the principal achievements in physics of the present century has been a difficult one. Experiments and hypotheses which seem important now may appear insignificant later. On recent events we lack perspective. The historic presentation of recent movements must necessarily be of only transient value. But a near view is better perhaps than no view at all.

The revision of this book does not consist simply in the annexation of new material relating to the researches made in the present century. Many additions and alterations have been made in the earlier part of this History.

I am indebted to Dr. V. F. Lenzen of the University of California for valuable suggestions and for assistance in the reading of proof.

FLORIAN CAJORI.

University of California,
December, 1928.

PREFACE TO THE FIRST EDITION

THIS history is intended mainly for the use of students and teachers of physics. The writer is convinced that some attention to the history of a science helps to make it attractive, and that the general view of the development of the human intellect, obtained by reading the history of science, is in itself stimulating and liberalizing.

In the announcement of Ostwald's *Klassiker der Exakten Wissenschaften* is the following, significant statement: "While, by the present methods of teaching, a knowledge of science in its present state of advancement is imparted very successfully, eminent and far-sighted men have repeatedly been obliged to point out a defect which too often attaches to the present scientific education of our youth. *It is the absence of the historical sense and the want of knowledge of the great researches upon which the edifice of science rests.*"

It is hoped that the survey of the progress of physics here presented may assist in remedying this defect so clearly pointed out by Professor Ostwald.

As it seems best not to increase the size of the book beyond the limit originally intended, it is necessary to omit a few subjects which properly belong to elementary physics.

It gives me great pleasure to acknowledge my obligations to Mr. S. J. Barnett, Ph.D., and Mr. P. E. Doudna, A.M., of Colorado College, for assistance in proof-reading and for important suggestions and criticisms.

F. C.

Colorado College, Colorado Springs,
November, 1898.

CONTENTS

A HISTORY OF PHYSICS

A HISTORY OF PHYSICS

THE BABYLONIANS AND EGYPTIANS

THE early Sumerians and Babylonians have contributed to later generations important units for the measurement of time and of angles. Babylonian in origin is the week of seven days, also the division of the day and of the night into twelve hours each. The Babylonians made quite extensive use of the sexagesimal scale in writing integral numbers and fractions; using the same scale, they divided the hour into 60 minutes and the minute into 60 seconds. The circle was subdivided into 360 degrees, the degree into 60 minutes of arc, and the minute into 60 seconds. The most humble worker of the present day measures the time of work by the hour, as did the Babylonians of perhaps 5000 years ago. The most noted engineer and the most distinguished astronomer of the present time measure angles in degrees, minutes and seconds, much as did the astronomers at the Euphrates and Tigris eons ago. These well-chosen units of measurement made it possible to accumulate early Babylonian astronomical records which indicate a surprising precision. An achievement of the first magnitude was the discovery of that slow motion of the equinoctial points on the ecliptic (about 1.2° per century) called the precession of the equinoxes. This was done by the Babylonian astronomer Cidenas, who directed an astronomical school at Sippra, on the Euphrates, about 343 B.C.[1] Cidenas antedates the Greek astronomer Hypparchus to whom this discovery has been attributed until recently.

Primitive sun-dials and water-clocks served for measuring time. For finding the angular altitude of the sun (at noon time), they used the gnomon which consisted essentially of a

[1] Paul Schnabel in *Zeitschrift für Assyriologie*, N. S., Vol. 3, 1926, p. 1–60.

vertical rod of known length. The length and direction of its solar shadow afforded the necessary data.

The beam-balance [1] served for weighing medicine and precious articles. The medical recipes described in the Egyptian papyrus *Ebers* indicate the use of weights as small as .71 grams.

[1] F. Dannemann, *Die Naturwissenschaften in ihrer Entwicklung und ihrem Zusammenhange*, 2d Ed., Vol. I, Leipzig, 1920, p. 39; Th. Ibel, *Die Wage im Altertum und Mittelalter*, Erlangen, 1908.

THE GREEKS

In mathematics, logic, metaphysics, literature, and art, the Greeks displayed wonderful creative genius; in astronomy and natural history they exhibited undoubted power of observation and capacity for cosmological speculation, but in physical science they achieved comparatively little.[1] The step from observation to experimentation proved to be a difficult one. Not till two thousand years after Plato and Aristotle did the experimental method acquire firm hold upon the procedure in physical science. In observation, the scientist simply takes notice of the phenomena nature happens to present to his unaided senses. In experimentation, the scientist creates new situations in nature and exacts a reply as to the consequences of these new situations. In general, the early Greeks were ignorant of this art of experimentation. Moreover, most of their early physical speculations were vague, trifling and worthless. Only in the later period of Greek scientific history, beginning about the time of Archimedes, do we find evidence of experimental procedure. As compared with the vast amount of theoretical deduction about nature, the number of experiments known to have been performed by the Greeks is surprisingly small. Little or no attempt was made to verify speculation by experimental evidence. As a conspicuous example of misty philosophizing we give Aristotle's proof that the world is *perfect*:[2] "The bodies of which the world is composed are solids, and therefore have three dimensions. Now, three is the most perfect number,—it is the first of numbers, for of *one* we do not speak as a number, for *two* we say both, but *three* is the first number of which we say *all*. Moreover, it has a beginning, a middle, and an end."

[1] For details relating to the early history of science in general, consult George Sarton, *Introduction to the History of Science*, Vol. I. Baltimore, 1927.

[2] *De Cœlo*, I. 1, as translated by Whewell.

3

MECHANICS

ARISTOTLE ON THE ACTION OF FORCES AND HIS LAW OF FALLING BODIES

Mechanical subjects are treated in the writings of **Aristotle.** The great peripatetic had grasped the notion of the parallelogram of forces for the special case of the rectangle. He attempted the theory of the lever, stating that a force at a greater distance from the fulcrum moves a weight more easily because it describes a greater circle. He resolved the motion of a weight at the end of the lever into tangential and normal components. The tangential motion he calls *according to nature;* the normal motion *contrary to nature.* The modern reader will readily see that the expression *contrary to nature* applied to a natural phenomenon is inappropriate and confusing.

Aristotle's views of falling bodies are very far from the truth. Nevertheless they demand our attention, for the reason that, during the Middle Ages and Renaissance, his authority was so great that they play an important rôle in scientific thought. He says: "That body is heavier than another which, in an equal bulk, moves downward quicker." [1] In another place he teaches that bodies fall quicker in exact proportion to their weight. [2] No statement could be further from the truth.

A modern writer endeavors to exonerate Aristotle as a physicist. "If he could have had any modern instrument of observation—such as the telescope or microscope, or even the thermometer or barometer—placed in his hands, how swiftly would he have used such an advantage!" [3] But in the case of

[1] *De Cœlo,* IV. 1, p. 308.
[2] This law is assumed by him in the following reasoning: ". . . suppose a without weight, but β possessing weight; and let a pass over a space $\gamma\delta$, but β in the same time pass over a space $\gamma\epsilon$,—for that which has weight will be carried through the larger space. If now the heavy body be divided in the proportion that space $\gamma\epsilon$ bears to $\gamma\delta$, . . . and *if the whole is carried through the whole space $\gamma\epsilon$, then it must be that a part in the same time would be carried through $\gamma\delta$. . . .*"—*De Cœlo,* Book III., Ch. II.
[3] Article "Aristotle" in *Encyclopædia Britannica,* Ninth Edition.

falling bodies, the experiment was within his reach. Taking two stones of unequal weight, and dropping them together, he could easily have seen that the one, say, ten times the weight of the other, did not descend ten times faster. The claim has been made recently that Aristotle has been misunderstood,[1] that what he actually had in mind was the "terminal velocity" of a body falling through a resisting medium (air), when the retardation of the medium is exactly equal to the acceleration of gravity. "A penny can never fall faster than about 30 feet a second through air." Such terminal motion is exemplified also in the motion of "a raindrop or hailstone falling vertically in the air, or of a smoke particle up the chimney." That the terminal velocities of globes of equal size falling through a resisting medium are proportional to their weights was justified by Newton in his experiments in St. Paul's cathedral and explained by him in the *Principia*, Bk. II, Prop. 40. Whether Aristotle was misinterpreted by Galileo and others can be settled only by reference to Aristotle's works.[2] He applies his law of falling bodies many times in discussions on the motions of bodies and the possibility of the existence of a vacuum. A critical examination of these passages shows that he considered his law applicable when the motion took place from rest, when the bodies are different weights of any one metal, like gold or lead, and when the time of motion was reduced or increased. He was willing to apply his law even to motion in a vacuum, were a vacuum possible. It appears therefore that Aristotle allowed his law a generality of application which did include the special conditions under which Galileo performed his memorable experiments about 2000 years later. Our conclusion is that Galileo interpreted Aristotle correctly.

[1] *Nature* (London, 1914), Vol. 92, pp. 584, 585, 606.
[2] Aristotle's *Physica*, Book IV, Chap. 8. Aristotle's *De Cælo*, Book I, Chaps. 6, 8; Book III, Chap. 2; Book IV, Chaps. 1, 2.

Archimedes on the Lever and on Hydrostatics

Immeasurably superior to Aristotle as a student of mechanics is **Archimedes** (287 (?)–212 B.C.).[1] He is the true originator of mechanics as a science. To him we owe the theory of the centre of gravity (centroid) and of the lever. In his *Equiponderance of Planes* he starts with the axiom that equal weights acting at equal distances on opposite sides of a pivot are in equilibrium, and then endeavors to establish the principle that "in the lever unequal weights are in equilibrium only when they are inversely proportional to the arms from which they are suspended." His appreciation of its efficiency is echoed in the exclamation attributed to him: "Give me a fulcrum on which to rest, and I will move the earth."

We reproduce from a mechanical work of Varignon, published in Paris in 1687, a figure (Fig. 1) illustrating this say-

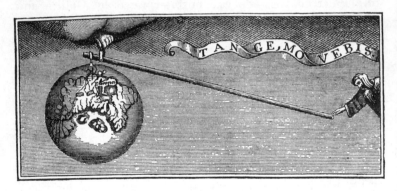

Fig. 1.

ing. The Latin motto in the figure may be rendered thus: "Touch it and you will move it."

While the *Equiponderance* treats of solids or the equilibrium of solids, the book on *Floating Bodies* treats of hydrostatics. His attention was first drawn to the subject of specific gravity

[1] Consult *The Works of Archimedes*, edited in modern notation, with introductory chapters, by T. L. Heath. Cambridge University Press.

when King Hieron asked him to test whether a crown, professed by the maker to be pure gold, was not alloyed with silver. The story goes that our philosopher was in a bath when the true method of solution flashed on his mind. He immediately leaped from the bath and ran home, shouting, "I have found it!" To solve the problem he took a piece of gold and a piece of silver, each weighing the same as the crown. According to one author,[1] he determined the volume of water displaced by the amount of gold, silver, and crown respectively, and calculated from that the amount of gold and silver in the crown. According to another writer,[2] he weighed separately the gold, silver, and crown, while immersed in water, thereby determining their loss of weight in water. From these data he easily found the solution. It is possible that Archimedes solved the problem by both methods.

In his *Floating Bodies* Archimedes established the important principle, known by his name, that the loss of weight of a body submerged in water is equal to the weight of the water displaced, and that a floating body displaces its own weight of water. Since the days of Archimedes able minds have drawn erroneous conclusions on liquid pressure. The expression "hydrostatic paradox" (applied to the fact that vessels whose bottoms are subjected to equal pressures do not necessarily transmit equal pressures to the stand on which they rest) indicates the slippery nature of the subject. All the more must we admire the clearness of conception and almost perfect logical rigor which characterize the investigations of Archimedes.[3]

Archimedes is said to have shown wonderful inventive genius in various mechanical inventions. It is reported that he astonished the court of Hieron by moving heavy ships by aid of a collection of pulleys. To him is ascribed the inven-

[1] Vitruvius, IX. 3.

[2] *Scriptores metrologici Romani* (ed. Hultsch, pp. 124–208).

[3] A valuable paper with numerous extracts from authors is Ch. Thurot's *Recherches Historiques sur le Principe d'Archimède*, Paris, 1869 (extrait de la *Revue Archéologique*, Années 1868–1869).

tion of war engines, and the endless screw ("screw of Archimedes") which was used to drain the holds of ships.

HERON AND OTHER GREEK INVENTORS

About a century or two after Archimedes, there flourished Ctesibius and **Heron,** both of Alexandria. They contributed little to the advancement of theoretical investigation, but they displayed wonderful mechanical ingenuity. The force-pump is probably the invention of Ctesibius. The suction pump is older and was known in the time of Aristotle. According to Vitruvius, Ctesibius designed the ancient fire-engine, consisting of the combination of two force-pumps, spraying alternately. The machine had no air-chamber, and therefore could not produce a steady stream. Heron describes the fire-engine in his *Pneumatica*. During the Middle Ages the fire-engine was unknown. It is said to have been first used in Augsburg in 1518.[1] Ctesibius is credited with the invention of the hydraulic organ, the water-clock, and the catapult. Heron showed the earliest application of steam as a motive power, in

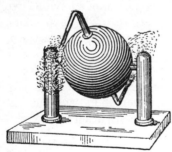

FIG. 2.

his toy, called the "eolipile" (Fig. 2). It consisted of a hollow sphere with two arms at right angles to its axis and bent in opposite directions at its ends. When steam was generated in the sphere, it escaped through the arms and caused the sphere to rotate. It was the forerunner of Barker's water-mill and the modern turbine. Heron wrote an important book on geodesy called *Dioptra*.[2]

The Greeks invented the hydrometer, probably in the fourth century A.D. There appears to be no good evidence for attribut-

[1] A. de Rochas in *La Nature*, Vol. XI., pp. 13, 14; 1883.
[2] For a full account of Heron, "the first engineer," see W. A. Truesdell in *Jour. of the Ass. of Engin. Soc.*, Vol. XIX., Philadelphia, 1897, pp. 1–19.

ing its origin to Archimedes. The hydrometer is described in
full by Bishop Synesius in a letter to Hypatia. It consisted of
a hollow, graduated, tin cylinder, weighted below. It was first
used in medicine, to determine the quality of drinking-water,
hard water being at that time considered unwholesome. According to Desaguliers it was used for this purpose as late as
the eighteenth century.[1]

LIGHT

The fragment of a Greek document, found in Egypt, speaks
of various optical illusions; for instance, that the sun appears
larger when at the horizon than when near the zenith.[2]
Optics is, indeed, one of the oldest branches of physics. A con-
verging lens of rock crystal is said to have been found in the
ruins of Nineveh.[3] In Greece, burning-glasses seem to have
been manufactured at an early date. Aristophanes, in the
comedy of *The Clouds,* Act II. (performed 424 B.C.), intro-
duces a conversation about "fine transparent stone (glass)
with which fires are kindled," and by which, standing in the
sun, one can, "though at a distance, melt all the writing"
traced on the surface of wax. The Platonic school taught the
rectilinear propagation of light and the equality of the angle
of incidence to that of reflection. The astronomer, **Claudius
Ptolemy,** who flourished in Alexandria in 139 A.D., measured
angles of incidence and of refraction, and arranged them in
tables. He found that the angles of incidence and refraction
are proportional, which is approximately correct in the case of
small angles.

Metallic mirrors seem to have been manufactured in remote antiquity. "Looking-glasses" are referred to in *Exodus*
38:8, and in *Job* 37:18; they have been found in graves of
Egyptian mummies. Spherical and parabolic mirrors were
known to the Greeks. To **Euclid** (about 300 B.C.) is attributed

---

[1] E. Gerland in *Wiedemann's Annalen*, Vol. 1, New Series, 1877, pp.
150–157. See also his *Gesch. d. Physik*, p. 40.
[2] See K. Wessely in *Wiener Studien*, Vol. 13, 1891, pp. 312–323.
Abstracted in *Wiedemann's Beiblätter*, Vol. 17, 1893.
[3] E. Gerland, *Geschichte der Physik*, Leipzig, 1892, p. 9.

a work on *Catoptrics*, dealing with phenomena of reflection. In it is found the earliest reference to the focus of a spherical mirror. In Theorem 30 it is stated [1] that concave mirrors turned toward the sun will cause ignition. In the "fragmentum Bobiense," a document written, perhaps, by Anthemius of Tralles, the focal property of parabolic reflectors is demonstrated. Several Greek authors appear to have written on concave mirrors. The story that, when the Romans were besieging Syracuse, Archimedes defended his native city by the use of mirrors reflecting the sun's rays, and setting on fire the ships when they came within bowshot of the walls, is probably a fiction.

The Greeks elaborated several theories of vision. According to the Pythagoreans, Democritus, and others, vision is caused by the projection of particles from the object seen, into the pupil of the eye. On the other hand, Empedocles (about 440 B.C.), the Platonists, and Euclid held the strange doctrine of ocular beams, according to which the eye itself sends out something which causes sight as soon as it meets something else emanated by the object. [2]

ELECTRICITY AND MAGNETISM

To the Greeks we owe a few isolated observations on electricity and magnetism. **Thales of Miletus** (640–546 B.C.), one of the "seven wise men" of early Greece, is credited with the knowledge that amber, when rubbed, will attract light bodies, and that a certain mineral, now called magnetite, or loadstone, possesses the power of attracting iron. Amber—a mineralized yellowish resin—was used in antiquity for decoration. In common with the bright shining silver-gold alloys, and gold itself, it was called "electron"; hence the word "electricity." About three centuries after Thales, Theophrastus, in his treatise *On Gems*, mentions another mineral which becomes

[1] *Euclidis Opera Omnia*, Vol. 7, Edidit I. L. Heiberg, Lipsiæ, 1895. See also E. Wiedemann in *Wied. Annalen*, Vol. 39, 1890, p. 123.

[2] For Plato's theory, see *The Dialogues of Plato*, Vol. II., translated by B. Jowett, C. Scribner's Sons, New York, pp. 537 *et seq.*

electrified by friction. We know now that all bodies can be thus electrified. Pliny says that ignorant people called the loadstone "quick-iron." The large extent to which this phenomenon of magnetic attraction excited the imagination of men is shown by the fable of the shepherd Magnes, who, on Mount Ida (on the island of Crete), was so strongly drawn to earth by the tacks in his sandals and the iron tip of his staff, that he could hardly pull himself away. He dug to ascertain the cause, and discovered a wonderful stone (magnetite). Another fable speaks of a powerful magnetic mountain, which pulled the nails out of ships, even when the latter were at considerable distance from it.[1]

Pliny tells another story concerning the loadstone. At Alexandria the construction of a vaulted roof of magnetite in the temple of Arsinoe was undertaken for the purpose of suspending in the air the iron statue of the queen. As time went on, the story was greatly embellished. Thus, according to the Venerable Bede, the horse of Bellerophon, on the island of Rhodes, weighed 5000 pounds, and was suspended by magnets.[2] A similar story is told of Mohammed's coffin. Of course, such a suspension in air is mechanically impossible.

During antiquity iron was mined chiefly along the coasts of the Ægean Sea and on the Mediterranean islands. Magnetic iron ore is said to have been found also near Magnesia in Asia Minor. According to Lucretius the term "magnet" is derived from "Magnesia." There were iron mines on the island of Samothrace. The miners of that locality showed the action of the loadstone in connection with the so-called Samothracian rings. Says Socrates: ". . . that stone not only attracts iron rings, but also imparts to them a similar power of attracting other rings; and sometimes you may see a number of pieces of iron and rings suspended from one another so as to form quite

[1] This story recurs frequently in literature; for instance, in the tale of the third mendicant in the *Arabian Nights*.

[2] Beda, *De Sept. Mirac. Mundi;* quoted by Park Benjamin in *The Intellectual Rise in Electricity,* New York, 1895, p. 46. (Hereafter this work will be referred to as Benjamin).

a long chain : and all of them derive their power of suspension
from the original stone.'' [1]

The polarity of magnets and the phenomena of repulsion
which may exist between the electric charges or magnetic poles
were unknown to Greek antiquity.

METEOROLOGY

Previous to the middle of the fifteenth century no systematic meteorological records are known to have been kept
anywhere.[2] Yet the Greeks paid some attention to meteorology. It is in Athens that we find the oldest contrivance
for observing the direction of the wind. There, in its essential
parts standing to this day, is the "tower of the winds", built
about 100 B.C. This small octagonal marble structure, devoted
to science, has interesting mythological ornamentation. In
the upper exterior there is a frieze in low relief, representing
the sons of Æolus, the god of winds; he kept the winds confined in a cavern and let them loose as he saw fit or as he was
bidden by the superior deities. The scientific instruments consisted of a sun-dial set against the tower to mark the time of
day, a water-clock kept inside, and a weather-vane, in form of
a triton, mounted on the highest part of the roof. It is improbable that weather-vanes were ever common in Greece or
Rome, for there is no Greek or Latin name to designate the
instrument.[3] Among the Greeks meteorology can hardly be
said to have risen to the dignity of a science. **Theophrastus of
Eresus** (371–286 B.C.), a disciple of Aristotle, wrote a book
On Winds and Weather Signs,[4] but like most other Greek
philosophers, he was hardly the man to adopt patient and
exact observation in place of dogmatic assertion and the teaching of authority. Aristotle makes a good observation on the

[1] Jowett, *Dialogues of Plato*, Vol. I., p. 223. (Ion.)
[2] G. Hellmann, *Himmel und Erde*, Vol. II., 1890, p. 113.
[3] Hellmann, *op. cit.*, p. 119.
[4] Translated by J. G. Wood, London, 1894, with an introduction and
an appendix of historical interest and value.

formation of dew; viz. dew is formed only on clear and quiet nights.[1]

Aratus of Soli, who lived about 275 B.C., wrote a book of *Prognostics*, giving predictions of the weather from observation of astronomical phenomena, and various accounts of the effect of weather on animals. Several editions of this and other works of Aratus were printed; one edition was brought out by Melanchthon.

SOUND

The pyramids of Egypt and the ruins of ancient cities bear testimony to the fact that practical geometry and practical mechanics antedated by many centuries the earliest records which we possess on abstract geometry and theoretical mechanics. In the same way, the knowledge of vocal and instrumental music, said to have been possessed by nations of great antiquity, demonstrates that the art of music is incomparably older than the theory of acoustics. The beginning of the theory of harmonics reaches back to **Pythagoras** (580 ?–500 ? B.C.), but the accounts of his researches are so intertwined with fable and with error, that it is difficult to ascertain just what Pythagoras did. Passing by a blacksmith's shop, he is said to have noticed that the hammers as they struck the anvil produced sounds having the intervals a "fourth," a "fifth," and an "octave." He found the weights of the hammers [2] to be, respectively, as $1 : \frac{3}{4} : \frac{2}{3} : \frac{1}{2}$. Subsequent experimentation with musical strings of the same material and equal lengths and thicknesses showed that weights proportionate to $1, \frac{3}{4}, \frac{2}{3}, \frac{1}{2}$, would give the above intervals. This research pointed to an arithmetical relation between musical intervals, and established a close connection between subjects so far apart as arithmetic and music.

It will readily be seen that the above account contains two

[1] J. C. Poggendorff, *Geschichte der Physik*, Leipzig, 1879, p. 42. (Hereafter this work will be quoted as Poggendorff.)

[2] Nicomachus, *Harmonices*, I., p. 10 (Ed. Meibomius); Porphyry, *Ptol. Harm.*, c. 3, p. 213; Diogenes Laertius, VIII., 12.

errors. Hammers of the weights given above will not yield the sounds in question. Nor is the law of weights for strings stated correctly; the pitch of tones varies, not as the weights, but as the square roots of the weights.

Some modern writers have been led to surmise that Pythagoras did not base his opinions upon experiment, that the smithy in which he got his information was the land of Egypt, whence he imported his knowledge.[1] Other writers assume that Pythagoras really did not vary the tensions of the strings, but varied their lengths, thereby arriving at the correct law that pitch changes inversely as the lengths of the strings.[2] It is said that Pythagoras was the first to establish the eight complete degrees in the diatonic scale.[3]

His speculations on harmony and musical intervals were uncontrolled by further inquiry into the facts. The seven planets are the seven strings of the lyre, which give us a beautiful "harmony of the spheres."[4] This idea was not advanced as poetry, but as physical philosophy. The fact that the human ear cannot detect such interplanetary music did not seem to weaken his belief in its existence!

The theory of sound was touched upon by Aristotle, who entertained correct ideas on the character of the motion of air constituting sound, and who knew that, if the length of a pipe is doubled, a vibration in it occupies double the time.

ATOMIC THEORY

It is worthy of notice that the atomic theory finds its earliest advocates in Greece. That the theory of the atomic constitution of matter is far from being a self-evident truth

[1] See article "Music" in *Encycl. Brit.*, 9th ed. The article contains much information on Greek musical scales.

[2] Helmholtz, *Sensations of Tone*, trans. by A. J. Ellis, London, 1885, p. 1. For fuller references and details regarding Pythagoras, see E. Zeller, *History of Greek Philosophy*, trans. by S. F. Alleyne, London, 1881, Vol. I., pp. 431–433. Consult also C. H. H. Parry, *The Evolution of the Art of Music*, New York, 1896, "Scales," pp. 15–47.

[3] Helmholtz, *op. cit.*, p. 266.

[4] Nicomachus, *op. cit.*, I., p. 6, II., p. 33; Pliny, H. N., II., p. 20; Simpl. in Arist. *de Cœlo. Schol.*, p. 496, 11.

follows at once from the fact that the two thinkers who have swayed philosophic thought most powerfully, Aristotle and Kant, teach that space is continuously filled.[1] The atomic theory originated with **Leucippus.** It is a curious circumstance that this theory was set up as a logical sequel to the subtle arguments against the possibility of motion advanced by the great dialectician, Zeno of Elea.[2] One of Zeno's arguments was that Achilles could not overtake a tortoise. For, Achilles must first reach the place from which the tortoise started. By that time the tortoise will have moved on a little way. Achilles must then traverse that, and still the tortoise will be ahead. Only in recent time has mathematical philosophy satisfactorily cleared up this matter. To Leucippus it seemed, apparently, that the escape from the impossible conclusion reached by Zeno, lay in denying the infinite divisibility of distance implied in Zeno's argument. Setting such a limit to divisibility led to the concept of the atom, the physically "indivisible." The great ancient expositor of the atomic theory is **Democritus of Abdera** (about 460–370 B.C.). He taught that the world consists of empty space and an infinite number of indivisible, invisibly small atoms. Bodies appear and disappear only by the union and separation of atoms. Even the phenomena of sensation and thought are the result of their combination. The atomic theory was adopted by the Greek philosopher Epicurus (341–270 B.C.) whose teaching otherwise marked a reaction against science. The atomic theory did not play any great rôle in scientific progress until after the discovery by Dalton of the chemical law of multiple proportions.

THE "FAILURE" OF GREEK PHYSICAL INQUIRY

While the Greeks achieved more in physical research than did other nations of antiquity, nevertheless they accomplished less in this field of intellectual activity than in other direc-

---

[1] Kurd Lasswitz, *Geschichte der Atomistik*, Vol. I., p. 2.
[2] John Burnet, *Early Greek Philosophy*, London, 1908, p. 387.

tions. The question why the Greeks made little progress in physics is an old puzzle, and is not easily answered. Francis Bacon says that "the proceeding has been to fly at once from the sense and particulars up to the most general propositions, as certain fixed poles for the argument to turn upon, and from these to derive the rest by middle terms: a short way, no doubt, but precipitate; and one which will never lead to nature, though it offers an easy and ready way to disputation." "The ancients proved themselves in everything that turns on wit and abstract meditation, wonderful men."[1] This, and other explanations offered by Whewell,[2] Mill,[3] and Robinson,[4] rest upon Greek intellectual endeavor as accomplished by early Greek thinkers, none later than the time of Aristotle. But it was during the five or six hundred years following Aristotle that Greek mathematics, astronomy and geography reached their full flowering time. According to some writers "the glorious period of Greek mind is commonly and rightfully assumed to have come to an end about the time of Aristotle's death," 322 B.C., but such an assumption ignores the real facts. Euclid, Apollonius, Archimedes, Diophantus, Eratosthenes, Hipparchus, Ptolemy, all flourished after the time of Aristotle. During this time empirical and experimental methods acquired a moderate foothold. Aristarchus, the "Copernicus of antiquity," belonged to this period. The observational astronomers Hipparchus and Ptolemy used the astrolabe and the quadrant in astronomical measurements; Archimedes used the experimental method in solving the "problem of the Crown"; his principle that the loss of weight of a body submerged in water is equal to the weight of the water displaced was empirical in origin. The

[1] F. Bacon, in Preface to the *Novum Organum* (*Works*, New York, 1878, Vol. I, pp. 42, 32.)

[2] W. Whewell, *History of the Inductive Sciences*, New York, 1858, Vol. I, p. 87.

[3] J. S. Mill, *System of Logic*, London, 1851, Vol. I, p. 367, where Mill adopts the view of a writer in the *Prospective Review*, February, 1850.

[4] James Harvey Robinson, *The Mind in the Making*, 1921, Chaps. IV, V.

story of his setting the Roman ships a-fire points to experimentation with mirrors reflecting the sun's rays. Eratosthenes measured the size of the earth with an accuracy which was not surpassed until Willebrord Snell's determination of 1617, in Holland. Eratosthenes measured the noon-day altitude of the sun at Alexandria, by the use of the gnomon. The difference of that altitude at Alexandria and at Syene, a town due south of Alexandria, yielded the difference in latitude, which, with the distance of Syene from Alexandria, afforded the data for computation of the circumference of the earth. Heron of Alexandria, the great engineer, developed surveying instruments. Another Greek invented the hydrometer. Ptolemy's experimental study of refraction and his elaborate study of atmospheric refraction, are "the most remarkable experimental research of antiquity." [1]

The consideration of these facts indicates that the Greeks had begun to develop experimental science, but the movement was soon checked by the intervention of external forces. Social causes, the absorption of the Hellenes in the vast Roman Empire, and the great struggle of Christianity with the ancient religions, brought an end to creative scientific research among the Greeks.

[1] George Sarton, *Introduction to the History of Science,* p. 274.

THE ROMANS

THE genius of the Roman people was exercised in war, conquest, government, and law, but no effort was put forth for the advancement of pure mathematics or science. The Roman scientific writers were contented to collect the researches of Greek predecessors. Among these are Marcus Vitruvius Pollio (85–26 B.C.), the architect of Emperor Augustus; **Titus Carus Lucretius** (95–52 (?) B.C.), the author of *De Rerum Natura;* Lucius Annœus Seneca (2–66 A.D.), the tutor of Emperor Nero; Pliny (23–79 A.D.), the compiler of a large work on natural history; and **Anicius Manlius Severinus Boethius** (480 ?–524), at one time a favorite of King Theodoric.

The *De rerum natura*[1] ("Concerning the nature of things") of Lucretius is a poem celebrated not only for its literary grandeur, but also for its keen scientific observations and brilliant anticipations of modern scientific thought. Lucretius is the first ancient writer who refers to the *repulsive* effect of a magnet and to the experiment with iron filings. The latter "will rave within brass basins," when the loadstone is placed beneath. Lucretius takes heat to be a substance, as the Greeks, Heraclitus and Democritus, had done before him. Lucretius speaks of "the several minute bodies of heat"[2] which "draws air along with it, there being no heat which has not air, too, mixed up with it." This great poem gives the completest and plainest ancient account of the Greek atomic theory. Atoms are little solids, indivisible, not all alike, but all in constant motion; they are infinite in number. Modern mathematicians find here conceptions of an infinite multitude which accord with the modern definition of those terms as being not variables, but constants. This infinite

[1] Lucretius, *De rerum natura*, Bk. I, lines 55, 600; Bk. II, lines 96–98, 478–568.
[2] *Loc. cit.*, Bk. II, lines 150–156; Bk. III, line 235.

18

multitude is of the denumerable variety; he made use of their whole-part property.[1] Lucretius supposed the atoms of a solid to be hooked so as to cling together. Hooked atoms were used in more recent times by John Bernoulli, and also by nineteenth century chemists to explain chemical combination and valency. Newton found in the great poem of Lucretius a clear statement of the Galileon principle of the falling body. In a vacuum, free of resistance, all atoms, whether light or heavy, descend with the same velocity. Lucretius attributes the phenomena of the world to necessity, or as we should say, to physical law. The conservation of matter is proclaimed by Lucretius with great clearness, and the conservation of energy almost as clearly. A recent biologist has found in the wonderful poem an expression of Mendel's celebrated law of heredity. As D'Arcy W. Thompson remarked, each generation of scientists may study Lucretius in the light of its own knowledge and find in it some prophetic vision.

Boethius wrote a work on *Music* which contains much information on Greek theories of harmony. Seneca taught the identity of rainbow colors with those formed by the edge of a piece of glass. He observed that a globular glass vessel, filled with water, magnifies objects, but he was led by this observation no further than to remark that nothing is so deceptive as our sight. His writings are replete with moral sentiment. This accounts, perhaps, for the fact that his *Naturalium quaestionum libri* VII was used for so long, during the Middle Ages, as a text-book of physics.[2] His grasp of mechanics is illustrated by the story which he gravely tells of a fish, less than a foot long, which, by clinging to a ship, completely stops its motion even in a gale. He claimed that, during the battle of Actium, Antonius's largest vessel was thus bound fast.

Cleomedes, whose place and time of birth are unknown, probably flourished about the time of the Emperor Augustus.

---

[1] C. J. Keyser, *Bull. Am. Math. Soc.*, Vol. 24, 1918, pp. 268, 321.

[2] F. Rosenberger, *Geschichte der Physik*, Part I., 1882, p. 45. (This work will be quoted after this as Rosenberger.)

He noticed, as did Archimedes and Euclid, that a ring on the bottom of an empty vessel, just hidden by the edge, becomes visible when the vessel is filled with water. But he goes further and suggests that in the same way the sun may be in sight when, as a matter of fact, it is a little below the horizon. He is the first after Ptolemy to consider atmospheric refraction.

THE ARABS

THE growth of the Arabic nation presents an extraordinary spectacle in intellectual history. Scattered barbaric tribes were suddenly fused in the furnace blast of religious enthusiasm into a powerful nation. A career of war and conquest was followed by a period of intellectual activity. About the eighth century A.D. the Mohammedans began to figure as the intellectual leaders of the world. With wonderful celerity they acquired the scientific and philosophic treasures of the Hindus and Greeks. Old books were translated from the Greek into Arabic. Chemistry, astronomy, mathematics, and geography became favorite subjects of study. In a few instances the Arabs made original contributions to science, but as a rule they did not distinguish themselves in original research; they were learned rather than creative.

There was only one branch of physics which was successfully cultivated on Arabic soil and but one man prominently identified with it. The branch was optics, and the man was **Al Hazen** (965 ?–1038). His full Arabic name was Abû 'Alî al Hasan ibn al Hasan ibn Al Haitam. He was born in Bosra on the Tigris and rose to the position of vizier. He was then called to Egypt by one of the caliphs who had heard that Al Hazen had thought out plans for so regulating the flow of the Nile that each year there should be plenty of water for irrigation. Closer inspection of the grounds compelled him to abandon the project. He committed other errors, which brought him into disfavor with the caliph. He feigned insanity and sought concealment until after the death of the caliph. Subsequently he made his living by copying manuscripts. He wrote on astronomy, mathematics, and optics.

His *Optics* was translated into Latin and printed at Bâle in 1572. To the law of the equality of the angles in reflection, which he learned from the Greeks, he added the law that both

21

angles lie in the same plane. He made a study of spherical and parabolic mirrors. The greater the number of rays which pass through a point, the more intense is the heat there. Rays incident upon a spherical mirror, and parallel to the principal axis, are reflected to this axis. All the rays reflected from points in the mirror lying on the circumference of a circle which is perpendicular to the axis (and these rays only) pass through one and the same point on the axis. He constructed a mirror out of a number of separate spherical rings, of which each has its own radius and its own centre, but so chosen that all rings reflect all the rays accurately to one and the same point. The following is known as "Al Hazen's problem": Given the position of a luminous point and of the eye, to find the point on the spherical, cylindrical, or conical mirror at which the reflection takes place. The beginnings of this problem are found in Ptolemy's optics; after Al Hazen's masterly but complicated discussion of it, it became famous in Europe on account of the geometrical difficulties to which the general problem gave rise.[1]

In repetition of what had been done by Ptolemy, Al Hazen took measurements of angles of incidence and of refraction, and showed that Ptolemy was in error in stating that the ratio of the angle of incidence to the angle of refraction is constant. But both failed to discover the true law of refraction. His apparatus consisted of a graduated circular copper ring, supported in a vertical position, and dipped half way into water. The incident ray passed through a hole in the rim of the ring and through a perforated disk at the centre. The apparatus closely resembles that utilized at the present time in elementary instruction, and has the great advantage of permitting the angles of incidence and refraction to be read directly.

The apparent increase in diameter of sun and moon, when

[1] For Al Hazen and his researches see Paul Bode, " Alhazensche Spiegel-Aufgabe," Separat-Abdruck aus dem *Jahresbericht des Physikalischen Vereins zu Frankfurt a. M.*, 1891–92; Leopold Schnaase, *Die Optik Alhazens*, Pr. Stargard, 1889; Baarman in *Zeitschr. d. deutschen Morgenl. Gesellschaft*, 36, 1882, p. 195; E. Wiedemann, *in Wiedemann's Annalen*, N. F., Vol. 39, pp. 110–130; also Vol. 7, p. 680.

near the horizon, he declares to be an illusion due to the fact that their size is estimated by that of the less distant terrestrial objects. This explanation has held its ground to the present day, but is not accepted by all. Al Hazen arrived at the conclusion that the planets and fixed stars do not receive their light from the sun, but are self-luminous.[1]

Al Hazen is the first physicist to give a detailed description and *drawing* of the human eye. He says that he took his account from works on anatomy. Some of our names for parts of the eye originated from the translation of Al Hazen's description into Latin—for instance, the terms "retina," "cornea," "vitreous humor" (glassy body), "aqueous humor."[2]

Some of his Arabic predecessors and contemporaries, as well as he himself, stoutly combat the theory of Euclid and the Platonists, that vision is due to rays given out by the eye; they supported the view of Democritus and Aristotle that the cause of vision proceeds from the object seen.[3]

The Arabs developed the notion of "specific gravity," and gave experimental methods for its determination. Al Biruni used for this purpose a vessel with a spout slanting downwards. It was filled with water up to the spout, then the solid was immersed, and the weight of the overflow determined. This, together with the weight of the solid in air, yielded the specific gravity. Al Khazin, in his *Book of the Balance of Wisdom,* written in 1137,[4] describes a curious beam balance, with five pans, for weighing in air and water. One pan was movable along the graduated beam. He points out that air, too must exert a buoyant force, causing bodies to weigh less.[5]

---

[1] His paper on this subject is published in German translation by E. Wiedemann in *Wochenschr. f. Astr., Meteor., u. Geogr.,* 1890, No. 17.

[2] Charles Singer *Studies in the History and Method of Science,* Oxford, 1917–1921, Vol. II., p. 389.

[3] E. Wiedemann in *Wiedemann's Annalen,* Vol. 39, 1890, p. 470.

[4] Extracts are translated in *Journal of American Oriental Society,* VI., pp. 1–128; consult also F. Rosenberger, Part I., pp. 81–86.

[5] Readers interested in water-clocks among the Arabs may consult A. Wittstein, "Ueber die Wasseruhr und das Astrolabium des Arzachel," in *Schlömilch's Zeitschr.,* Vol. 39, 1894, Hist. Lit. Abtheilung, p. 43.

EUROPE DURING THE MIDDLE AGES

WITH the third century of our era there began a migration of barbaric nations in Europe. The powerful Goths from the north swept onward in a southwesterly direction, crossing into Italy and shattering the Roman Empire. The Dark Ages which followed were the germinating season of the institutions and nations of Europe. Christianity was introduced, and Latin became the language of intercourse in ecclesiastical and learned circles.

Obscurity and servility of thought, indistinctness of ideas, and mysticism characterize the Middle Ages. Writers on science were mainly commentators, and never thought of bringing the statements of ancient authors to the test of experiment. At first the science of the Middle Ages was drawn largely from Latin sources. The insignificance of Roman science has been already pointed out. But Roman writers frequently refer to Greek authors, and the desire naturally arose to read Greek authors directly. This craving was partly satisfied by the acquisition, in the twelfth century, of Arabic translations of Greek treatises. The writings of Aristotle became well known and began to assume supreme authority. Woe unto him who dared to contradict a statement made by Aristotle! Witness Petrus Ramus (1515–1572), who in Paris was forbidden on pain of corporal punishment to teach or write against the great philosopher. In physics, Aristotle's authority remained unshaken until the time of Galileo. It is no fault of Aristotle that his works were used in the Middle Ages to hamper the further progress of science. He was the most penetrating thinker of antiquity; his writings should have served as a stimulus and challenge to all investigators—as they actually did serve to Galileo.[1]

[1] Fuller details than can be given here, relating to Physics in the Middle Ages, are found in George Sarton's *Introduction to the History of Science*, and in Lynn Thorndike's *History of Magic and Experimental Science*, New York, 1923.

GUNPOWDER AND THE MARINER'S COMPASS

The Europeans of this period came into possession of two inventions which have greatly influenced the progress of civilization, viz. gunpowder and the compass. Their origin is shrouded in darkness. The preparation of gunpowder out of sulphur, saltpetre, and charcoal was known to Marcus Græcus in the eighth (?) century, and to Albertus Magnus about 1250. It is said to have been used in Europe for blasting in the twelfth century. Firearms do not appear to have been manufactured before the close of the fourteenth century.[1]

There are obscure passages in Chinese legends regarding south-pointing chariots which have been believed by some to prove that the land compass was used in remotest antiquity.[2] No definite testimony concerning the land compass occurs before the eleventh century. "The earliest clear mention in any literature of a magnetic needle" is found in the writings of the Chinese mathematician and instrument maker, Shên Kua, who died in 1093 A.D.[3] A Chinese author of that time says that "the soothsayers rub a needle with the magnet stone, so that it may mark the south; however, it declines constantly a little to the east. It does not indicate the south exactly."[4] This passage discloses a knowledge of magnetic declination.

The earliest mention of the use of the magnetic needle for navigation occurs a little after 1100, in a Chinese writer who refers to the period 1086 to 1099, when it was used, not by Chinese, but by foreign sailors (probably Muslims), sailing between Canton and Sumatra.[5]

In Europe, the first mention of the mariner's compass is made in the twelfth century by Alexander Neckam of St. Albans, England. Another reference occurs in a poem published about the close of that century by the Frenchman Guyot de Provins, who speaks of the ugly brown stone to

---

[1] Rosenberger, *op. cit.*, Part I., p. 97.
[2] Benjamin, *op. cit.*, pp. 63–74.
[3] George Sarton, *op. cit.*, pp. 756, 764.
[4] Quoted by Benjamin, *op. cit.*, p. 75.
[5] George Sarton, *op. cit.*, p. 764.

which iron turns, through which navigators possess an art that cannot fail them. A bishop of Palestine in 1218 says that the needle is "most necessary for such as sail at sea."

The old mariner's compass was operated in a very primitive manner. In a work of 1282 an Arabic writer says that the needle was floated in a basin of water by being placed inside a reed or upon a splinter of wood. When brought to rest the magnet pointed north and south. A similar practice seems to have prevailed among the early Italians.

Remarkable progress in the knowledge of magnetism and the construction of the compass is indicated in a letter written August 12, 1269, by Master Peter de Maricourt of France, commonly called **Peregrinus.** This man was greatly admired by Roger Bacon, and for good reason. His letter discloses a knowledge of magnetic polarity, states that the fragments of a divided magnet have each two poles, gives the law that unlike poles attract each other, and mentions that a strong magnet will reverse the polarity of a weaker magnet. Peregrinus invented a compass with a graduated scale and pivoted needle. He designed perpetual-motion machines based on magnetic attraction, but was very politic, throwing the burden of success or failure upon the makers. He himself was at that time a soldier and probably had no tools for the construction of complicated machines. His letter was written from the trenches in front of Lucera (a town in southern Italy, then besieged by Charles of Anjou).[1]

After Peregrinus the graduated circle was replaced by the "Rose of the Winds," consisting of a star of, usually, thirty-two points.[2] In recent years there has been a tendency to return to Peregrinus's circle, graduated in degrees.

In the Exchange in Naples is a brass statue erected to Flavio

[1] Peregrinus's letter was printed in 1558. It is reprinted in Hellmann's *Neudrucke von Schriften u. Karten über Meteor. u. Erdmagn.*, No. 10, Berlin, 1898. See also Benjamin, pp. 165–187, and especially P. F. Mottelay, *Biographical History of Electricity and Magnetism*, London, 1922, pp. 45–54.

[2] For their various forms consult A. Breusing, *Die Nautischen Instrumente bis zur Erfindung des Spiegelsextanten*, Bremen, 1890, pp. 5–24.

Gioja as the inventor of the compass in 1302. This man, a resident of Amalfi in southern Italy, has long been considered its originator. We know now that it was used in Europe before his day, but he probably identified himself with it by introducing improvements in its construction.

An important innovation was the suspension of the magnet in gimbal rings, known as "Cardan's suspension." But Cardan (1501–1576) does not claim the invention, nor was it first designed for use with the compass. He describes a chair which had been constructed for an emperor, permitting that royal personage to sit in it during a drive without experiencing the least jolting. Cardan remarks that the same arrangement had been used previously in connection with oil lamps.[1]

HYDROSTATICS

The application of the principle of Archimedes to the famous problem of the crown alleged by its maker to be pure gold, though really alloyed with silver, is explained in a manuscript of the tenth century.[2] A treatise, prepared perhaps in the thirteenth century, explains how to find the volume of irregular bodies by the method of Archimedes, and emphasizes the practical value of this procedure by pointing out that the prices of some kinds of merchandise depend upon size. In this manuscript for the first time, says Thurot, occurs the name "specific gravity."

The Archimedean principle and the crown problem became favorite subjects with mathematicians, but received less attention from philosophers. As late as 1614 Keckerman, a prominent student of Aristotle, promulgated absurdities like the following: "Gravity is a motive quality, arising from cold, density, and bulk, by which the elements are carried downwards." "Water is the lower, intermediate element, cold and

[1] Breusing, *op. cit.*, p. 16; Cardan, *De subtilitate, Lib. XVII., de artibus artificiosisque rebus*, Basil, 1560, p. 1028. A remarkable form of compass was patented in 1876 by Sir William Thomson. See article "Compass" in the *Encyclopædia Britannica*, 9th ed.

[2] Ch. Thurot, *Principe d'Archmède*, p. 27.

moist." [1] It was taught by the philosophers that water has no
gravity in or on water, since it is in its own place, that air has
no gravity on water, that water rises in a pump, because nature
abhors a vacuum.[2] So firmly established were these false
maxims regarding pressure that when Boyle published his
experimental results on the mechanics of fluids, which con-
tradicted Aristotelian opinions, he felt constrained to advance
his views under the title of "hydrostatic paradoxes." [3]

LIGHT

In the thirteenth century Europe was assimilating the science of optics as obtained from the Arabs. Wilhelm von Moer-
beck, in 1278 Archbishop of Corinth, translated into Latin
Al Hazen's treatise on parabolic mirrors. About 1270 his
friend Witelo, or Vitellio, a Thuringian monk, prepared a
work on optics less diffuse and more systematic than that of
Al Hazen, on which it was based. Witelo explained the
twinkling of stars as due to the motion of the air, and
showed that the effect was intensified, if the star was viewed
through water in motion. He pointed out that the rainbow
was not formed by reflection alone, as was taught by Aristotle,
but was due to both reflection and refraction.

Prominent among writers of the Middle Ages who drew
from Arabic sources was **Roger Bacon** (1214 ?-1294). He
wrote on optics, and by mistake has been credited with the
invention of the refracting telescope. No doubt, Bacon suspected the possibility of designing an instrument which should
enable one to. "read the smallest writing at enormous distances" from the eye. But Bacon never constructed, or tried
to construct, such an instrument. The claim set up for him
grew out of a mistranslation of a passage in his works.[4]

Bacon was one of the most gifted minds of the Middle
Ages. Educated at Oxford and Paris, he became famous as

---

[1] Whewell, Vol. I., 1858, p. 236.
[2] *Ibidem.*, p. 236.
[3] *Ibidem*, pp. 189, 236.
[4] E. Wiedemann in *Wiedemann's Annalen,* Vol. 39, 1890, p. 130.

professor at Oxford. His open contempt for scholasticism and for immorality among the clergy led to the charge of heresy and to imprisonment. From his Oxford cell he sent out an appeal for *experimental science* which nearly converted his old friend Pope Clement IV. But Bacon's ideas were in advance of his time and bore no immediate fruit. In Paris he was imprisoned a second time for a period of ten years. Thus the genius of this remarkable man was crushed by the political and mental despotism of his time.

THE RENAISSANCE

THE sixteenth century was a period of intense intellectual activity. The minds of men were cut adrift from their ancient moorings and launched forth on the wide sea of inquiry.

The movement was of great breadth. Here we witness the revival of classic learning, there the production of masterpieces in art by Michel Angelo, Raphael, and Da Vinci. Yonder we behold the stupendous struggle against Church authority, known as the Reformation. The secluded mathematician infuses new life into algebra and trigonometry. The astronomer gazes at the stars and creates a new system of the universe. The physicist abandons scholastic speculation and begins to study nature in the language of experiment.

THE COPERNICAN SYSTEM

The first great scientific victory during the Renaissance was the overthrow of the Ptolemaic and the establishment of the Copernican System. We shall pause a moment to consider briefly this great epoch in the development of our sister science, astronomy, and insert a few remarks on Greek astronomy.

The sphericity of the earth and of the heavenly bodies was held by the Pythagoreans who embodied the idea in their doctrine of the "harmony of the spheres." That the earth is spherical was the prevailing view among the Greeks after the time of Pythagoras. Aristotle justified it on the ground that in a partial eclipse of the moon the shadow of the earth on the moon was circular. The sphericity of the earth was fully accepted by the greatest of observational astronomers, **Hipparchus** and Ptolemy. But during the early Middle Ages (before 600) Hebrew ideas relating to the earth—the flatness of the earth—came to be popularly accepted in Christendom. However, a few later medieval writers, for instance, Bede the

Venerable, Abelard, Grosseteste, and Raymond Lull held that the earth was round.[1]

GREEK ANTICIPATIONS OF COPERNICUS

Not only did Greek astronomers teach that the earth is round, but some of them, particularly Heraclides of Pontus and **Aristarchus** of Samos, entertained modern ideas relating to the solar system. Aristarchus in part actually anticipated the hypothesis of Copernicus and has been called "the Copernicus of antiquity." [2] He advanced the heliocentric hypothesis. Archimedes describes it thus: "His hypotheses are that the fixed stars and the sun remain unmoved, that the earth revolves about the sun in the circumference of a circle, the sun lying in the middle of the orbit." Plutarch says that Aristarchus taught also that the earth "rotates, at the same time, about its own axis." About a century after Aristarchus, Hipparchus rejected the heliocentric hypothesis, presumably because it did not seem to account for the irregularities of planetary motion (the retrograde motion, as seen by an observer on the earth), which he could explain satisfactorily on the theory of "epicycles." And so Hipparchus rejected the brilliant hypothesis of Aristarchus, though he retained the sphericity of the earth; he turned from the heliocentric to the geocentric view point.

GREEK THEORY OF EPICYCLES AND ECCENTRICS

The Greek astronomers, Eudoxus and Hipparchus, explained plantetary motions by the famous theory of epicycles and eccentrics. The apparent sweep of an outer planet around the earth was represented by the combination of two motions: (1) the yearly motion of the planet along the cir-

[1] On views of the sphericity of the earth, during the Middle Ages, see Lynn Thorndike, *History of Magic and Experimental Science*, Vol. I, pp. 480, 481; Vol. II, p. 35, 864; J. L. E. Dreyer in Charles J. Singer's *Studies in the History and Method of Science*, Oxford, 1917–1921, Vol. II., pp. 102–120.

[2] Sir Thomas Heath, *Aristarchus of Samos, the Copernicus of Antiquity*, London, 1920.

cumference of a small circle, called the *epicycle;* (2) the motion of the centre of that epicycle along the circumference of a second circle which surrounds the earth. We know now that the latter circle represents approximately the true orbit of the planet around the sun and that the epicyclic motion is only apparent. This apparent motion is due to the real motion of the earth itself. If an observer is carried around in a circle, then an object at rest will appear to him to move in a circle of equal size. The ancient theory is, therefore, approximately correct. Hipparchus observed that the theory of epicycles could not explain the motions of the planets, if the earth must be assumed to be exactly in the centre of the second circle mentioned above. This led him to establish the theory of the *eccentric.*

This ancient system was elaborated by and named after the distinguished Alexandrian astronomer Claudius Ptolemy (100–178 A.D.). It made the earth immovable at the centre of the universe. Around it revolved in successively wider spheres the Moon, Mercury, Venus, Sun, Mars, Jupiter, Saturn, and lastly the eighth sphere of the fixed stars.

The Studies of Copernicus

This geocentric theory of the universe has always had its opponents, but it was first vigorously attacked by **Nicolaus Copernicus** (1473–1543). He was probably of Polish descent and was born at Thorn, in Prussia, near the Polish boundary. For twenty-three years he was engaged in the threefold occupation of discharging ecclesiastical duties, practising medicine, and studying astronomy. With the hope of finding an explanation of less complexity than that offered by the Ptolemaic system, he zealously studied all sources of information at his command. He studied the various opinions of the ancients about the motion of the earth and planets. It is not generally known that Copernicus states in his work that the heliocentric theory was taught by Aristarchus. Aided by suggestions found in ancient sources, Copernicus gradually matured his own system. For many years he withheld from publication the manuscript of his *De orbium cœlestium revolutionibus,* but finally, in 1542, he consented to have it printed. He died before the printing was completed. This saved him from persecution. Others—Giordano Bruno and Galileo—had to suffer for the Copernican system.

Copernicus taught that the earth was spherical, rotated on its axis and revolved around the sun; that the motions of the heavenly bodies are either circular and uniform or compounded of circular and uniform motions. He explained for the first time the variation of the seasons and the cause of the apparent oscillations of the planets. A great defect in his system was his notion that all celestial motions are compounded of circular ones. It cannot be said that the argument made by Copernicus against the Ptolemaic system was conclusive. To overthrow completely the ancient theory required the genius of another man—Kepler.

Nor is it quite proper, according to modern notions, to state that the heliocentric theory is ''correct'' and the geocentric theory is ''wrong.'' They are both correct, but represent different viewpoints. One refers motions in the solar system to the sun as a point of reference (origin of coordinates), the other refers these motions to the earth as a point of reference. The superiority of the first procedure over the second is that we find it more ''convenient'' in describing the dynamics of the solar system.

Kepler's Inductive Researches

Johannes Kepler (1571–1630) was at one time in Prague assistant to the Danish astronomer Tycho Brahe. Unlike Tycho, Kepler had no talent for observation and experimentation. But he was a great thinker and excelled as a mathematician. He absorbed Copernican ideas, and early grappled with the problem of determining the real paths of the planets. In his first attempts he worked on the dreams of the Pythagoreans concerning figure and number. Intercourse with

Tycho led him to reject such mysticism and to study the observations on the planets recorded by his master. He took the planet Mars, and found that no combinations of circles would give a path which could be reconciled with the actual observations. In one case the difference between the observed and his computed values was eight minutes, and he knew that so accurate an observer as Tycho could not make an error so great. He tried an oval orbit for Mars, and rejected it; he tried an ellipse, and it fitted! Thus, after more than four years of assiduous computation, and after trying nineteen imaginary paths and rejecting each because it was more or less inconsistent with observation, Kepler at last discovered the truth. An ellipse! Why did he not think of it before? What a simple matter—after the puzzle is once solved. He worked out what are known as "Kepler's Laws," which are as follows: (1) Each planet moves in an ellipse, having the sun in one of its foci (published in 1609); (2) The radius vector joining the sun with the planet moves over equal areas in equal times (published in 1609); (3) The squares of the times of revolution of any two planets are proportional to the cubes of their mean distance from the sun, i.e. $T^2 : T_1^2 = D^3 : D_1^3$ (discovered in 1618).[1] It is seen that these laws find easy expression when it is assumed that the sun is fixed and the planets are revolving around it. The laws were interpreted by astronomers as overthrowing the Ptolemaic system. But only after a bitter struggle between science and theology did the Copernican system find general acceptance.[2]

[1] The first and second laws appear in Kepler's *Astronomia nova.* See Kepler's *Opera,* ed. Frisch, Vol. III, pp. 337, 408; the third law appeared in the *De Harmonica mundi,* lib. V, chap. 3. See *Opera,* Vol. V, p. 279.

[2] For an account of this struggle, consult A. D. White, *The Warfare of Science with Christian Theology,* New York, 1896, Vol. I., pp. 114–170.

MECHANICS

Stevin's Doctrine of Equilibrium

The sixteenth century witnessed the revival of statics and the creation of dynamics. The science of statics, which, since the time of Archimedes, had been nearly stationary, was first taken up by **Simon Stevin** (1548–1620) of Bruges in Belgium, a man remarkable for varied attainments in science, independence of thought, and extreme lack of respect for authority. He is the inventor of decimal fractions. In 1605 he published at Leyden a work written in Dutch, which in 1608 was brought out in Latin translation under the title *Hypomnemata mathematica*. Stevin accurately determined the force necessary to sustain a body on an inclined plane and investigated the equilibrium of pulleys. He employed the principle of the parallelogram of forces, but did not expressly formulate it. In fact, he was in possession of a complete doctrine of equilibrium.[1] Da Vinci, the famous painter, Guido Ubaldi, and Galileo paid some attention to statics.

Life of Galileo

The creation of the science of dynamics is due to **Galileo Galilei** (1564–1642), a native of Pisa. He studied medicine at the University of Pisa, but in a few years he abandoned it for the more congenial pursuit of mathematics and science carried on at Florence where his parents had taken up their residence. In 1589, he received the appointment, for three years, to the mathematical chair in Pisa. During this time he performed memorable experiments on falling bodies, but his new views met with so much opposition that he was obliged to resign in 1591. From 1592 to 1610 he was professor at Padua. It was there that he manufactured telescopes, microscopes, and his air thermometers. With his telescopes he made important astronomical observations. Encircled by the lustre of

[1] For details consult E. Mach, *Science of Mechanics* (ed. McCormack), pp. 24–34.

these achievements, he departed from Padua and accepted the invitation to Florence, as philosopher and mathematician to the Grand Duke of Tuscany. A few years later his conflict with the church began. He boldly preached Copernican doctrines, and in consequence was summoned before the Inquisition at Rome. The theory of the earth's motion was condemned by the Inquisition, and Galileo received an injunction to silence. For some years Galileo remained silent, though always at work. In 1632 he published, contrary to the edict of 1616, a new work, the *Dialogo,* which was a brilliant success as an argument in favor of the Copernican theory. This brought about a second trial. The old man of seventy was subjected to indignity, imprisonment, and threats. On his knees he was forced publicly to "abjure, curse, and detest the error and the heresy of the movement of the earth."[1] At first he was kept in separation from his family and friends, but was allowed a little more liberty, after he became blind and wasted with disease.[2]

Galileo was among the first to teach that the Holy Scriptures were not intended as a text-book on science—a truth which the world has been slow to recognize.

The first years after 1632 were given to the study of dynamics. In 1638 appeared, not in Italy, but in Holland, his dialogues on motion, under the title *Discourses on Two New Sciences pertaining to Mechanics and Local Motions.* These are now considered his greatest and most substantial achievements.

Recent criticism has endeavored to sift the truth from what some have suspected to be legendary in the life of Galileo. Did he actually perform the experiment from the leaning tower

[1] Quoted by A. D. White, *op. cit.,* Vol. I., p. 142. After the abjuration, as Galileo arose from his kneeling posture, he is said to have murmured the words, "Eppur si muove" ("and yet it moves"). Upon a careful study of documents, G. Berthold comes to the conclusion that this story is legendary. Yet there can be no doubt that the "Eppur si muove" expresses what must have been Galileo's innermost conviction. See Berthold, *Zeitschr. f. Math.* und *Phys.,* Vol. 42, 1897, pp. 5–9; R. Wolf, *Gesch. d. Astronomie,* München, 1877, p. 262.

[2] A. D. White, *op. cit.,* pp. 142, 143.

at Pisa, before a university gathering? Did he actually count the oscillations of the chandelier in the cathedral at Pisa? What are the facts relating to his trial, conviction and punishment by the Inquisition? Is the earliest life of Galileo, written by his pupil Vincenzo Viviani, trustworthy? These and many other questions, the answers to which are partly foreshadowed in what we have already stated relating to Galileo's life, received the attention of many writers, but particularly of the German Wohlwill,[1] and the Italian Antonio Favaro, the editor of the magnificent twenty-volume National Edition of the works of Galileo.

GALILEO'S EXPERIMENTS AT THE LEANING TOWER

That Galileo publicly performed the experiments at the leaning tower of Pisa, rests upon the authority of his pupil Viviani who knew Galileo only during his last years of life. Suspecting this account to be legendary, Wohlwill sought for other sources of information, and was surprised by the fact that contemporary writers, four of whom wrote on falling bodies, make no mention of such public experiments by Galileo. Of course, the failure of these four writers, who did *not* write lives of Galileo, to mention the Pisan experiments, does not prove Viviani wrong, who *did* write a life of Galileo. Wohlwill frankly admits that this evidence by itself is inconclusive. He examined also a long tract on motion written by Galileo, probably during the first year as lecturer at Pisa, called *De motu*. Galileo never published this tract; it was first printed on the two hundredth anniversary of his death and is included in the first volume of Favaro's National Edition. Wohlwill considered the *De motu* a decidedly immature production, indicating an uncertain state of mind on the part of Galileo, that is incompatible with the aggressive, challenging attitude which alone could lead to the public experimentation at Pisa, that Viviani attributes to him. From the study of the

[1] Emil Wohwill, *Galilei und sein Kampf für die Copernicanische Lehre*, Vol. I, 1909, pp. 80–118.

De motu Wohlwill concludes that Galileo never publicly performed the Pisan experiments. Such is not the conclusion of Favaro, who found from a life-long study of the Galileon period and records drawn from many sources, that Viviani was quite reliable. Our own inference with respect to the *De motu* differs from that of Wohlwill. True, young Galileo's ideas of motion *in a vacuum* were faulty. He was impressed by the views of the Spanish-Arabic philosopher Averroës, that in a vacuum, the lighter body fell the faster. Here speculation was rampant, because no direct appeal to experiment was then possible. But under conditions of fall through the air, when Galileo could experiment, the *De motu* indicates that Galileo had reached clear, quite accurate, and convincing results on falling bodies. While Galileo nowhere in his writings refers specifically to the leaning tower of Pisa, he speaks in his *De motu* half a dozen times of experiments on bodies falling from a tower—"ex turri," "ex alta turri," "ab alta turri." He maintained a critical attitude toward Aristotle. There are ten chapters which in their very headings indicate his strong opposition to Stagirite teachings: "contra Aristotelem," "in quo error Aristotelis manifestatur." He derides those who "take things for granted simply because Aristotle says so." These are the words of a young man who felt intensely and would not hesitate to appear openly before a university assembly to demonstrate the errors of Aristotle. We are safe in concluding that Viviani's account of the Pisan experiments is correct.

The criticism of Aristotle's law of falling bodies having met with opposition at the University, it appears that Galileo decided to give to his opponents an ocular proof. He did this with the enthusiasm, courage and imprudence of youth. That bodies fall with equal velocity, allowing for the resistance of the air, he proved, as Viviani says, "by repeated experiments made from the height of the Campanile of Pisa in the presence of the other professors and philosophers and the whole student body." Apocryphal in modern accounts of these experiments are the statements of the exact weight of the shot which Galileo used. These statements are probably suggested by the passage written by Galileo in 1638 (about 47 years later) where in his *Discourses* he lets Sagredo say: "But I, Simplicio, who have made the test, can assure you that a cannon ball weighing one or two hundred pounds, or even more, will not reach the ground by as much as a span ahead of a musket ball weighing only half a pound, provided both are dropped from a height of 200 cubits." [1]

It must be emphasized that, before the time of Galileo, the law of Aristotle on falling bodies, though generally accepted, was not universally held. The Frenchman N. Oresme, the Portuguese Alverus Thomas, the Oxford don William Heytesbury, and probably Leonardo da Vinci had all arrived at correct notions on falling bodies.[2] As far as known, these men did not experiment. Reasoning upon their general observations of moving bodies, they arrived at the relation $s = \frac{1}{2} g t^2$. The great achievement of Galileo was the stress placed upon experiment, so as to remove all doubt. His emphasis on experimentation revolutionized physics.

GALILEO'S DISCOURSES ON TWO NEW SCIENCES

And yet, an interesting feature in Galileo's *Discourses on two New Sciences* is the fact that the book is not purely a presentation of experimental data; it contains much deductive reasoning. For example, discussing the nature of uniformly accelerated motion, the question arose, is the velocity proportional to the distance passed over? This question is answered, not by actual physical measurement, but by what may be called a thought experiment. "If the velocity with which a body overcomes four yards is double the velocity with which it passed over the first two yards, then the times necessary

[1] See Henry Crew and Alfonso de Salvio's translation, under the title, *Dialogues concerning Two New Sciences,* New York, 1914, p. 62. A translation into German is given in *Ostwald's Klassiker der exacten Wissenschaften* Nos. 11, 24, 25.

[2] See H. Wieleitner in *Zeitschrift für mathematischen und Naturwissenschaftlichen Unterricht,* Vol. 44, 1913, p. 209–228.

for these processes must be equal; but four yards can be overcome in the same time as two yards only if there is an instantaneous motion. We see, however, that the body takes time in falling and requires, indeed, less time for a fall of two than of four yards. Hence it is not true that the velocity increases proportionally to the distance fallen."[1]

Galileo then proceeds to a second assumption,—velocity is proportional to the time of falling,—and, finding no self-contradiction in it, he goes about to test it experimentally. In a board twelve yards long a trough one inch wide was cut out in a straight line and lined with very smooth parchment. A brass ball, perfectly round and polished, was allowed to run down the inclined plane. About one hundred trials were made for different inclinations and lengths of the plane. The distance of descent was found always to vary closely as the squares of the times. It is interesting to notice how Galileo measured the time. Accurate clocks or watches were then not available. He attached a very small spout to the bottom of a water pail and caught in a cup the water escaping through the spout during the time when the body travelled through a given distance. The water was weighed accurately and at the times of descent taken proportional to the ascertained weight.[2]

FIG. 3.

To exhibit the relation between velocity and distance, Galileo establishes the theorem that the time in which a body moving from rest with uniformly accelerated velocity travels a given distance is the same as the time it would require to travel the same distance with a uniform velocity equal to half its actual final velocity. This truth he illustrated by Fig. 3.[3] The line *EB* represents the final velocity which varies directly as the time represented by *AB*. The area *ABE* stands for the

1 Crew and De Salvio, *op. cit.*, p. 168.
2 Crew and De Salvio, *op. cit.*, p. 179.
3 *Ibidem*, p. 173.

distance gone over. This area is evidently equal to that of the rectangle *ABFG,* where *FB* stands for the average velocity. This geometrical illustration has retained a place in some modern text-books. Still more common is the illustration (Fig. 4) showing the path of a body projected horizontally and acted upon by gravity.[1] In the dialogue on this subject Galileo permites Sagredo to remark naïvely, "Truly the conception is new, ingenious, and incisive; it rests on an assumption, namely, that the transverse motion remains constant and that, at the same time, the naturally accelerated motion maintains itself, proportional to the squares of the times, and that

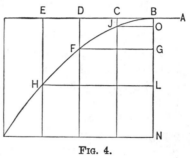

Fig. 4.

such motions mix, indeed, but do not disturb, change, and impede each other, so that finally, by the progressive motion, the path of the projectile is not degenerated—a behavior hardly comprehensible to me."

Galileo was the first to show that the path of a projectile is a parabola. Previously it was believed by some that a cannon ball moved forward at first in a straight line and then suddenly fell vertically to the ground.

Galileo had an understanding of *centrifugal force* and gave a correct definition of *momentum.* This emphasis of momentum as a fundamental quantity in dynamics is of prime importance. He measured momentum by the product of velocity and weight; mass is a later Huygenian and Newtonian concept. In the swinging of a simple pendulum, Galileo says that "every momentum acquired in the descent along an arc is equal to that which causes the same moving body to ascend through the same arc." His explanation of the path of projectiles indicates that Galileo had grasped the

[1] *Ibidem,* p. 249.

first law and the second law of motion. He did not generalize them so as to make them applicable to bodies not subject to the earth's gravitation. That step was taken by Newton. The term "inertia" was used by Kepler who applied it to bodies at rest.[1] The first law of motion is now often called the law of inertia.

Galileo did not fully grasp the third law of motion,—the law of the equality of action and reaction, though he corrected some errors of Aristotle. He discusses this topic the sixth day of his *Discourses*. That Galileo did not advance this third law needs emphasis, since in some recent popular science publications this law is pronounced one of Galileo's glorious achievements.

With Stevin and others Galileo also wrote on statics. He formulated the principle of the *parallelogram of forces*, but he did not fully recognize its scope.

Still another subject engaging Galileo's attention was the laws of the pendulum. As in case of falling bodies, so here the first observations were made while he was a young man. Tradition has it that in 1583, while he was praying in the cathedral at Pisa, his attention was arrested by the motion of the great lamp which after being lighted had been left swinging. Galileo proceeded to time its oscillations by the only watch in his possession, namely, his own pulse. He found the times, as near as he could tell, to remain the same, even after the motion had greatly diminished. Thus was discovered the isochronism of the pendulum. Galileo was at that time studying medicine, and he applied the pendulum to pulse measurements at the sick-bed. He also proposed its use in astronomical observations. More careful experiments carried out by him later, and described in his *Discourses*, showed that the time of oscillation was independent of the mass and material of the pendulum and varied as the square root of its length.[2] His last contribution to the art of time measurement was made after he had become blind. In 1641 he dictated

[1] Kepler, *Opera omnia* (Ed. Frisch) Vol. VI., p. 341, 342.
[2] Crew and De Salvio, *op. cit.*, p. 96.

to his son Vicenzo and his pupil Viviani the description and drawing of a pendulum clock. The original drawing is extant, but a model, said to have been constructed by Viviani in 1649, has been lost. Galileo's invention did not become generally known at that time, and fifteen years later, in 1656, Christian Huygens independently invented a pendulum clock, which met with general and rapid appreciation. The honor of this great invention belongs, therefore, to Galileo and Huygens.[1]

Galileo's *Discourses* of 1638 are masterpieces of popular exposition, which fact alone renders them worthy of perusal. But they contain other points of merit. W. G. Adams well says: "The true method of teaching mechanics is illustrated by the way in which Galileo established the first principles of dynamics and placed them before his pupils. Due weight should be given both to experimental and to rational mechanics, and the best way of bringing the subject before students is to have parallel but distinct courses of experimental and theoretical lectures attended by students at the same time." [2]

Among his contemporaries it was chiefly the novelties he detected in the skies that made him celebrated, but Lagrange claims that his astronomical discoveries required only a telescope and perseverance, while, in the case of dynamics, it took an extraordinary genius to discover laws from phenomena which we see constantly and of which the true explanation escaped all earlier philosophers.

[1] The invention of the pendulum clock has been claimed also for the Swiss Joost Bürgi (R. Wolf, *Geschichte der Astronomie*, 1877, p. 369), for Richard Harris of London (*Edinburgh Encyclopædia*, 1830, Vol. 11, p. 117), and for others, but these claims have been rejected by later authorities. On the history of this invention consult E. Gerland, *Zeitschr. f. Instrumenten Kunde*, Vol. VIII., 1888, p. 77: W. C. L. v. Schaïk in same journal, Vol. VII., pp. 350 and 428; S. Günther, *Vermischte Untersuchungen*, Leipzig, 1876, pp. 308–344; G. Berthold, *Schlömilch's Zeitschr.*, Vol. 38, 1893, Hist. Lit. Abth., p. 123.

[2] *Nature*, Vol. V., 1871–1872, p. 389.

LIGHT

Invention of the Telescope and Microscope

The greatest achievement in optics during the Renaissance was the invention of instruments, giving an observer a glimpse of the infinitely distant and of the infinitely small. We refer to the telescope and the microscope.

According to tradition the telescope was invented by accident. The great Huygens in his *Dioptrica* asserts that a man capable of inventing the telescope by mere thinking and application of geometrical principles, without the concurrence of accident, would have been gifted with superhuman genius. To this remarkable statement Mach adds that it does not follow that accident alone is sufficient to produce an invention. The inventor "must *distinguish* the new feature, impress it upon his memory, unite and interweave it with the rest of his thought; in short, he must possess the capacity to *profit by experience*." [1]

There have been brought forward numerous candidates for the honor of the invention of these marvellous instruments. Four nations, the English, Italian, Dutch, and German, have each endeavored to secure a decision in favor of one of its own countrymen.

The evidence we possess favors the Dutch. The first telescope was probably constructed in 1608 by **Hans Lippershey,** a native of Wesel, and a manufacturer of spectacles in Middleburg. [2] He prepared his lenses, not of glass, but of rock crystal. A document found in the archives at the Hague shows that on October 2, 1608, he applied for a patent. He was told to modify his construction and make an instrument enabling the observer to see through it with both eyes. This he accomplished the same year. He did not receive his patent, but the government of the United Netherlands paid him in-

---

[1] E. Mach, "On the Part Played by Accident in Invention and Discovery," *Monist*, Vol. VI., p. 166.

[2] Dr. H. Servus, *Die Geschichte des Fernrohrs*, Berlin, 1886, p. 39.

stead 900 gulden for the instrument and an equal sum for two other binocular telescopes, completed in 1609.[1]

The invention of the microscope is nearly contemporaneous with that of the telescope. It is now usually ascribed to Zacharias Joannides and his father, though Huygens assigned it to Cornelius Drebbel.[2] At first the eye-pieces consisted of concave lenses. Franciscus Fontana of Naples appears to have been the first to replace the concave eye-lens by a convex one. Kepler was the first to suggest a similar change in the telescope. All the artisans whom we have mentioned in connection with the microscope are known to have been prominent in the manufacture of telescopes.

The use of the new instruments spread over Europe with

[1] *Ibidem.*, p. 40. The claim that Roger Bacon invented the telescope is now generally abandoned. The Italian *Giambattista della Porta*, known as the inventor of the *camera obscura*, has. been named in this connection on the strength of passages in his *Magia Naturalis* (2d Ed., 1589) to the effect that by judicious combination of two lenses, one convex and the other concave, objects at a distance as well as objects near at hand may be magnified to the eye. But his experiments appear to have been confined to the preparation of suitable eye-glasses for persons with abnormal vision; the invention of the telescope is here out of the question. In 1571 Leonard Digges of Bristol published a book in which the effect of combining concave and convex lenses is explained, somewhat as in Porta's book of 1589, but all statements of this sort must be regarded as having prepared for the invention rather than as having actually constituted it. Previous to 1831 the best evidence at hand seemed to point to Zacharias Joannides of Middleburg in Netherlands as the inventor of the telescope, though his countrymen, Adrian Metius and Cornelius Drebbel, the Germans Simon Marius and Kepler, and the Italians Franciscus Fontana and Galileo have all had their supporters. All of these except Kepler, were actually engaged in the manufacture of telescopes.

[2] G. Govi claims the invention of the microscope for Galileo. From a document printed in 1610 he proves that Galileo had modified the telescope to see very small and very near objects. Consult G. Govi in *Rendic. Accad. Napol.*, (2) I., 1887; C. R. 107, No. 14, 1888; *Poske's Zeitschr.*, Zweiter Jahrgang, 1888, p. 93. Galileo says in his *Sidereus Nuncius*, which was published at the beginning of the year 1610, that he first heard of the invention of the telescope "about ten months ago." His microscope was a modified telescope. Hence his microscope must have been made in 1609 or 1610. Now, if we may trust the testimony contained in a letter by the Dutch ambassador, Borelius, written in 1655, then Zacharias Joannides did not construct a telescope until 1610, "long after" (longe post) he had invented the microscope. See H. Servus, *op. cit.*, pp. 17, 18. According to this Joannides anticipated Galileo.

rapidity. In England the mathematician Thomas Harriot had a telescope magnifying fifty times, and he observed the satellites of Jupiter in 1610, almost as early as did Galileo.[1]

The news of the invention of the telescope incited Kepler, who had already given much time to the study of optics, to fresh efforts. In 1611 he published his *Dioptrica*, which is the earliest work containing an attempt to elaborate the theory of the telescope. Such an attempt demands a knowledge of the law of refraction. Kepler arrived at an empirical expression which was merely an approximation. He failed to discover the accurate law, as had Ptolemy and Al Hazen. His approximate result for small angles $(i < 30°)$ was $i = nr$, where n is a constant, equal to 3/2 for a ray passing from air to glass. This was near enough to the truth to enable him to give in broad outline the correct theory of the telescope.

First Use of the Telescope in Scientific Investigation

The earliest important scientific discoveries with the aid of the telescope were made by Galileo. He was led to take up this line of research by rumors which had reached him regarding the invention in Belgium of an instrument through which distant objects could be seen distinctly. He probably heard that this had been effected by the combination of a concave and a convex lens, and he set to work to devise such an instrument himself. Guided by the hints he had received and by his knowledge of dioptrics, he soon succeeded. He made a rough telescope with two glasses fixed at the end of a leaden tube, both having one side flat; the other side of the one lens being concave, and of the other lens convex. It made objects appear three times nearer and nine times larger. Thereupon, sparing neither expense nor labor, he got so far as to construct

[1] In 1585 Sir Walter Raleigh sent Harriot to Virginia as surveyor with Sir Richard Grenville's expedition. Among the mathematical instruments by which the wonder of the Indians was aroused, Harriot mentions "a perspective glass whereby was showed many strange sights." See *Dic. of Nat. Biography*.

an instrument which magnified an object nearly a thousand times and brought it more than thirty times nearer.[1]

Galileo went to Venice and showed it to the signoria. Says he: "Many noblemen and senators, although of great age, mounted the steps of the highest church towers at Venice to watch the ships, which were visible through my glass two hours before they were seen entering the harbor."

Galileo's telescopes were much sought after, and he received numerous orders from learned men, princes, and governments —Holland, the birthplace of the telescope, not excepted.[2]

Galileo turned his telescope toward the moon and discovered mountains and craters; he turned it to Jupiter and saw its satellites (January 7, 1610); he pointed it at Saturn and saw the planet threefold—now known to have been due to an imperfect view of the ring; he examined the sun, saw its spots moving, and concluded that the sun rotates. All this was achieved in 1610. His observations seemed to confirm the Copernican theory. The cloud of opposition to Galileo began to gather. Some refused to believe their eyes, and asserted that, while the telescope answered well enough for terrestrial objects, it was false and illusory when pointed at celestial bodies. Others refused to look through it. Among the latter was a university professor. Galileo wrote to Kepler: "Oh, my dear Kepler, how I wish that we could have one hearty laugh together! Here, at Padua, is the principal professor of philosophy, whom I have repeatedly and urgently requested to look at the moon and planets through my glass, which he pertinaciously refuses to do. Why are you not here? What shouts of laughter we should have at this glorious folly! And to hear the professor of philosophy at Pisa laboring before the Grand Duke with logical arguments, as if with magical incantations to charm the new planets out of the sky."[3] The

[1] Consult *Sidereus Nuncius* of 1610, reprinted in editions of Galileo's works; also Karl von Gebler, *Galileo Galilei and the Roman Curia* trans. by Mrs. George Sturge, London, 1879, p. 17.

[2] Gebler, *op. cit.*, p. 18.

[3] This translation is taken from O. Lodge, *Pioneers of Science*, 1893, p. 106.

antagonism to Galileo and his hated telescope became stronger. The clergy began to denounce him and his methods. Father Caccini became known as a punster by preaching a sermon from the text, "Ye men of Galilee, why stand ye gazing up into heaven?"[1]

ELECTRICITY AND MAGNETISM

GILBERT'S EXPERIMENTATION

By the side of Galileo, "the originator of modern physics," we may well place Gilbert, "the father of the magnetic philosophy." **William Gilbert** (1540–1603) of Colchester, county of Essex, England, studied at St. John's College, Cambridge, then travelled on the Continent. There, as well as in England, he "practised as a physician with great success and applause." He was appointed by Queen Elizabeth her physician-in-ordinary, and she settled upon him an annual pension for the purpose of aiding him in the prosecution of his philosophical studies. His first investigations were in chemistry; but later, for eighteen years or more, he experimented on electricity and magnetism. In 1600 he published his great work, the *De Magnete*. J. F. W. Herschel speaks of this book as "full of valuable facts and experiments ingeniously reasoned on." It is the first great work on physical science produced in England. Galileo pronounced it "great to a degree that is enviable," but at home it was not appreciated so highly.[2] In subsequent generations the book was quite forgotten.

Gilbert's contempt for the methods of the schoolmen crops out everywhere in his book. In fact, his criticisms of worthy predecessors are at times ungenerous. He withheld his work from publication for many years. "Why should I," says he in his preface, "submit this noble and . . . this new and inadmissible philosophy to the judgment of men who have taken

[1] A. D. White, *op. cit.*, Vol. I., p. 133.
[2] See William Gilbert of Colchester, *On the Loadstone and Magnetic Bodies, and on the Great Magnet, the Earth,* trans. by P. F. Mottelay, London, 1893, "Biographical Memoir," pp. ix–xxvii. All our references will be to this edition of the *De Magnete*.

oath to follow the opinion of others, to the most senseless corrupters of the arts, to lettered clowns, grammatists, sophists, spouters, and the wrong-headed rabble, to be denounced, torn to tatters, and heaped with contumely. To you alone, true philosophers, ingenious minds, who not only in books but in things themselves look for knowledge, have I dedicated these foundations of magnetic science—a new style of philosophizing" (p. xlix.). Modern philosophers "must be made to quit the sort of learning that comes only from books, and that rests only on vain arguments from probability and upon conjectures" (p. 47). "Men of acute intelligence, without actual knowledge of facts, and in the absence of experiment, easily slip and err" (p. 82). Gilbert was the first to use the terms "electric force," "electric attraction," magnetic "pole." Bodies which attract in the same way as amber he called "electrics." Metals and some other bodies he called "non-electrics," because he could not make them attract by friction.

Pupils beginning physics sometimes fail to discriminate between magnetic action and electric attraction or repulsion. History reveals the same error on the part of some early writers. The differentiation between the two was first clearly made by the Milanese mathematician, **Hieronimo Cardano** (1501–1576).[1] English writers usually give his name as Cardan. Gilbert complains of those who "are ignorant that the causes of the loadstone's movements are very different from those which give to amber its properties" (p. 75). The Italian Baptista Porta had taught that iron rubbed with diamond turns to the north, as if it had been rubbed on a loadstone. To this Gilbert says, "We made the experiment ourselves with seventy-five diamonds in presence of many witnesses, employing a number of iron bars and pieces of wire, manipulating them with the greatest care while they floated in water, supported by corks; but never was it granted me to see the effect mentioned by Porta" (p. 218). Gilbert wages war

[1] Consult P. Benjamin, p. 249.

against Cardan, who "asks why no other metal is drawn by any stone; and his answer is, because no other metal is so cold as iron; as if, forsooth, cold were cause of attraction, or iron were much colder than lead, which neither follows the loadstone nor leans toward it. But this is sorry trifling, no better than old wives' gossip" (p. 101). "A needle turns no less rapidly, no less eagerly, to the loadstone though a flame intervenes than if only air stands between" (p. 107). He then makes the interesting observation, "But were the iron itself red-hot, it certainly would not be attracted," though it will be "as soon as the temperature has fallen somewhat" (p. 107). Some modern texts give the elegant experiment performed by Gilbert of magnetizing an iron bar or wire, while held so as to point north and south, by being "stretched or hammered or pulled," or by being hammered while cooling from a red heat (pp. 211, 212).

Gilbert's experiments on terrestrial magnetism are epoch making. To him we owe the "new and till now unheard-of

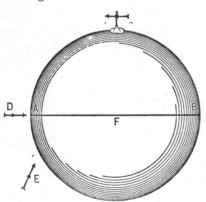

FIG. 5. Gilbert's Terrella.

view of the earth" as a great magnet (p. 64).[1] Gilbert followed partly in the steps of Peregrinus and used a little loadstone formed into the shape of a globe. Placing pivoted needles near this magnetic globe, he observed the directive and attractive force which it exerted upon them. In that small body he found many properties of the earth. Hence he called it the "terrella" or "little earth." The loadstone pos-

[1] The theory that the earth has a magnetic pole had been advanced in 1546 by *Gerhard Mercator*, but the letter on this subject was not printed until 1869. It is reprinted in Hellmann's *Neudrucke*, No. 10, Berlin 1898.

sesses the actions peculiar to the globe, of attraction, polarity, revolution, of taking position in the universe according to the law of the whole" (p. 66). "Toward it, as we see in the case of the earth, magnetic bodies tend from all sides, and adhere to it" (p. 67). "Like the earth it has an equator, . . . [it] has the power of direction and of standing still at north and south" (p. 67).

Since the earth has magnetic poles, it follows from the law of magnetic action that the north-pointing pole of a needle is the *south* pole; "all instrument makers, and navigators, are egregiously mistaken in taking for the north pole of the loadstone the part of the stone that inclines to the north" (p. 27). Gilbert's discovery that the earth is a huge magnet made it easy to explain why the needle points north. Prior to Gilbert all sorts of reasons had been assigned. "The common herd of philosophizers, in search of the causes of magnetic movements, called in causes remote and far away. Martinus Cortesius . . . dreamt of an attractive magnetic point beyond the heavens, acting on iron. Petrus Peregrinus holds that direction has its rise at the celestial poles. Cardan was of the opinion that the rotation of iron is caused by the star in the tail of Ursa Major. The Frenchman Bessard thinks that the magnetic needle turns to the pole of the zodiac. . . . So has ever been the wont of mankind; homely things are vile; things from abroad and things afar are dear to them and the object of longing" (p. 179).

Gilbert was a strong adherent of the Copernican system. One object of his book was to furnish additional arguments in support of the new doctrine. His experiments exhibit throughout painstaking accuracy, but his application of experimental results to cosmology was inconclusive. Thus, he endeavored to prove that the earth rotated because of its magnetic quality. No doubt these unfortunate speculations were the cause of the undue neglect from which his book suffered so long.

Declination Different in Different Places. Dip

That the needle does not point true north and south was known to the Chinese as early as the eleventh century. That there are variations in declination was clearly recognized by Columbus on his memorable voyage of 1492. An atlas issued in 1436 by Andrea Blanco was formerly believed to disclose the knowledge that the declination is not everywhere the same, but Bertelli denies him this knowledge and interprets the indicated corrections for variation in a different manner.[1] Columbus was certainly the first to make known a place of no declination which he found not far from the island of Corvo, one of the Azores. Baptista Porta had taught that the declination varied regularly with the longitude, so that terrestrial longitude could be found readily from the observed declination. Gilbert had data on hand to show that this "is false as false can be" (p. 251). However, Gilbert himself falls into error by assuming the declination at any one place to be invariable, and by presuming that the magnetic and geographic equators were identical and that lines of equal dip coincided with the geographic parallels. These are instances showing that the propensity to speculation without checking the results by "sure experiment" sometimes secured control even of Gilbert.

The existence of dip is usually believed to have been discovered in 1576 by **Robert Norman,** a "skilled navigator and ingenious artificer" of Bristol, who announced the new fact in a treatise of 1581, entitled, *The Newe Attractiue.* To Norman's treatise was added a supplement prepared in 1581 by William Borough, who dwells more particularly on rules for finding the declination. Hellmann attributes the discovery of dip to Georg Hartmann in 1544, but admits that his determination was very inaccurate. Hartmann's letter was not published till 1831.[2]

---

[1] Bertelli, *Sulla Epistola di P. Peregrino,* Rome, 1868, mem. III., 77; Benjamin, p. 197.
[2] Hartmann's, Norman's, and Borough's interesting papers are reprinted in Hellmann's *Neudrucke,* No. 10.

METEOROLOGY

One of the earliest systematic meteorological records is that
kept in the years 1582–1597 by the astronomer **Tycho Brahe**
at his observatory in Prague.[1] Instruments for weather observations were still few. The windvane, first found among
the Greeks, was placed in Christian Europe on top of church-
steeples, and received the form of a cock, because that bird
was the emblem of clerical vigilance.[2]

About 1570 the astronomer Egnatio Danti had erected in
Bologna and Florence a number of pendulum anemometers
(Fig. 6) for measuring the force of the wind. In modern
times this instrument has been used extensively in Europe.
Its first invention is often wrongly attributed to Robert
Hooke.[3]

The earliest known hygroscope is described in the works of
the German cardinal **Nico-
laus de Cusa** (1401–1464).
He says: "If you suspend
from one side of a large
balance a large quantity
of wool, and from the
other sides stones, so that
they weigh equally in dry
air, then you will see that
when the air inclines to-
ward dampness, the weight
of the wool increases, and
when the air tends to dryness, it decreases." The
Italians attribute the first
hygrometers to Da Vinci. About the middle of the sixteenth
century Mizauld[4] noticed the effect of moisture on gut-strings.

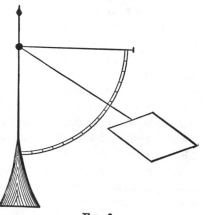

FIG. 6.

[1] G. Hellmann, *Himmel und Erde*, Vol. II., 1890, p. 113, etc.
[2] *Ibidem*, p. 119.
[3] *Ibidem*, p. 121; Sprat, *Hist. of Royal Soc.*, 1667, p. 173.
[4] *Ephemerides aëris perpetuae*, Lutetiae, 1554, p. 49; Hellmann, *op.
cit.*, p. 122.

This has since been used repeatedly in the design of hygrometers. About the same time Baptista Porta called attention to the hygroscopic properties of the beards of wild oats. He saw children paste to a beard small pieces of paper, which would bend one way or another, according as the air was dry or moist. In the early part of the seventeenth century wild oats were used extensively as a hygroscopic substance.

THE INDUCTIVE METHOD OF SCIENTIFIC INQUIRY

The necessity of observation and experiment in scientific research was emphasized in the writings of **Francis Bacon.** He was a man of extraordinary literary gifts, and his works on scientific method contain many bright passages, with which popular authors delight to ornament their title-pages and chapter-headings. People unacquainted with the history of scientific progress have even imagined that to Francis Bacon and his *Novum Organum* are principally due the reawakening of the world, the overthrow of the Aristotelian physical philosophy, and the introduction into science of the inductive method. Macaulay [1] writes: "The *Novum organum* takes in at once all the domains of science—all the past, the present and the future, all the errors of two thousand years, all the encouraging signs of the passing times, all the bright hopes of the coming ages." Bacon "moved the intellects which have moved the world."

As a matter of fact, Bacon was not a scientific man; he had little practical experience in experimentation; he lacked the scientific instinct to pursue in detail the great truth that nature must be studied directly by observation and experiment. He appears to have rejected the Copernican system, and he treated with contempt the researches of Galileo and Gilbert—the two greatest experimentalists of his day. He observes that "Gilbert has attemped to raise a general system

[1] T. B. Macaulay, *Essays*, 1855, Vol. II., pp. 142–254 (*Edinburgh Review, July* 1837); *Miscellaneous Works of Lord Macaulay*, Vol. 2, New York, 1880, pp. 455, 456.

upon the magnet, endeavoring to build a ship out of materials not sufficient to make the rowing-pins of a boat.''[1] Bacon
undertook to give an infallible rule by which any one could,
with perseverance, make scientific discoveries. We "must
analyze Nature by proper rejections and exclusions, and then,
after a sufficient number of negatives, come to a conclusion
on the affirmative instances.''[2] He thought nature could be
studied by rule, without the aid of hypotheses and scientific
imagination. The scientist who passed the severest criticism
upon Bacon's method was the chemist J. Liebig,[3] who said:
"Bacon meant therewith experiments which one undertakes
without knowing what one is seeking, they are endeavors to
compare without the motive therefor, and their results are
therefore purposeless and aimless.'' "The true method does
not progress, as Bacon would have it, from many cases,
but from a single case; when this is explained then all
analogous cases are explained; our method is the old Aristotelian method, only applied with immensely greater skill
and experience. . . .'' "The result reached by his method is
always zero.'' "Such a procedure can never lead to discovery of truth.'' "The real method of natural science excludes
chance (Willkür) and is diametrically the opposite of Bacon's
method.'' Such is the dictum of the great German chemist.
E. Mach says:[4] "I do not know whether Swift's academy of
schemers in Lagado, in which great discoveries and inventions
were made by a sort of verbal game of dice, was intended as
a satire on Francis Bacon's method of making discoveries by
means of huge synoptic tables constructed by scribes. It certainly would not have been illplaced.'' Similar views have

[1] F. Bacon, *De augmentis scientiarum.*
[2] *Novum Organum*, I., Aphorism CV.
[3] Justus von Liebig, *Ueber Francis Bacon von Verulam und die
Methode der Naturforschung*, München, 1863, pp. 11, 47, 48.
[4] *Monist*, Vol. VI, 1893, p. 174. Consult further Jevons, *Principles
of Science*, 1892, p. 507; P. Duhem, *L'Évolution des Théories Physiques*,
Louvain, 1896, pp. 8–10; Justus von Liebig, *Reden und Abhandlung*,
Leipzig, 1874; Draper, *Hist. of the Intell. Develop. of Europe*, 1875,
Vol. II., p. 259; Whewell, *op. cit.*, Vol. I., p. 339.

been expressed by George Howard Darwin,[1] Augustus De Morgan [2] and Oliver Lodge.[3]

Such great praise and censure must signify great merits and great defects. This much is certain, Bacon ranks as the earliest prominent methodologist of scientific inquiry. Bacon insists that men should mark when they miss as well as when they hit; they should observe many cases—the more the better. He compares his method to a pair of compasses which enables any beginner to draw a perfect circle. Needless to say, his method did not stand the test of experience. It was not generally followed in the actual pursuit of physical investigation, but in zoology and botany it was used extensively in the work of classification, before the time of Charles Darwin. But the great advance in these two sciences came through the aid of the hypothesis advanced by Darwin.

A revision of the methodology of science, as stated by Bacon, was undertaken by John Stuart Mill, who assigned to hypotheses their legitimate place. But even his scheme lacks completeness. He, like Bacon, underrated the importance of mathematics, and of exact measurement. Neither clearly provided a place for mathematical physics. Both underrated the rôle of the scientific imagination, the importance of which has been brought out very strongly by Tyndall and more recently by Rutherford.

[1] G. H. Darwin's Presidential Address, *Report of British Association*, 1886, p. 511.
[2] A. De Morgan, *A Budget of Paradoxes*, Chicago, Vol. I., 1915, pp. 82, 84.
[3] O. Lodge, *Pioneers of Science*, London, 1905, p. 136.

THE SEVENTEENTH CENTURY

THE first effects of the Reformation were favorable for the progress of science in Germany. But during and after the Thirty Years' War (1618–1648) civil and religious strife, as well as a political dismemberment into a lax confederation of petty despotisms, ensued. In consequence, science almost died out in Germany.

In France the ascension of Henry IV. to the throne, and the promulgation of the Edict of Nantes (1598), somewhat lessened religious strife; the genius of the French people began to flourish. At the time when the blossoms of science withered away in Germany, they were budding forth in France.

In Italy the fate of Galileo dampened scientific enthusiasm, while in England, where religious contention never fully engrossed the attention of the people, the time of Gilbert was followed by a period of extraordinary scientific achievement.

In the present epoch we shall contemplate the scientific labors of Torricelli in Italy, Guericke in Germany, Huygens in Holland, Pascal, Mariotte, and Descartes in France, Boyle, Hooke, Halley, and Newton in England. It was a period of great experimental as well as theoretical activity.

MECHANICS

LAWS OF MOTION

As we have seen, Galileo, in his explanation of the path of a projectile in a vacuum, had successfully mastered the first and the second law of motion. Later Descartes wrote on mechanics, but he hardly advanced beyond Galileo. Descartes's statement of the first law of motion (*Principia Philosophiæ,* 1644) was an improvement in form, but his third law is false in substance. The motion of bodies in their direct impact was imperfectly understood by Galileo, erroneously given by

Descartes, and first correctly stated by Christopher Wren, John Wallis, and Christian Huygens. The laws of motion in their present form were first given by Newton in his *Principia*.

Descartes's achievements in geometry and in philosophy are immeasurably superior to those in physics. He was a metaphysician, and, from a limited amount of experimentation or experience, confidently deduced a large amount of inference, without allowing himself to be disturbed by any possible discrepancy between his final conclusions and the actual facts. He had no appreciation of the slow-going process of Galileo.[1]

Says Descartes: "Without considering the first causes of nature, he (Galileo) sought only for the causes of a few particular effects and thus built without a foundation." "What Galileo says regarding velocity of falling bodies in a vacuum has no foundation; he should have told what gravity is; had he known its nature, then he would have seen that there is none in empty space." "I see nothing in his books which I envy and almost nothing which I would acknowledge as my own."[2] According to his own *a priori* principles, Descartes thought he could easily explain all that Galileo had worked out, while, as a matter of fact, Descartes had no true notion of acceleration, and committed errors avoided by Galileo.

DISPUTE BETWEEN THE CARTESIANS AND LEIBNIZIANS

There arose a curious dispute between the Cartesians and the Leibnizians on the measure of the efficacy of a moving body. Descartes took the efficacy to be proportional to the *velocity;* Leibniz took it to vary as the *square of the velocity*.[3] The controversy lasted over half a century, until, finally, it was brought to a close by Jean-le-Rond D'Alembert's remarks in

[1] "Of the mechanical truths which were easily attainable in the beginning of the seventeenth century, Galileo took hold of as many, and Descartes of as few, as was well possible for a man of genius." Whewell, Vol. I., p. 338.

[2] Descartes, *Lettres*, Vol. II., Paris, 1659, Letter 91, p. 391; Dühring, *Krit. Geschichte d. allgem. Princ. d. Mechanik*, Leipzig, 1887, pp. 106–108; Kästner, *Geschichte d. Mathematik*, Vol. IV., pp. 22–26.

[3] *Acta Eruditorum*, 1686, "Demonstratio erroris memorabilis cartesii," etc.

the preface to his *Dynamique,* 1743, though before this date Huygens's thought on this subject was perfectly clear. The long dispute was merely one of words; both views were correct. The efficiency of a body in motion varies as its *velocity,* if we consider the *time.* A body thrown vertically upward with double the velocity ascends twice as long a time. The efficiency varies as the *square of the velocity,* if we consider the *distance.* A body thrown vertically upward with double the velocity ascends four times as far. The reference to time leads to what Descartes called the "quantity of motion" (our "momentum"), *mv,* and makes the notion of *force* the primary concept. The reference to the distance leads to the expression *fs,* which makes *work* the primary notion. The former view made $ft = mv$ the fundamental equation; the latter made $fs = mv^2/2$ the fundamental equation. With the Cartesians *work* was a derived notion; with the Leibnizians *force* was a derived notion.[1] The Cartesian view, followed by Newton and modern writers of elementary text-books, makes *force, mass, momentum,* the original notions; the Leibnizian view, followed usually by Huygens and by the school of Poncelet, makes *work, mass, vis viva* (energy), the original notions.[2] If certain modern thinkers are correct in affirming the objective reality of kinetic energy and denying the objective reality of force, then the Leibnizian method would seem to be the more philosophical.[3]

[1] For the term *ft* the Frenchman **J. B. Bélanger** proposed in 1847 the name *impulse,* which term is used in the same sense by **J. Clerk Maxwell** in his *Matter and Motion.* Leibniz (1695) called *mv²* the *vis viva* or *living force.* **G. G. Coriolis** preferred to call ½ *mv²* the *vis viva,* a term now called *kinetic energy* by the English. Coriolis employed the name *work* for *fs* and was sustained in this usage by **J. V. Poncelet,** who adopted the *kilogramme-metre* as the unit of work. Coriolis and Poncelet were among the first promoters of reform in the teaching of rational mechanics. See Mach, *Science of Mechanics* (Ed. McCormack), pp. 271, 272; Marie, *Histoire d. Sciences Math. et Phys.,* Vol. XII., 1888, pp. 191, 192.

[2] Mach., *op. cit.,* pp. 148, 250, 270–276; H. Klein, *Principien der Mechanik,* Leipzig, 1872, pp. 17, 18.

[3] Consult P. G. Tait, *Recent Advances in Physical Science,* London, 1885, pp. 16, 343–368.

DISTINCTION BETWEEN WEIGHT AND MASS

The teacher will observe that those parts of mechanics which a beginner usually finds "hard to learn" are the parts which, in the development of the science, were difficult to overcome. Take, for instance, the difference between force and energy, or the concept of mass. Early writers, such as Galileo, Descartes, Leibniz, Huygens, had no clear notion of mass; *weight* and *mass* were taken interchangeably; these terms were one and the same thing. The real distinction between the two became evident when it was discovered that the same body may receive different accelerations by gravity on different parts of the earth's surface. When **Jean Richer** in 1671 went from Paris to Cayenne in French Guiana to make astronomical observations, he found that his pendulum clock, which in Paris kept correct time, fell daily two and a half minutes behind mean solar time. The pendulum was shortened, but after his return to Paris it was found to be too short.[1] The keen-minded Huygens at once discerned the cause, and found a partial explanation in the greater centrifugal tendency of the earth in Cayenne.[2] The distinction between *mass* and *weight* was clearly perceived by Newton in his extension of the laws of dynamics to heavenly bodies.[3] On the same spot of the earth, mass and weight are proportional to each other. This is not a self-evident fact; Newton proved it in course of a remarkable series of tests on pendulums. "By experiments made with the greatest accuracy, I have always found the quantity of matter in bodies to be proportional to their weight."[4]

The mathematical theory of the pendulum was first worked out by Huygens in his *De horologio oscillatorio* (Paris, 1673),

[1] Marie, *op. cit.*, Vol. V., 1884, p. 102.
[2] Huygens calculated that centrifugal action renders the second's pendulum at the poles 1/289 shorter than at the equator, and that the centrifugal force at the equator is 1/289 of the absolute weight of a body. See Huygens, *Ursache d. Schwere*, trans. by R. Mewes, Berlin, 1896, p. 34.
[3] Mach, *op. cit.*, pp. 161, 251.
[4] *Principia*, Book II., Prop. XXIV., Cor. 7.

a work that ranks second only to the *Principia* of Newton. The book opens with a description of pendulum clocks. Of his new theorems, the one on the interchangeability of the point of suspension and centre of oscillation has found its way into elementary text-books.

DESCARTES'S VORTICES

Before proceeding to Newton's discovery of the law of gravitation, we pass in brief review **Descartes's** theory of vortices. After the overthrow of the Ptolemaic system and the rejection of the ancient crystalline spheres, the puzzle stared philosophers in the face, what is it that causes the planets to move in their orbits? The answer given in Descartes's theory was eagerly accepted.[1] All space is filled with a fluid, or ether, the parts of which act on each other and cause circular motion. Thus the fluid was formed into a multitude of vortices of different size, velocity, and density. There is an immense vortex around the sun, carrying in its whirl the earth and the other planets. The denser bodies, being slower and less subject to centrifugal action, are forced toward the sun, the centre of the vortex. Each planet is in the centre of another vortex by which the ordinary phenomena of gravity are produced. Still smaller vortices produce cohesion between parts of a body. Figure 7 is Descartes's diagram of vortices in his *Principia Philosophiæ*, 1644.

This theory is of interest, because it is the faith on which Newton was brought up; it was taught in English and European universities. In 1671 Jacques Rohault, a Cartesian, wrote his *Traité de Physique*. This became a classic text in France, and was taught in England and America. **Samuel Clarke's** translation of it into Latin appeared, in London, in 1697, 1703, and 1710. An English translation of Clarke's

---

[1] It is an interesting fact that, by his theory, Descartes aimed primarily to reconcile the teachings of Copernicus with the doctrine of the immobility of the earth. He taught "that the earth is at rest in its heaven, which does not prevent its being carried along with it, and that it is the same with all the planets."

edition was published as late as 1730, three years after the death of Newton. The editions of 1710 and 1730 (but not the edition of 1697) contained Clarke's notes to the original text aiming to expose the fallacies of the Cartesian system. One of these notes is a long quotation from Newton's *Principia*

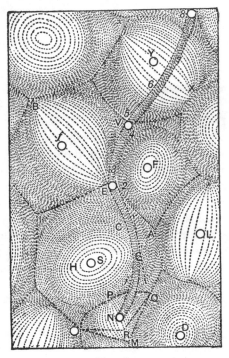

FIG. 7.

disproving the theory of vortices. Some of the college tutors in British Universities at this time were not trained in Newtonian science and were adherents of Cartesian tenets. Clarke's translation was popular because it was acceptable to followers of Descartes and also to followers of Newton. Both sides were fairly represented and each instructor could take his choice. This text was used at Yale College as late as 1743.[1] In France the Newtonian theory did not completely dispel the belief in Descartes's vortices until the middle of the eighteenth century.[2]

Descartes's theory of vortices can hardly be ranked among the great scientific theories, such as the Ptolemaic or Copernican system, or the emission theory of light. Descartes made no attempt to reconcile it with Kepler's laws; in fact, it did not explain a single phenomenon satisfactorily. Nor did it lead to the discovery of new truths. However, it referred planetary motions to mechanical causes. It is of philosophical importance, because it is an attempt to explain the universe on mechanical, rather than on animistic conceptions. Its general features were easily grasped, for a whirlwind or an eddy of water at once suggested a picture to the mind. Then, too, these vortices helped to overthrow the Aristotelian system.[3]

EARLY YEARS OF NEWTON

Isaac Newton (1642–1727) was born at Woolsthorpe, in Lincolnshire, the same year in which Galileo died. In his twelfth year his mother sent him to the public school at Grantham, where he began to show decided taste for mechanical inventions. He constructed a water-clock, a windmill, a carriage moved by the person who sat in it, and other toys. He entered Trinity College, Cambridge, in 1660. Cambridge was the birthplace of Newton's genius. Among the physical works read by him while an undergraduate are Kep-

[1] *Teaching and History of Mathematics in the U. S.*, Washington, 1890, p. 30.

[2] Voltaire, who visited England in 1727, and afterward became a staunch supporter of Newton's philosophy, says, "A Frenchman who arrives in London finds a great alteration in philosophy, as in other things. He left the world full [*a plenum*], he finds it empty. At Paris you see the universe composed of vortices of subtle matter, in London we see nothing of the kind," Whewell, *op. cit.*, Vol. I., p. 431. We cannot blame the Europeans for not believing in "empty" space. In this respect Newton himself was not a Newtonian. See *Correspondence of R. Bentley*, Vol. I., p. 70; *Proc. Roy. Soc. of London*, Vol. 54., 1893, p. 381.

[3] John Playfair, "Dissertation Fourth" in *Encyclop. Brit.*, 8th ed., Vol. I., pp. 609, 610; O. Lodge, *Pioneers of Science*, pp. 152–156.

ler's *Optics* and Barrow's *Lectures.* The first ideas of some of his greatest discoveries suggested themselves to him at this time. In 1664 he made some observations on halos.[1]

First Thoughts on Gravitation

In 1666, "I began," he says, "to think of gravity extending to the orb of the moon, . . . and thereby compared the force requisite to keep the moon in her orb with the force of gravity at the surface of the earth."[2]

The above thoughts on gravitation occurred to him while he was at his home in Lincolnshire, where he had gone to escape the plague at that time raging in Cambridge. Pemberton gives the following details: "As he sat alone in the garden, he fell into a speculation on the power of gravity; that as this power is not found sensibly diminished at the remotest distance from the centre of the earth to which we can rise, neither at the tops of the loftiest buildings, nor even on the summits of the highest mountains; it appeared to him reasonable to conclude, that this power must extend much farther than was usually thought; why not as high as the moon, said he to himself? And if so, her motion must be influenced by it; perhaps she is retained in her orbit thereby."[3] It was conjectured by Newton, as also by Hooke, Huygens, Halley, Wren, and others, that if Kepler's third law (the square of the time of revolution of the planets is proportional to the cube of their mean distance from the sun) was true, then the attraction between the earth and other members of the solar system varied inversely as the square of the distance. The accuracy of Kepler's third law was doubted at that time. To show that the above conjecture was true required the genius of Newton.

[1] Newton, *Opticks,* London, 1704, Book II., Part IV., obs. 13, p. 111.
[2] *Portsmouth Collection,* Sect. I., Division XI., No. 41; W. W. R. Ball, *An Essay on Newton's "Principia,"* London, 1893, p. 7.
[3] Pemberton, *View of Sir Isaac Newton's Philosophy,* London, 1728; W. W. R. Ball, *op. cit.,* p. 9. The well-known anecdote that the idea of universal gravitation was suggested to Newton by the fall of an apple is by some considered legendary, but Ball argues in its favor, and gives the authorities bearing on it, pp. 11, 12.

Cause of the Twenty Years' Delay in Announcing His Law of Gravitation

His first studies of gravitation were made in 1665 or 1666, but strangely he did not announce his law of gravitation until about twenty years later. There are two explanations [1] of Newton's long delay of twenty years. The old account of the discovery rests mainly on the authority of Henry Pemberton, who knew Newton during the last years of his life. According to Pemberton, Newton in 1666 based his estimate of the earth's radius on the supposition that there are 60 miles to a degree of latitude, "the common estimate in use among geographers and seamen," but the true value being "about $69\frac{1}{2}$ of our miles." In consequence, Newton's "computation did not answer expectation" and "he laid aside for that time any further thoughts on this matter." About 1684 he obtained **Jean Picard's** more correct measurement of the arc of the meridian and was able to verify the law of inverse squares. This is briefly Pemberton's narrative. Later the legend grew that in going over the calculation with the new data, Newton was taken with such intense emotion that he could not proceed and had to secure the assistance of a friend. This story first appeared in print in Robison's *Mechanical Philosophy*, 1804, p. 288. It has been beautifully expressed in verse by Alfred Noyes in his "Watchers of the Sky."

The second explanation was offered by the astronomer J. C. Adams and the mathematician J. W. L. Glaisher in 1887, at the time of the two-hundredth anniversary of the publication of Newton's *Principia*. They were able to quote from a written draft of the early history of Newton's scientific discovery, found in the "Portsmouth Collection" of Newtonian manuscripts. This draft contains a statement that Newton in 1666 compared the theoretical and the experimental values for the acceleration due to gravity, "and found them answer pretty nearly." [2] This statement, written by Newton him-

[1] For details see *Sir Isaac Newton 1727–1927*, Baltimore, 1928, pp. 127–188.
[2] W. W. R. Ball, *op. cit.*, p. 9.

self, is in conflict with Pemberton's assertion, based on hear-say evidence. Moreover, Pemberton's "69½ miles to the degree" shows that he is using "English statute miles" of 5280 feet each. But it has recently been shown that English seamen of the seventeenth century, before 1666, did not count the degree of latitude to be 60 English statute miles, but 60 miles of only 5000 feet each. Had Newton used 60 such short miles, his calculation would have differed 18% from the experimental value, and Newton could not have "found them answer pretty nearly." That Newton in 1666, or soon after that date, could not obtain fairly accurate values for the size of the earth is unbelievable. Norwood's careful measurement of the degree of latitude published in his *Seaman's Practice* of 1636, gave 69½ English statute miles per degree which is only slightly above Picard's later value of 69.1 miles, and Norwood's figure was quoted in many English publications prior to 1666. Snell's measurement of 1617 gave 66⅔ statute miles, a good result quoted by Edmund Gunter in his *Description of the Sector and Crosse-staffe* which appears to be the very "Gunter's Book and Sector" purchased by Newton in 1666.[1] Snell's value was referred to in Varenius's *Geography,* an edition of which was prepared in 1672 by Newton himself. Nevertheless, Newton did not announce his law of gravitation for many years. Why this delay?

An examination of Newton's correspondence during the years preceding the publication of his *Principia* indicates, as J. C. Adams pointed out in 1887, that Newton's difficulties were of a different nature, that the numerical verification was fairly complete in 1666 (as shown by Newton's own statement), but that Newton had not been able to determine what the attraction of a spherical body upon an external point would be. His letters to Halley show that he did not suppose the earth to attract as though all its mass were concentrated into a point at the centre. He could not assert, therefore, that the assumed law of gravity was verified by the figures,

[1] See D. Brewster's *Memoirs of Sir Isaac Newton,* Edinburgh, 1860, Vol. I., chap. II, pp. 27–29.

though for long distances he might have claimed that it yielded close approximations. When Halley visited Newton in 1684, he requested Newton to determine what the orbit of a planet would be if the law of attraction were that of inverse squares. Newton had solved a similar problem for Hooke in 1679, and replied at once that it was an ellipse. Newton resumed the study of gravitation, and in 1685 was able to complete his discovery by resolving the problem which had baffled him so long. He showed that the sphere whose density at any point depends only on the distance from the centre, attracts an external particle as though its whole mass were concentrated at the centre.[1] It was thus proved that the force of attraction between two spheres is the same as it would be if the mass of each sphere were concentrated at its centre. "No sooner," says Glaisher, "had Newton proved this superb theorem— and we know from his own words that he had no expectation of so beautiful a result till it emerged from his mathematical investigation—that all the mechanism of the universe at once lay spread before him."

Of the two explanations of Newton's delay in announcing the law of gravitation, the one of Pemberton must be rejected as being in conflict with Newton's own statement and with the practice among seamen. The second explanation rests upon facts taken from Newton's papers and correspondence which constitute a consistent though in some respects an incomplete account of the progress of his great discovery.

NEWTON'S EARTH-MOON TEST OF HIS LAW

We proceed, with the aid of Fig. 8, to explain Newton's verification of the law of inverse squares, as given in his

[1] Consult theorems in *Principia*, Book I., Sec. XII., also Book III., Prop. VIII. For further details on the discovery of the law of gravitation, consult W. W. R. Ball, *op. cit.*; J. W. L. Glaisher, "Bicentenary Address," *Cambridge Chronicle*, April 20, 1888. We have used also Ball, *Hist. of Math.*, 1888, pp. 295–297. Rosenberger's *Isaac Newton und seine Physikalischen Principien* is worthy of reference, even though the author made no use whatever of the information obtained through the *Portsmouth Collection*.

Principia, Book III, Prop. IV. Geodetic measurements gave the circumference of the earth as 123,249,600 Paris feet. The moon's mean distance is about 60 times the earth's radius. Hence, the moon's orbit, assumed to be circular, is 123,249,600 × 60 = 7,394,976,000 feet. The moon revolves around the earth once in 27 d. 7 h. 43 m., or in 39,343 minutes. Hence her orbital velocity is 7,394,976,000 ÷ 39,343 = 187,961.67 ft. per minute. Let the arc MM' represent this velocity, where M is the moon's position in its orbit and E is the earth's centre. Then, evidently, NM', which for a very small angle, MEM', nearly equals MO, represents the distance the moon falls per minute toward the earth. Since

$$\overline{MM'}^2 = MP \, . \, MO, \text{ (Book I., Prop. IV., Cor. 9)},$$

we get

$$MO = \overline{MM'}^2 \div MP = 15 \text{ } 1/12 \text{ ft. per minute, nearly.}$$

Since ME equals 60 radii of the earth, the distance a body

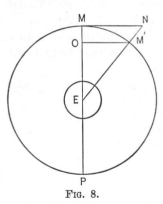

FIG. 8.

falls per minute on the earth's surface should be, by the law of inverse squares, $60^2 \times 15$ 1/12 ft. per minute, or 15 1/12 ft. per second. More accurately it is "15 ft., 1 inch, and 1 line 4/9." Now, pendulum experiments made by Huygens gave as the distance per second through which a body falls from rest at Paris as "15 ft., 1 inch, 1 line 7/9" (Book III., Prop. IV.). Hence the law of inverse squares is proved to be true.

In the scholium to Prop. IV., Book I., Newton acknowledges his indebtedness to Huygens for the laws of contrifugal force employed in the above calculation.

When Newton presented his *Principia* to the Royal Society, **Robert Hooke** (1635–1703) claimed the law of inverse squares for himself. Newton's reply is contained in a letter to Edmund

Halley.[1] The *Principia* was published in 1687 under the direction and at the expense of Halley.

Though the law expressing the variation in the intensity of gravitational attraction became known over three centuries ago, and though scientific discovery since that time has been more rapid than ever before, we are still unable to explain what causes a stone to fall to the ground. This is indeed a strange fact in the progress of science. That the earth and the moon act upon each other through empty space, without the aid of some medium between them or surrounding them, modern physicists find it difficult to believe. No little interest attaches to the question as to Newton's view on this subject. Did he believe in "action at a distance," or in the idea that matter can act where it is not? In a letter to Bentley he says:

"That gravity should be innate, inherent, and essential to matter, so that one body may act upon another at a distance through a vacuum without the mediation of anything else, by and through which their action and force may be conveyed from one to another, is to me so great an absurdity that I believe no man who has in philosophical matters a competent faculty of thinking can ever fall into." [2]

Yet the opposite belief has sometimes been ascribed to Newton. The doctrine of action at a distance has for its author, not Newton, but **Roger Cotes** (1682–1716), who edited the second edition of the *Principia* in 1713 and asserted the doctrine in his preface. When later the Newtonian philosophy gained ground in Europe, it was the opinion of Cotes, rather than that of Newton, which prevailed.[3]

[1] See letter in Ball, *op. cit.*, p. 155.

[2] *Corresp. of R. Bentley*, Vol. I., p. 70; *Proc. of Royal Soc. of London*, Vol. 54, 1893, p. 381. For other passages from Newton favoring an ether-hypothesis, see his *Opticks*, Queries 18, 22; also *Phil. Trans. Abr.*, Vol. I., p. 145, Nov., 1672; Birch, *Hist. of Royal Society*, Vol. III., p. 249, 1675.

[3] C. Maxwell, Lecture "On Action at a Distance," *Nature*, Vol. VII., 1872–73, p. 325. Cotes's preface is given in *Sir Isaac Newton's Principia reprinted for Sir William Thomson and Hugh Blackburn*, Glasgow, 1871. Our inability to explain gravity is not due to want of attempts.

LIQUIDS AND GASES

Proceeding to the mechanics of liquids and gases, we begin with researches on liquid pressure by **Blaise Pascal** (1623–1662), who is celebrated not only as a precocious mathematician and as the author of the *Provincial Letters*, but also as a physicist. He was born at Clermont in Auvergne. In his brief *Traité de l'équilibre des liqueurs*,[1] written in 1653 and first published in 1663, one year after his death, he enunciates the law, known as "Pascal's Law," that the pressure exerted upon a liquid is transmitted undiminished in all directions and acts with the same force on all equal surfaces in a direction at right angles to them. He shows by experiments identical with those carried out in our modern laboratories with Masson's apparatus that pressure against a surface, in virtue of the weight of the liquid, depends simply upon its depth. Several vessels of different shapes having movable bottoms of equal areas are suspended, one after the other, from one arm of a balance. The vessels are filled with water to such a height that the pressure is just sufficient to force down the bottom and raise a weight on the other arm of the balance. Pascal also takes two sliding plugs or pistons pressing against a fluid in a closed vessel, the surface of the first being one hundred

The first important effort in this line was made by C. Huygens in his *Discours sur la cause de la pésanteur,* part of which was written after the appearance of Newton's *Principia* in 1687. A German translation of the *Discours* has been brought out by Rudolf Mewes, Berlin, 1896. A mechanical gravitation theory was advanced by C. Le Sage, born at Geneva in 1724. See Le Sage, "Lucrèce Newtonien," *Mémoires de l'Académie des Sciences,* Berlin, 1782, pp. 404–432. He teaches that gravity is caused by streams of atoms coming in all directions from space. Later speculations on the cause of gravity were made by Clerk Maxwell, Lord Kelvin, C. Isenkrahe, Bernhard Riemann, Leonhard Euler, N. v. Dellingshausen, Tolver Preston, Adalbert Rysáneck, Paul du Bois-Reymond, Vaschy, Schramm, Anderson, Möller, and others. For critical and historical summaries, see C. Isenkrahe, "Ueber die Zurück-führung der Schwere auf Absorption" in *Zeitsch. f. Math. and Physik,* 1892, *Suppl.,* pp. 163–204; S. Tolver Preston, "Comparative Review of some Dynamical Theories of Gravitation," *Philosophical Magazine,* (5) Vol. 39, 1895, pp. 145 *et seq.;* W. B. Taylor, "Kinetic Theories of Gravitation," *Smithsonian Report,* 1876, pp. 205–282. Discussions involving the theory of relativity will be noted later.

[1] *Œuvres Complètes de Blaise Pascal,* Paris, 1866, Vol. III., pp. 83–98.

times greater than the surface of the other; the force of one man acting at the first plug will balance the force of one hundred men at the other. "Hence it follows that a vessel full of water is a new principle of mechanics and a new machine for multiplying forces to any degree we choose."[1]

THE "HORROR VACUI"

Except the telescope, no scientific discovery of the seventeenth century excited wonder and curiosity to a greater degree than did the experiments with the barometer and air-pump. Chance expressions that air has weight are already found in Aristotle and Plato, but nothing was *known* till the time of Galileo and Torricelli. A great deal of vague speculation was indulged in regarding the vacuum. Aristotle believed that a vacuum could not exist, and as late a writer as Descartes held the same view. For two thousand years philosophers spoke of the horror that nature has for empty space,—the *horror vacui*,—as if inanimate objects could have *feeling*. Because of this horror, nature was said to prevent the formation of a vacuum by laying hold of anything near by and with it instantly filling up any vacated space. Even Galileo could not quite free himself from this unphilosophical doctrine. He was astonished when told that a suction-pump with a very long suction-pipe, which had just been constructed, would not raise water higher than about thirty-three feet. He remarked that the *horror vacui* was a force which had its limitations and could be measured. That air has weight he convinced himself by the difference in weight of a glass balloon filled with air under ordinary pressure and then with air under high pressure.[2] He estimated the density of air to be 400 times less than that of water.

Thus Galileo knew (1) that air has weight; he knew also (2) what the "resistance to a vacuum" was when measured by

[1] *Œuvres Complètes de Blaise Pascal,* Paris, 1866, Vol. III., p. 85.
[2] H. Crew and A. de Salvio's translation of Galileo's *Dialogues concerning Two New Sciences,* New York, 1914, pp. 78, 79. See also Mach, *op. cit.,* pp. 112–114.

the height of a water column, and also when determined by the weight against a piston. But the two ideas dwelt separately in his mind.[1] It remained for his pupil Toricelli to vary the experiments, to unite and interweave the two ideas, and to place air in the list of pressure-exerting fluids.

The Torricellian Experiment

Evangelista Torricelli (1608–1647) began his mathematical studies in a Jesuit school, and continued them under Benedict Castelli at Rome. He made himself familiar with Galileo's writings, and published some articles on mechanics. Galileo was anxious to become acquainted with the author of these tracts and pressed Torricelli to join him at Florence. He accepted the invitation, and it is said that his society and conversation contributed greatly to soothe the last days of the blind physicist. Galileo died three months later. Galileo's patron, the Grand Duke of Tuscany, made Torricelli Galileo's successor as professor of mathematics at the Accademia.

Torricelli devised the scheme of determining the resistance of a vacuum by a vertical column of mercury, which he expected to be about 1/14 the length of the corresponding water column. The "Torricellian experiment" was carried out in 1643 in Florence by **Vincenzo Viviani** (1622–1703), who at seventeen had become a pupil of Galileo, and was now studying under the direction of Torricelli.

Torricelli never published an account of his research. He was at this time too deeply absorbed in mathematical investigations on the cycloid, and he died a few years later. However, he described his experiments in two letters of 1644, to his friend, M. A. Ricci, in Rome, and these are extant.[2] He says that the aim of his investigation was "not simply to produce a vacuum, but to make an instrument which shows the

[1] Mach, in *Monist*, Vol. 6, 1896, p. 170.
[2] They were first published in 1663. See a recent reprint by G. Hellmann; *Neudrucke*, No. 7.

mutations of the air, now heavier and dense, and now lighter and thin."[1]

In 1644 Ricci wrote a letter, describing the Torricellian experiment to Père Mersenne, in Paris, who, by his extensive correspondence, acted as an intermediary between scientific men. The news created a sensation among French savants. But the experiment was not repeated in France until the summer of 1646 (by Pierre Petit, of Rouen, in conjunction with Pascal), as no suitable glass tubes were available before that date.

The account of the Italian experiment which reached Pascal must have been quite incomplete, for he found it necessary to reflect on the phenomenon independently. He concludes "that the vacuum is not impossible in nature, and that she does not shun it with so great a horror as many imagine."[2]

Pascal reasoned that, if the mercury column was held up simply by the pressure of the air, then the column ought to be shorter at a high altitude. He tried it on a church-steeple in Paris, but desiring more decisive results, he wrote to his brother-in-law to try the experiment on the Puy de Dôme, a high mountain in Auvergne. There was a difference of three inches in the height of the mercury, "which ravished us with admiration and astonishment." Pascal repeated the Torricellian experiment, using red wine and a glass tube forty-six feet long. (Evidently glass tubing had become more plentiful.) He experimented with the siphon, and explained its theory. A balloon, half full of air, was found to appear inflated on being taken up on a mountain, and to flatten again, gradually, during the descent.

---

[1] At the close of the letter, he says, "My principal object is, therefore, not altogether successful . . . because the level [of the mercury] . . . changes for another cause which I never thought of, namely, by the heat and cold, and that very appreciably." Yet only since the time of Amontons (1704) has it been thought necessary to make corrections for temperature. See G. Hellmann, *op cit.*, pp. 16 (3).

[2] Nouvelles expériences touchant le vide," *Œuvres Compl. de B. Pascal*, Paris, 1866, Vol. III., p. 1. See also his *Traité de la pesanteur de la masse de l'air*, pp. 98–129.

GUERICKE'S EXPERIMENTS ON AIR PRESSURE

The doctrine of the *horror vacui* was overthrown through experimental research in Italy and France. A repetition of the process took place in Germany. The early work of the German investigator was carried on independently. **Otto von Guericke** (1602–1686) came of a prominent family in Magdeburg. He studied at German universities, also at Leyden, and then travelled in England and France. In the course of the Thirty Years' War Magdeburg was devastated in 1631, and Guericke and his family barely escaped with their lives. Later he earned a livelihood as engineer in the army of Gustavus Adolphus. In 1646 he became burgomaster of Magdeburg.

The disputations regarding the vacuum made him curious to find out the facts experimentally. Says he, "Oratory, elegance of words, or skill in disputation avails nothing in the field of natural science." In 1663 he completed the manuscript for his work *De vacuo spatio,* but it was not published until 1672.[1]

Guericke first took a tight wine-cask, full of water, and attempted to remove the liquid with a brass pump applied to the cask below. But the bands and iron screws holding the pump to the cask gave way. It was attached more securely, then three strong men pulling at the piston at last succeeded in drawing out the water. Thereupon a noise was heard, as if the residual water within were boiling violently, and this continued until air had replaced the water pumped out.

The leaky wooden cask was replaced by a copper globe, then water and air were drawn out as before. At first the piston moved easily, but later the strength of two men could hardly move it, when "suddenly with a loud clap and to the

---

[1] The work consists of seven books, of which the third contains his own experiments and has been recently brought out in German translation in *Ostwald's Klassiker,* No. 59. The first accounts of Guericke's air-pump and experiments were published by Kaspar Schott in his *Mechanica hydraulico-pneumatica,* 1657, and in his *Technica curiosa,* 1664. Through the publication of 1657 Robert Boyle became acquainted with Guericke's experiments.

terror of all'' the sphere collapsed. A more massive and
more exactly spherical metallic vessel, Fig. 9, was secured
and exhausted. "On opening the stop-cock the air rushed

FIG. 9.

with such force into the copper globe, as if it wanted to drag
to itself a person near by. Though you held your face at considerable distance, your breath was taken away; indeed, you
could not hold your hand over the stop-cock without danger
that it would be violently forced down.''

Guericke next invented air-pumps, the first form of which
is illustrated in Fig. 10. Its tap with the stop-cock was
detachable, so that objects to be experimented upon might
be placed in the receiver. As an extra precaution against
leakage, the stop-cock was made to stand under water which
was poured into the conical vessel. Numerous experiments
were made with this pump. A clock in a vacuum cannot be
heard to strike; a flame dies out in it; a bird opens its bill

wide, struggles for air, and dies; fishes perish; grapes can be preserved six months *in vacuo*. A long tube, connected with an exhausted globe above and dipping in water below, was his

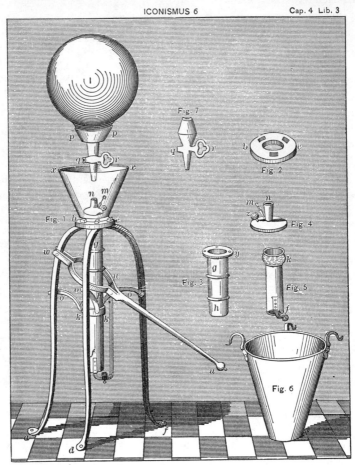

Fɪɢ. 10.

water barometer. He explains the rise of the water in the tube by the pressure of the air. He observes fluctuations in the height of the water column and uses the instrument for weather predictions. A miniature man of wood, floating on the water, moved up and down inside the tube and by his finger indicated the pressure of the air at any moment. Guericke's experiment of weighing a receiver, first when full of air and again when exhausted, has held its place in elementary books The same is true of his "Magdeburg hemispheres." He constructed such hemispheres, about 1.2 ft. in diameter, and made a test in 1654 at Regensburg before the Reichstag and Emperor Ferdinand III. According to his calculations, a force of 2686 pounds was needed to overcome the atmospheric pressure holding the hemispheres together. They were pulled apart only after applying sixteen horses, four pairs on each hemisphere. His book contains a large engraving, naïvely illustrating how the experiment was made.

On that occcasion Guericke made other experiments, and he happened to assert that if you were to blow your breath into a large exhausted receiver, you would that moment breathe your last. The truth of this being doubted, he illustrated the power of "suction" by a new experiment. A cylinder of a large pump had a rope attached to its piston, which led over a pulley and was divided into branches on which twenty or thirty men could pull. As soon as the cylinder was connected with an exhausted receiver, the piston was suddenly pushed down by the atmospheric pressure and the men at the ropes were thrown forward.

It was on this occasion that Guericke heard for the first time of the Torricellian experiments made eleven years earlier.[1]

LIFE OF BOYLE

In England the mechanics of the air was first studied by **Robert Boyle** (1627–1691). He was born at Lismore Castle in Ireland. In his autobiography he speaks of "his acquaintance with some children of his own age, whose stuttering habi-

[1] A pair of Guericke's "Magdeburg hemispheres" were on exhibition at the Columbian Exposition in Chicago in 1893. As to the fate of Guericke's original air-pump, consult G. Berthold in *Wiedem. Annalen*, Neue Folge, 54, 1895, pp. 724–726. Guericke is said to have spent 20,000 thaler for apparatus.

tude he so long counterfeited that at last he contracted it;"
diverse cures "we tried with as much successlessness as
diligence."[1] After spending nearly four years at Eton
College, he left in 1638 for the Continent. At Geneva, one
night, a terrific thunder-storm made him fear that the day of
judgment was at hand. At this time he became converted to
religion, and many of his later writings are on theology.
On his return home, in 1644, a youth of eighteen, he found
the country in great confusion; nevertheless he received a
strong impetus for scientific research from the meetings in
London, in 1645, of a philosophical society,—the *Invisible
College*, as he called it,—which after the Restoration was
incorporated as the Royal Society. In 1654 he settled at
Oxford, where he erected a laboratory, kept several operators
at work, and engaged Robert Hooke as his chemical assistant.[2]
After reading of Guericke's air-pump, he let Hooke make a
less clumsy pump, which was completed in 1659. As early as
1660 Boyle published his *New Experiments . . . touching the
Spring of the Air.*

He left Oxford for London in 1668. For forty years he
was in feeble health. His memory was so treacherous that
he was often tempted to abandon study, yet he was a volumi-
nous writer, and possessed an immense reputation both at
home and abroad. Before 1657 he purposely refrained from
"seriously and orderly" reading the works of Gassendi, Descartes, or Francis Bacon, "that I might not be prepossessed
with any theory or principles till I spent some time in trying
what things themselves would incline me to think."[3]

Boyle placed the barometer in the receiver of the air-pump
and observed the ebullition of heated liquids and the freezing
of water on exhaustion.

[1] *The works of the Honourable Robert Boyle,* in five volumes, to which
is prefixed the Life of the Author, edited by Thomas Birch, London,
1743, Vol. I., p. 6 (of biography).
[2] See article "Boyle, Robert," in *Dic. of Nat. Biog.*
[3] *Works,* Vol. I., p. 194.

BOYLE'S AND MARIOTTE'S LAW OF GASES

Except for an absurd criticism by a would-be physicist, Boyle would probably never have discovered the law bearing his name. Franciscus Linus, professor at Lüttich in the Netherlands, had read Boyle's *New Experiments,* and declared that the air is very insufficient to perform such great matters as the counterpoising of a mercurial cylinder of 29 inches; he claimed to have found that the mercury hangs by invisible threads (*funiculi*) from the upper end of the tube, and to have felt them when he closed the upper end of the tube with his finger. This criticism incited Boyle to renewed research. "We shall now endeavor to manifest by experiments purposely made, that the spring of the air is capable of doing far more than it is necessary for us to ascribe to it, to solve the phenomena of the Torricellian experiment." [1] "We took then a long glass tube, which by a dexterous hand and the help of a lamp was in such a manner crooked at the bottom, that the part turned up was almost parallel to the rest of the tube and, the orifice of this shorter leg . . . being hermetically sealed, the length of it was divided into inches (each of which was divided into eight parts) by a straight list of paper, which containing those divisions, was carefully pasted all along it." A similar strip of paper was pasted on the longer leg. Then "as much quicksilver as served to fill the arch or bended part of the siphon" was poured in so as to be at the same height in both legs. "This done, we began pouring quicksilver into the longer leg . . . till the air in the shorter leg was by condensation reduced to take up but half the space it possessed . . . we cast our eyes upon the longer leg of the glass . . . and we observed, not without delight and satisfaction, that the quicksilver in that longer part of the tube was 29 inches higher than the other." This tube was broken by accident, and a new one, about eight feet long, was prepared. It was too long to be used in his chamber, so he took it on "a pair of stairs" and suspended it by strings so "that it did scarce

[1] See "Defence against Linus," 1662, *Works,* Vol. I., p. 100.

touch the box" placed underneath. Pressures less than one atmosphere were also obtained. Altogether he subjected the enclosed air to pressures varying from 1 2/8 inches of mercury to 117 9/16 inches, passing from one extreme to the other in about forty steps, and every time comparing the observed pressures with what they should be "according to the hypothesis that supposes the pressures and expansions to be in reciprocal proportions." The observed and theoretical values agree fairly well.

In 1666 Boyle published his *Hydrostatical Paradoxes,* in which he takes pains to refute the old doctrine that a light liquid can exert no pressure against a heavier liquid. That such refutations seemed necessary at so late a date indicates the slow assimilation of correct ideas on fluid pressure.

"Boyle's Law" was rediscovered independently, fourteen years after Boyle's publication of it, by the prominent French physicist, **Edme Mariotte** (1620–1684). In France it is often called "Mariotte's Law." Mariotte published it in his treatise, *Sur la nature d l'air,* 1676. He says, "We employed a tube of 40 inches, which I filled with mercury up to $27\frac{1}{2}$ inches, $12\frac{1}{2}$ inches of air being left, which, being plunged 1 inch into a vessel of mercury, leaving 39 inches above, contained 14 inches of mercury and 25 inches of air expanded to double its volume." By repeated experimentation "it became sufficiently evident that one may take it as a certain rule or law of nature that air condenses in proportion to the weight by which it is loaded." He had a clearer realization of the importance of this law than had Boyle.

To Mariotte is attributed the instauration of experimental physics in France. As Boyle was prominent in the organization of the Royal Society of London, so Mariotte was one of the first and leading members of the Académie des Sciences, founded in 1666. By carefully measuring the height of the mercury column in a deep cellar, and then at the newly built astronomical observatory, located on high ground in Paris, he obtained an approximate formula for estimating height by the barometer. He wrote an important article on percussion.

In 1674 **Denis Papin** described an air-pump in which the flask-like receptacle with a stop-cock, such as had been employed by Guericke and Boyle, was replaced by a plate and bell glass. The credit for this improvement is usually given to Papin, but he himself ascribes it to Huygens, who is now known to have made this desirable innovation in 1661.[1] Papin was a pupil and assistant to Huygens.

MOTION OF PROJECTILES

In the study of falling bodies and the motions of projectiles the resistance of the air has always complicated the phenomena, has usually perplexed the investigators, and has often supplied critics with all sorts of objections. Galileo made allowances for the resistance of the air. About 1670 Mariotte concluded from experiments at the Paris observatory that the resistance to falling bodies is proportional to the square of the time. Newton inclined to the same conclusion, while La Hire favored the cube of the time.

In 1679 Newton remarked "that a falling body ought by reason of the earth's diurnall motion to advance eastward and not fall to the west as the vulgar opinion is." We may here state, parenthetically, that in France Mersenne and Petit fired bullets vertically upward, expecting them to strike the ground far to the westward.[2] But the bullets could not be found! Descartes, the French oracle of the time, was consulted, and he seriously replied that the bullets had received such intense velocity that they lost their weight and flew away from the earth.

Newton's prediction applied, not to a body rising and then falling, but to one falling from rest. The experiment was

[1] E. Gerland, *Wiedemann's Annalen*, Vol. II., 1878, p. 666.
[2] If disturbances due to the atmosphere are negligible, then the bullets should fall a small distance to the west. See W. Ferrel, *A Popular Treatise on the Winds*, New York, 1889, p. 88.

tried by his contemporary, Robert Hooke, who reported to the Royal Society that he "had found the ball in every one of the said experiments fall to the southeast of the perpendicular point found by the same ball hanging perpendicular." The experiments were made in the open air, and the results were somewhat discordant. "But," says Hooke, "within doors it succeeded also." [1] The strange southerly component of the deviation was probably ascribed to errors of observation, but careful experiments made by G. B. Guglielmini in 1791 from a tower at Bologna, by J. F. Benzenberg in 1802 from St. Michael's tower in Hamburg, and by F. Reich in 1831 down a mine shaft at Freiberg in Saxony, all showed, in addition to the predicted easterly deviation, also a small southerly displacement.[2] All writers agree that a body will deviate to the eastward with respect to the plumb-line hung from the initial point, but there has been disagreement, on theoretical grounds, regarding the deviation measured along the meridian. Laplace found no meridional deviation, Gauss did find a small value toward the south. Gauss' general conclusion was confirmed more recently by W. H. Röver of Washington University.[3]

In projectiles the actual path, as represented by the ballistic curve, deviates, considerably from Galileo's parabolas. It is mathematically almost unmanageable. The path appears in the northern hemisphere to be slightly bent to the right, owing to the rotation of the earth. That the resistance of the air complicates the path of a rotating sphere is known to every base-ball or tennis player.[4]

[1] Birch, *History of the Royal Society,* London, 1757, Vol. III., p. 519. Vol. IV., p. 5.   See also Ball, *An Essay on Newton's "Principia,"* pp. 146, 149, 150.

[2] Rosenberger, Part III., pp. 96, 97, 432–437.   J. F. W. Gronau, *Historische Entwicklung der Lehre vom Luftwiderstande,* Danzig, 1868, pp. 1–28.

[3] See *Washington University Studies,* Vol. III., 1916, p. 153–168.

[4] For the effect of the earth's rotation, consult Ferrel, *op. cit.,* p. 86; Poisson, *Journ. École Polytechnique,* XXVI., 1838.   In *ibidem,* XXVII., 1839, Poisson considers the effect of their rotation in the air.   See also Magnus, *Poggendorff Annalen,* LXXXVIII., 1853, p. 1.

LIGHT

Law of Refraction

The law of refraction was discovered by **Willebrord Snell** (1591–1626), professor of mechanics at Leyden. He never published his discovery, but both Huygens and Isaak Voss claim to have examined Snell's manuscript. He stated the law in inconvenient form as follows: For the same media the ratio of the cosecants of the angle of incidence and of refraction retains always the same value. As the cosecants vary inversely as the sines, the equivalence of this to the modern form becomes evident. As far as known, Snell did not attempt a theoretical deduction of the law, but he verified it experimentally. The law of sines, as found in modern books, was given by Descartes in his *La Dioptrique*, 1637. He does not mention Snell, and probably discovered the law independently.[1] Descartes made no experiments, but deduced the law theoretically from the following assumptions: (1) the velocity of light is greater in a denser medium (now known to be wrong); (2) for the same media these velocities have the same ratio for all angles of incidence; (3) the velocity component parallel to the refracting surface remains unchanged during refraction (now known to be wrong). The improbability of the correctness of these assumptions brought about attacks upon the demonstration from the mathematician Fermat and others. Fermat deduced the law from the assumption that light travels from a point in one medium to a point in another medium *in the least time,* and that the velocity is less in the denser medium.[2]

[1] Various opinions have been held on this point. Heller, Vol. II., pp. 65, 78, argues in favor of the independent discovery; Poggendorff, p. 312, and Rosenberger, Part II., p. 113, incline to the opinion that Descartes plagiarized from Snell. Arago, on the other hand, declared Descartes the sole discoverer. See ''Fresnel'' in Arago's *Biographies,* 2d series, Boston, 1859, pp. 187, 188. The question is minutely discussed by P. Kramer, *Zeitsch. f. Math. u. Phys.,* Vol. 27, 1882, Supplement, p. 235, and, after the discovery of some new documents, again by D. J. Korteweg, *Revue de Métaphysique et de Morale,* July, 1896, pp. 489–501.

[2] Rosenberger, Part II., p. 114.

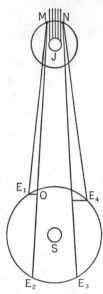

FIG. 11. **Römer's determination of the velocity of light.** When the earth moves from E_1 to E_2 the eclipses of the first satellite of Jupiter occurred several minutes later than the time computed from its average period of revolution. Römer interpreted this difference to be due to the time it takes light to travel the distance OE_2. When the earth passed from E_3 to E_4 the eclipses occurred earlier than predicted.

VELOCITY OF LIGHT

A great achievement of the seventeenth century was the discovery of the gradual propagation of light. Previously its speed was usually supposed to be infinite. The first attempt to measure the velocity was made by Galileo.[1] He ascertained the time required for a person A to signal with a lantern to B and receive back a signal from B. This was tried in nighttime, when the two observers were stationed close together, and also when they were nearly a mile apart. If a difference in time could be detected, then light would travel with finite velocity. Galileo was not able to settle the question from his experiments. But he made a suggestion on a wholly different problem which accidentally led another investigator to success. He remarked that the frequent disappearance of Jupiter's satellites behind the planet might be made to serve in longitude determinations. About 1642 the Italian astronomer, **Giovanni Domenico Cassini,** one of a number of great scientists called to Paris by Louis XIV., undertook a prolonged study of the Jovian system. About thirty years later a young Dane, **Olaf Römer** (1644–1710), was induced to settle in Paris. He was a native of Aarhus and had studied at Copenhagen. At Paris he observed, together with Jean Picard, the eclipses of Jupiter's moons. It was noticed that the times of revolu-

[1] Crew and de Salvio, *op. cit.*, pp. 43, 44.

tion of these moons in their orbits were not the same at all periods of the year, and were greater than the average when the apparent size of Jupiter was diminishing. Considering it in the highest degree improbable that the actual motions should be affected with any inequality of this sort Römer became convinced that the observed irregularities must be explained on the supposition that the velocity of light is finite. In September, 1676, Römer stated to the French Academy of Sciences that in November next the eclipses of the first satellite would be about ten minutes later than the time gotten from computations based on the observations of the preceding August, and that the discrepancy could be explained by assuming that it took time for light to come from Jupiter to the earth. (See Fig. 11.) On November 9 an eclipse took place at 5 h. 35 m. 45 s., while by computation it should have been at 5 h. 25 m. 45 s. On November 22 he explained his theory to the Academy more fully, and said that it required light 22 minutes to cross the earth's orbit. (The more correct value is now known to be 16 minutes and 36 seconds.) The Academy did not at once accept Römer's theory. Picard favored it, but Cassini did not. Römer had based his computation on the

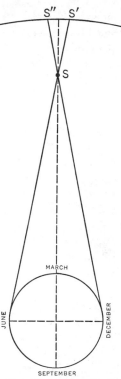

FIG. 12. Bradley's attempt to measure the parallax of γ draconis. He expected the star to show apparent motion from S' to S'' from June to December, and in March and September to occupy an intermediate position on the celestial sphere. In fact, the positions were the same for June and December. He found no effect of parallax. But strangely, in March and September the star did not appear in the same place!

first satellite, and he frankly stated that similar calculations from observations on the three other moons would not have led to success. In Cassini's mind this fact operated strongly against the acceptance of Römer's explanation. Regarding the behavior of these three bodies, Römer could only say that "they have irregularities not yet determined." In 1680 Cassini published improved ephemerides of Jupiter's moons, but made no mention of Römer's hypothesis.

The young Dane's fame increased to such an extent that he was made tutor to the Dauphin, and in 1681 Christian V. called him to Denmark as astronomer-royal. After Römer's return to his native country confidence in his theory waned at Paris. It is not known how much more he worked on the problem, and whether he removed the objection arising in connection with the other moons. He left behind many astronomical observations, nearly all of which were destroyed by the fire which devastated the town of Copenhagen in 1728.[1]

In England Römer's theory was enthusiastically supported by Edmund Halley and verified in an unexpected manner by **James Bradley** (1693–1762), then Savilian Professor of Astronomy at Oxford. While endeavoring to determine the parallax of a star, he was surprised to find that its displacement was not at all as he expected it to be. (See Fig 12.) He had almost despaired of being able to explain this, when an unexpected light fell upon him. "Accompanying a pleasure party in a sail on the Thames one day about September, 1728, he noticed that the wind seemed to shift each time that the boat put about, and a question put to the boatman brought the (to him) significant reply that the changes in direction of the vane at the top of the mast were merely due to changes in the boat's course, the wind remaining steady throughout. This was the clue he needed. He divined at once that the progressive transmission of light, combined with the advance of the earth in its orbit, must cause an annual shifting of the

[1] We have used an article on Olaf Römer by Alex. Wernicke, *Zeitsch. f. Math. u. Physik*, Vol. 25, 1880, Hist. Abtheil., pp. 1–6; also W. Doberck in *Nature*, Vol. 17, 1877, p. 105.

direction in which the heavenly bodies are seen by an amount depending upon the ratio of the two velocities."[1] (See Fig. 13.) From the value of this "aberration of light" Bradley estimated that solar rays reach the earth in 8 m. 13 s. This value was more nearly correct than Römer's 11 m., determined half a century earlier. Thus Bradley verified Römer's theory, and the gradual propagation of light came to be accepted as an established fact.

Bradley found an easy explanation of the aberration of light on Newton's corpuscular theory of light. The corpuscle acted similarly to the raindrop which falls vertically, yet seems, when we run forward, to be coming into our faces. The corpuscle of light moves down the tube of the telescope which is tipped forward, while the telescope itself is being carried forward by the earth's motion. On Fresnel and Young's undulatory theory of light the explanation is less simple. As we shall see, it involved the question of the existence and behavior of the ether.

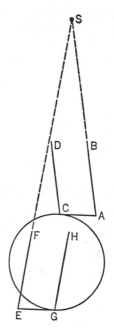

FIG. 13. **The effect called aberration.** Let *AB* be the direction of a telescope. While the earth's motion carries the observer from *A* to *C*, the ray of light travels the length of the telescope. When the ray reaches the eye, the telescope is in the position *CD*. Similarly, six months later, an observer at *G* has the telescope pointing in the direction *GH*. *CD* and *GH* differ in declination by about 40 seconds.

Huygens's Wave Theory

At a meeting of the French Academy of Sciences, in 1678, in the presence of Römer, Cassini, and others, a remarkable paper on the theory of light was presented by **Christian Huygens** (1629–1695). He was a native of The Hague,

[1] "Bradley, James," in *Dic. Nat. Biog.*

and had studied at the university in Leyden. The perusal of some of his earliest mathematical theorems led Descartes to predict his future greatness. He was induced by Louis XIV. to settle in Paris, where he remained from 1666 to 1681. Like his great contemporaries, Newton and Leibniz, Huygens never married.

Huygens's *Traité de la lumière,* of 1678, referred to above, was printed in 1690.[1] It is the earliest important attempt at an exposition of the wave theory of light. Before Huygens, a rough outline of such a theory had been given in 1665, by Robert Hooke. Huygens develops the important principle, known by his name, relating to the propagation of waves. Around each particle of a vibrating medium as a centre, a wave is formed. Thus, if, in Fig. 14, *DCF* is a spherical wave

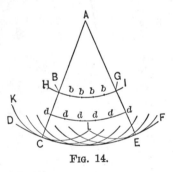

FIG. 14.

which starts from *A* as centre, then a particle *B* within this sphere will be the centre of a special wave *KCL*, touching *DCF* at *C*. In the same way every other particle inside the sphere *DCL* forms a wave of its own. All these innumerable feeble wavelets are spheres, each touching *DCL* at one point, and contributing to its formation. Huygens assumes the existence of an all-pervading ether, and explains reflection and refraction of light by the wave theory in the manner current in modern texts. Atmospheric refraction, and the marvels of double refraction in the Iceland spar, are dwelt upon. This division of a ray was first observed in Iceland spar in 1669 by **Erasmus Bartholinus,** of Copenhagen. Huygens gave the method of constructing the path of the ordinary and extraordinary ray, and observed that these rays were polarized. He assumed

[1] Reprinted in German translation in *Ostwald's Klassiker,* No. 20. Consult also *Œuvres Complètes de Christiaăn Huygens, publicées par la Société Hollandaise des Sciences,* La Haye, 1888–1895.

the vibrations in the ether to be longitudinal, as in sound, and was, therefore, not able to explain the strange phenomenon of polarization. Nor could he, by his theory, explain the origin of colors. He endeavored to deduce from the wave theory the fact that light travels rectilinearly in a homogeneous medium. His argument was not conclusive. The main reason why Newton rejected the undulatory theory was its apparent inability to explain satisfactorily why light travels in straight lines. Newton threw the weight of his great authority on the side of the emission theory, and for over a century Huygens's ideas were laid aside and neglected.

NEWTON'S EXPERIMENTS WITH PRISMS

Newton's researches on light are of the greatest importance, and give evidence of extraordinary powers. Newton's first observations are on coronas, and date back to his student days in 1664. Later come his experiments of dispersion. "In the year 1666 (at which time I applied myself to the grinding of optick glasses of other figures than spherical) I procured me a triangular glass prism to try therewith the celebrated phenomena of colors."

The formation of colors from white light had been observed long ago. Seneca (2–66 A.D.) spoke of the identity of rainbow colors and those formed by the edges of a piece of glass. The breaking up or condensation of white light into colors was discussed by Marcus Marci, professor of medicine at Prague (1648), by Grimaldi, Descartes, Hooke, and others.[1] Isaac Barrow, Newton's teacher at Cambridge, held a theory resembling one of Marcus Marci, that red was strongly condensed light, that violet was strongly rarefied light. It remained for Newton to remove the cobwebs. Before him refraction due to a prism was supposed *actually to produce color*, instead of merely to *separate what already existed*.

[1] Pater Trigautius, in the description of his mission to China, narrates that prisms were highly valued for their color effects, and were usually owned only by persons in high authority, and that a single piece sold for 500 pieces of gold. Priestley, *Gesch. d. Optik*, trans. by *G. S. Klügel*, Leipzig, 1776, p. 132.

In a darkened room he made a small circular opening in the shutter and placed the prism inside, near the hole, so that the light was refracted to the opposite wall. "Comparing the length of this colored spectrum with its breadth, I found it about five times greater—a disproportion so extravagant, that it excited me to a more than ordinary curiosity of examining from whence it might proceed." [1]

Before reaching the right explanation he advanced several hypotheses, only to find that each was disproved by the facts. One of these guesses is of particular interest to the college students of to-day, as it shows that Newton's profound mind had dwelt upon a subject prominent in modern athletics, namely, the subject of "curved pitching." Surely the modern student would find it hard to guess what possible relation there might be supposed to exist between the performance of a twirler on the diamond and optical theories. Here is what Newton said: "Then I began to suspect, whether the rays, after their trajection through the prism, did not move in curve lines and according to their more or less curvity tend to divers parts of the wall. And it increased my suspicion, when I remembered that I had often seen a tennis ball struck with an oblique racket, describe such a curve line. For, a circular as well as a progressive motion being communicated to it by that stroke, its parts on that side, where the motions conspire, must press and beat the contiguous air more violently than on the other, and there excite a reluctancy and reaction of the air proportionably greater. And for the same reason, if the rays of light should possibly be globular bodies, and by their oblique passage out of one medium into another, acquire a circulating motion, they ought to feel the greater resistance from the ambient æther, on that side, where the motions conspire, and thence be continually bowed to the other. But nothwithstanding this plausible ground of suspicion, when I came to examine it, I could observe no such curvity in them. And besides (which was enough for my purpose) I observed, that

[1] *Phil. Trans.*, Abr., Vol. I., p. 128. Newton sent this article to the Royal Society in 1672.

the difference betwixt the length of the image, and the diameter of the hole, through which the light was transmitted, was proportionable to their distance.

"The gradual removal of these suspicions at length led me to the *experimentum crucis,* which was this: I took two boards, and placed one of them close *behind the prism at the window,* so that the light might pass through a small hole, made in it for the purpose, and fall on the other board, which I placed at about twelve feet distance, having first made a small hole in it also, for some of that incident light to pass through. Then, I placed another prism behind the second board." On turning the first prism about its axis, the image which fell on the second board was made to move up and down upon that board, so that all its parts could successively pass through the hole in that board, and fall upon the prism behind it. The places where the light fell against the wall were noted. It was seen that the blue light, which was most refracted in the first prism, was also most refracted in the second prism, the red being

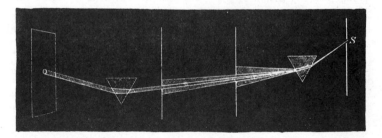

Fig. 15.

least refracted in both prisms. "And so the true cause of the length of that image was detected to be no other than that light is not similar or homogeneal, but consists of *diform rays, some of which are more refrangible than others.*" [1] (See Fig. 15.)

When Newton made these experiments, he was interested in

[1] *Phil. Trans. Abr.,* Vol. I., p. 130. These experiments are also described in Newton's *Opticks,* Book I., Props. I.–V.

the improvement of the refracting telescope. The deficiencies noticed in that instrument had always been attributed to spherical aberration and the attempt was being made so to alter the spherical form of lenses as to give clear images. Newton satisfied himself that, besides spherical aberration, there was another source of trouble, namely, chromatic aberration. "The confused vision of objects seen through refracting bodies by heterogeneal light arises from the different refrangibility of several sorts of rays." (*Opticks,* Book I., Prop. V.) Could this evil be removed? Probably, if different substances possessed different dispersive powers. So Newton contrived an experiment. In a prismatic vessel filled with water (probably it was impregnated with *saccharum saturni*—sugar of lead),[1] he placed a glass prism and examined rays passing through. From his tests he thought he could conclude that refraction must always be accompanied by dispersion. Achromatic lenses seemed to him an impossibility. Evidently, here Newton did not exercise his usual caution. He happened to have used a prism of glass and one of water of equal dispersive powers. Other liquids than his impregnated water would have given different results. From very limited experimental evidence he drew a broad inference, to which he adhered with marvellous tenacity, but which later experimenters have found to be erroneous. Newton failed to examine with proper care a criticism passed by the Jesuit, Lucas of Liège. In repeating Newton's experiment with the prism, Lucas found that the length of the spectrum was not five times its width, as claimed by Newton, but only three and one-half times its width. Here was a wide divergence in a simple comparison of the length and width of the spectrum—one of the simplest measurements conceivable. How could it happen that two able experimenters should differ so widely? This question did not receive adequate study. Doubtless Newton felt that his measurement had been made repeatedly and that he could not be mistaken. Though interested in chemistry, it did not occur

---

[1] *Opticks,* p. 51; "Newton Isaac," in *Dic. Nat. Biog.*

to him that, possibly, the kind of glass of which the prism was made, might play a role in the experiment. Thus, by a strange perversity of fate, he missed the important discovery of the variability of dispersive power, and the possibility of producing achromatic lenses.

Invention of the Reflecting Telescope

While Newton failed to reach the goal in relation to the refracting telescope, he made a brilliant touchdown with regard to the reflecting telescope. He is justly regarded as one of the inventors of the latter. At that time, the reflecting telescope had been the subject of considerable attention: **Niccolò Zucchi** (1586–1670), a Jesuit in Rome, is considered the earliest designer of such an instrument. Another Jesuit, **Marin Mersenne,** in France, suggested a type of reflector, as did also the Scotch mathematician and astronomer, **James Gregory** (1638–1675). But they did not carry out their designs. Newton prepared a design of his own and he was the first to construct a reflecting telescope. This was in 1668. It was six inches long, had a diameter of one inch, and magnified 30 to 40 times. Later he made a larger instrument, which he presented to the Royal Society in 1672. It bears the inscription, "Invented by Sir Isaac Newton and made with his own hands, 1671." It was shown to the king and was examined by Robert Hooke, Christopher Wren, and others. It was greatly admired, and a description of it was sent to Huygens in Paris.[1] The telescope is preserved in the library of the Royal Society.

Newton's Further Researches. His Critics

Newton's discoveries were well received by the Royal Society, but as soon as they were published in the *Philosophical Transactions* he was opposed by several critics,— Linus, Lucas, Pardies, Hooke, Huygens. Newton was over-

[1] H. Servus, *Gesch. d. Fernrohrs,* 1886, pp. 121–132; D. Brewster, *Life of Sir Isaac Newton,* New York, 1831, p. 40.

sensitive to criticism, and on December 9, 1675, wrote to Leibniz, "I was so persecuted with discussions arising from the publication of my theory of light, that I blamed my own imprudence for parting with so substantial a blessing as my quiet, to run after a shadow."

Hooke upheld the undulatory theory of light as against Newton's corpuscular theory. Newton's reply to Hooke, as well as other papers communicated between 1672 and 1676, show that he had carefully weighed the arguments for and against each hypothesis. We can readily imagine how the young scientist pondered over the two rival theories; and when he hesitatingly rejected the wave theory, he little dreamed that his views would ever command such great authority, and bias the minds of physicists to such an extent as to delay for a whole century the acceptance of the wave theory. Newton had experimented on colors formed by thin plates.[1] He saw plainly how the phenomena might be explained by the undulatory theory. "Since the vibrations which make blue and violet are supposed shorter than those which make red and yellow, they must be reflected at a less thickness of the plate; which is sufficient to explicate all the ordinary phenomena of those plates or bubbles, and also of all natural bodies, whose parts are like so many fragments of such plates. These seem to be the most plain, genuine, and necessary conditions of this hypothesis; and they agree so justly with my theory, that, if the animadversor think fit to apply them, he need not, on that account, apprehend a divorce from it; but yet, how he will defend it from other difficulties I know not." [2] In Newton's mind the insuperable barrier to the acceptance of the wave theory, as it was developed at that time, was its inability to explain the rectilinear

---

[1] "Newton's Rings" are explained in Newton's *Opticks*, published in 1704, Book II., Obs. I. *et seq.* The colors of thin plates had been observed by Boyle and Hooke. The latter gave correct accounts of the leading phenomena as exhibited in the colored rings in soap-bubbles and between plates of glass compressed together.

[2] *Phil. Trans.*, Abr., Vol. I., p. 145; quoted in G. Peacock, *Miscellaneous Works of the Late Thomas Young*, Vol. I., pp. 145, 146.

path of rays. He says: "To me the fundametal supposition itself seems impossible, namely, that the waves or vibrations of any fluid can, like the rays of light, be propagated in straight lines, without a continual and very extravagant spreading and bending every way into the quiescent medium, where they are terminated by it. I mistake if there be not both experiment and demonstration to the contrary."[1] If light consisted of vibrations, it would, like sound, "bend into the shadow."

The emission theory, on the other hand, offered an easy explanation. A luminous body emits streams of minute particles moving in straight lines, which cause vision by their impact of the retina. Refraction was explained by assuming that the flying particle begins to be attracted towards the refracting surface when it comes very near, so that the component of its velocity along the normal is increased. When the particle passes from a denser to a rarer medium, this component is decreased, while the component velocity perpendicular to the normal remains unaltered in both cases. Thus the bending of the ray is explained. As a consequence, the velocity of the particle is greater through the denser medium.[2] The fact that, in a transparent substance, there exists both reflection and refraction was very difficult to explain on the emission theory. How can a surface at one time refract and at another time reflect an impinging particle? To account for this, Newton advanced the theory of "fits" of easy reflection and easy transmission, communicated to the particles by the all-pervading ether.[3] The procession of flying particles sets the ether near the surface into agitation resulting in successive compressions and rarefactions of the ether. A flying particle reaching the surface at a moment of compression is thrown back; if the particle arrives at a moment

[1] *Phil. Trans.*, Abr., Vol. I., p. 146; *Miscellaneous Works of Thomas Young*, Vol. I., p. 152.

[2] Newton's *Opticks*, 1704, Book II., Part III., Prop. X.

[3] *Opticks*, Book II., Part III., Prop. XIII.; see also T. Preston, *The Theory of Light*, 2d ed., 1895, p. 19. Preston gives a good résumé of the emission theory.

of rarefaction, its path is less obstructed and it passes through. This is Newton's explanation, how a surface of glass or water partly reflects and partly refracts rays of light composed of flying particles. Observe that Newton's emission theory postulates the existence, not only of the flying particles constituting light, but also of an ether—all the mechanism needed for the wave theory, and more.

Newton gave an explanation of the rainbow, the correct outline of which had been given previously by Archbishop Antonius de Domini in a book published in 1611, as also by Descartes and Huygens.

Newton experimented also on diffraction ("inflection") of light. The discovery of this phenomenon was made by **Francesco Maria Grimaldi** (1618–1663), professor of mathematics at the Jesuit College in Bologna. It was described in his work, *Physico-mathesis de lumine,* 1666. Through a small hole Grimaldi introduced a pencil of light into a dark room. The shadow cast by a rod held in the cone of light was allowed to fall upon a white surface. To his surprise he found the shadow wider than the computed geometrical shadow; moreover, it was bordered by one, two, and sometimes three colored bands. When the light was very strong, he saw, in addition, colored bands inside the shadow itself. On replacing the rod by an opaque plate with a small hole in it, the illuminated circle was found larger than it should have been, on the supposition that the rays travelled past the edges of the hole in exactly straight lines. This and other experiments established the fact that light bends very slightly around a corner. He called the new phenomenon "diffraction."[1]

Grimaldi's experiments were ably conducted, but he was unable to contribute anything substantial to their theory. Newton repeated Grimaldi's experiments in modified form and endeavored to explain them by the emission theory.[2]

It is remarkable that Newton should have experimented so much with the solar spectrum and have failed to observe the

[1] Rosenberger, Part II., pp. 131, 132.
[2] See *Opticks,* Book III., pp. 113–137.

Fraunhofer lines. We cannot attribute this failure to his introduction of light through a circular opening, for in some cases (*Opticks*, I, Prop. IV., p. 49) he employed a narrow slit. It cannot be ascribed to his placing the prism close to the opening so as to receive upon it very divergent light, since in the case just referred to the prism was at a distance of 10 or 12 feet from the slit. The fact that he received the spectrum on paper would not necessarily debar him from seeing dark lines; at any rate, he sometimes "looked through the prism upon the hole" (Book I., Prop. II., Exp. 4, p. 22). In the experiment (p. 49), the conditions were about the same as those under which Wollaston later saw a few of the lines. Unfortunately, during the very experiments in which the discovery of the lines would have been easiest, Newton was obliged to rely on the observations of an assistant with "more critical" eyes than his own,[1] but who was probably less alert for unexpected phenomena.

HEAT

DEVELOPMENT OF THE THERMOMETER

During the seventeenth century we witness the early development of the thermometer, a physical instrument which has enjoyed wider application than almost any other. Modern historical research concurs in ascribing its invention to Galileo.[2] A glass bulb of the size of a hen's egg, with a long stem of the thickness of a straw, and dipping into water, which was made to rise part way up the tube by previous warming

[1] Book I., Part II., Exp. 7, p. 92; see also an article on "Newton, Wollaston, and Fraunhofer Lines," by Alexander Johnson in *Nature*, Vol. 26, 1882, p. 572.

[2] E. Wohlwill, "Zur Geschichte der Erfindung und Verbreitung des Thermometers," *Poggendorff's Annalen*, Vol. 124, 1865, pp. 163–178; F. Burckhardt, *Die Erfindung des Thermometers und seine Gestaltung im 17. Jahrhundert*. Basel, 1867; E. Gerland, *Das Thermometer*, Berlin, 1885. Of Gerland's publication we have made extensive use. The invention of the thermometer has been variously ascribed to the famous mechanic, Cornelius Drebbel of Holland, to the anatomist, Sanctorius of Padua, to Father Paul of Cracow, to the London physician, Robert Fludd, to the German, Otto von Guericke.

of the bulb, constituted Galileo's first thermometer. It was affected, of course, by fluctuations of atmospheric pressure as well as of temperature, and was really a thermo-baroscope. Galileo's pupil, Viviani, gives 1593 as the date of the invention; Castelli, another pupil, says that in 1603 he saw Galileo use it in experimental lectures. All the early thermometers contained air, and the stem was arbitrarily graduated. Being affected by changes in atmospheric pressure, Galileo's air thermometer was very imperfect.

The first improvement was introduced by the French physician, **Jean Rey**,[1] who simply *inverted* Galileo's instrument, filling the bulb with water and the stem with air. Thus, water was made the thermometric substance. On January 1, 1632, he communicated this method to the great intermediary among scientists, Pater Mersenne. As Rey could not bring himself to close the upper end of the stem, there was constant danger of errors from evaporation of the water. Schwenter says that before 1636 artisans had succeeded in so choosing the relative dimensions of bulb and stem, that the liquid rose and fell the whole length of the stem in the course of one year.

To some minds the rise and fall of the thermometer presented an example of perpetual motion, and one writer actually called the instrument a *"perpetuum mobile* showing degrees of heat and cold.*"* [2]

A quarter of a century after Rey's innovation, the idea of sealing the tube was carried out by the Florentine academicians, probably on the suggestion of Grand Duke Ferdinand II. of Tuscany. The tube was filled with spirit of wine and a graduated scale was attached to the stem.

These academicians, not more numerous than the muses, were pupils of Galileo, and made the *Accademia del Cimento* (academy of experiment) famous. In this small organization the spirit of Galileo revived for a time in Italy; but the society lasted only ten years, 1657–1667. What was the cause of

[1] G. Hellmann in *Himmel und Erde*, Vol. II., p. 172; E. Gerland, *op. cit.*, p. 10.
[2] See E. Wohlwill, *op. cit.*, p. 169.

this early dissolution? According to some writers,[1] Leopold de' Medici, the brother of the Grand Duke, and with him founder and patron of the organization, was given the cardinal's hat only on condition that the Academy be broken up. According to others[2] there arose dissensions among the members themselves.

Before the organization of this academy, the Italians had already done much for meteorology. Besides the invention of the thermometer and barometer, they invented the rain-gauge, first used by Benedetto Castelli in 1639.[3] The problem of selecting two fixed temperatures for the thermometer and of subdividing the interval into a suitable number of degrees was taken up by the *Accademia del Cimento*. Following the example of the philosophers and physicians, they chose as fixed points the cold of winter and the heat of summer, dividing the intervening space into 80 or 40 equal spaces. To determine more accurately the position of these points, they defined the one to be the temperature of snow or ice in the severest frost, and the other to be the temperature in the bodies of cows and deer. The melting-point of ice was found by them to be invariable, and, in their medical scale, to be at $13\frac{1}{2}°$. In 1829 some of the Florentine thermometers were discovered among old glass-ware, and Libri actually found them to read $13\frac{1}{2}°$ in melting ice. They had been used in Florence sixteen years in meteorological observations, and by reducing the average temperature to one of the modern scales, and comparing with modern observations, Libri thought he could draw the inference that the climate of Florence had remained unaltered during the two hundred years.[4]

The fixed points chosen by the Florentine Academy did not prove satisfactory, and all sorts of improvements were suggested. Dalencé in 1688 adopted (1) the temperature of air

[1] Poggendorff, p. 351; Rosenberger, Part II., p. 162.
[2] Gerland, *op. cit.*, p. 45; also his article in *Wiedemann's Annalen* Vol. IV., p. 604.
[3] G. Hellmann, *op. cit.*, p. 176.
[4] Libri, *Poggendorff's Annalen*, Vol. 21, p. 325; see also Gerland, *Das Thermometer*, p. 45.

during freezing, and (2) that of melting butter. The final adoption of the temperatures of melting ice and boiling water was not reached until the eighteenth century, though Huygens had recommended the use of one or the other of these as early as 1665.[1]

The Florentine thermometers became famous. They were introduced into England by Boyle. They reached France by way of Poland. An envoy of the Queen of Poland was presented in 1657 by the Grand Duke with thermometers and other instruments. Her secretary forwarded one of the thermometers to the astronomer Ismaël Boulliau in Paris and stated that "the Grand Duke always carries one in his pocket."[2] The thermometer was about one decimeter long and contained alcohol. Boulliau himself constructed in 1659 a thermometer in which mercury was used for the first time (so far as known) as a thermometric substance. Recently a record of temperature observations by Boulliau, extending from May, 1658, to September, 1660, has been found. Next to the Florentine record, begun in 1655, it is the oldest in existence.[3]

HEAT DUE TO MOTION

We are surprised to find that Newton's immediate predecessors had anticipated our modern theory of heat. *Heat a Mode of Motion* is the title of Tyndall's well-known work (1862), yet Descartes, Amontons, Boyle, Francis Bacon, Hooke, and Newton already looked upon heat as a mode of motion. Of course, in the seventeenth century, this theory rested upon somewhat slender experimental evidence, else the doctrine could hardly have been cast to the winds by the eighteenth-century philosophers. Boyle experimented on the mechanical production of heat and illustrated the heating due to arrested motion by such examples as the hammer driving a nail.

[1] E. Gerland, *Zeitschr. f. Instrk.*, Vol. 13, 1893, p. 390.
[2] Maze, *Comptes Rendus*, Vol. 121, 1895, p. 230.
[3] Maze, *Comptes Rendus*, Vol. 120, 1895, p. 732.

Boyle observed also the effects of atmospheric pressure on ebullition and experimented with freezing mixtures. Newton, in 1701, made a statement in the *Philosophical Transactions* which involves the hypothesis that the rate of cooling of a body is proportional to its excess of temperature over the surrounding medium.[1] This surmise has since been tested experimentally by Dulong and Petit, and has been shown to be true only within a small range of temperature.[2]

ELECTRICITY AND MAGNETISM

SECULAR VARIATION OF DECLINATION

The correction of Gilbert's error in asserting that magnetic declination "is constant at a given place," and the discovery of the "secular variation of the declination," is usually attributed to **Henry Gellibrand** (1597–1637), professor at Gresham College. He pointed out that in 1580, *"Mr. Burrows* (a man of unquestionable abilities in the mathematiques)" found the declination near London to be 11° 15′ E.; that in 1622 **Edmund Gunter** found it to be at the same place 6° 13′; that in 1634 he himself found it to be not much more than 4° E.[3] This subject received the careful attention of **Edmund Halley** (1656–1742), who was professor at Oxford and later astronomer-royal. He endeavored to explain magnetic variation by assuming four fixed magnetic poles. As this did not account for the facts, he supposed that the earth consisted of two concentric magnetic shells with poles differently placed and not coincident with the geographic poles, the inner shell rotating slowly. In 1698, William III. was induced to send Halley upon a long voyage on the Atlantic and Pacific oceans for the purpose of testing his hypothesis.[4] He came back, not with the desired proof, but with useful observations on "varia-

[1] Mach, *Princ. d. Wärmelehre*, p. 132.
[2] *Ann. de chim. et de Phys.* 2ᵉ, Vol. VII., 1817, pp. 225, 237.
[3] Consult Henry Gellibrand, *A Discourse Mathematical on the Variation of the Magneticall Needle*, London, 1635. Reprinted in G. Hellmann's *Neudrucke*, No. 9, Berlin, 1897.
[4] Benjamin, p. 448.

tion." About the beginning of the eighteenth century he constructed charts of equal variation (declination), which became famous. One of his original isogonic maps has been found recently in the British Museum. It seems that he published two totally distinct charts.[1]

Some interesting observations were recorded in the *Philosophical Transactions* of 1676 and 1684 regarding the magnetic effects of lightning. Thus in 1681, a ship bound for Boston was struck by lightning. Observations of the stars showed that "the compasses were changed"; "the north point was turn'd clear south." The ship was steered to Boston with the compass reversed.[2]

EXPERIMENTS ON ELECTRIC ATTRACTION AND REPULSION

Phenomena due to electric attraction and repulsion continued to interest and amuse investigators. Thus, Boyle observed that dry hair is easily electrified by friction. "That false locks of hair, brought to a certain degree of dryness, will be attracted by the flesh of some persons, I had proof in two beautiful ladies who wore them; for, at some times, I observed that they could not keep them from flying to their cheeks, and from striking there, tho' neither of them had occasion for or did use paint." One of the ladies "gave me leave to satisfy myself farther; and desiring her to hold her warm hand at a convenient distance from one of those locks taken off and placed in the free air, as soon as she did this, the lower end of the lock, which was free, applied itself presently to her hand."[3]

[1] L. A. Bauer, "Halley's Earliest Equal variation Chart," *Terrestrial Magnetism*, Vol. I., 1896, p. 29; L. A. Bauer, *Nature*, May 23, 1895. It is worthy of remark that Halley constructed in 1686, and published in the *Philosophical Transactions*, 1688, No. 183, the earliest *wind map*. It is reprinted in Hellmann's *Neudrucke*, No. 8, Berlin, 1897.

[2] E. Hoppe, *Entw. d. Lehre v. d. Elektricität bis auf Hauksbee*, Hamburg, 1887, p. 18.

[3] *Boyle's Works*, by Peter Shaw, 2d ed., London, 1738, Vol. I., p. 506 *et seq.;* E. Hoppe, *op. cit.*, p. 17.

Again, Newton astonished the Royal Society by the description of an experiment with a round piece of glass set in a brass ring and supported by it about one-eighth of an inch from the table. "Rubbing a pretty while the glass briskly with some rough and raking stuff, till some very little fragments of very thin paper, laid on the table under the glass, began to be attracted and move nimbly to and fro . . . leaping up to the glass and resting there awhile; then leaping down and resting there; then leaping up and perhaps down and up again." [1]

Otto von Guericke of Magdeburg generated electricity by holding his hands against a rotating sphere of sulphur. This once famous contrivance is the forerunner of the friction electric machine. He discovered electric induction and made a number of other interesting observations, but his speculations on electricity—his "mundane virtues"—were as unfortunate as were Gilbert's cosmological magnetic theories.

Boyle made an important experiment showing that electric attraction takes place through a vacuum. In 1676 Picard, while carrying one evening a mercury barometer from the observatory in Paris to the Porte Saint Michel, saw that each motion of the mercury caused a glow in the Torricellian vacuum. The cause of this light was attributed to a substance called mercurial phosphorus. This name was suggested by the new glow phenomena (phosphorescence) of phosphorus, which were then astonishing the scientific world. The origin of Picard's light was studied in England by **Francis Hauksbee**. He let air rush from above into a vacuum through a tube dipping into a basin of mercury under the bell-jar, and watched the air blowing the mercury up "with violence against the sides of the glass that held it, appearing all round as a body of fire, made up of abundance of glowing globules descending again into itself." [2] From this and other tests with mercury Hauksbee concluded that no light could be

---

[1] T. Birch, *Hist. of Royal Society*, Vol. III., London, 1757, p. 250; E. Hoppe, *op. cit.*, p. 14.

[2] *Phil. Trans.*, 1705, No. 303, p. 2129; Hoppe, *op. cit.*, p. 21.

obtained without motion and without a partial vacuum. He observed that attraction accompanied the phenomena and concluded that the light is due to electricity. He was the first to show that an electric charge resides only on the surface of a body, and that metals may become electrified by friction.

SOUND

Vibratory strings were made the subject of investigation by Galileo and Marin Mersenne. Galileo pointed out the dependence of pitch upon the number of vibrations perceived in unit of time. Mersenne noticed that a string gives, besides its fundamental, two overtones. At Oxford, **William Noble** and **Thomas Pigott** showed by paper riders put at different places on a vibrating string that it vibrates not only as a whole, but also in halves, thirds, etc.[1] Mersenne determined the velocity of sound in air by the difference in time between the flash and the report of fire-arms at known distances. He got 1380 feet per second. **Pierre Gassendi** (1592–1655) used cannon as well as pistols, and disproved the peripatetic tenet that the velocity depends upon its source and its pitch. His test gave 1473 Paris feet. The illustrious members of the Paris Academy, D. Cassini, Picard, Römer, Huygens, found the value 1172 Paris feet per second.

Newton published in his *Principia* (Book II., Props. XLVIII., XLIX., L.) a theoretical deduction for the velocity of sound. He concluded that this velocity varied directly as the square root of the "elastic force," and inversely as the square root of the "density of the medium"; the velocity is "equal to that which heavy bodies acquire by falling with an equally accelerated motion, and in their fall describing half the altitude A," where A is the height of a homogeneous atmosphere, taken as 29,725 feet. This gave 979 feet as the velocity, while experiment indicated about 1142 English feet. Newton threw out conjectures as to the cause of the discrep-

[1] *Phil. Trans.*, 1677; Heller, Vol. II., p. 339.

ancy between the experimental and theoretical values, but the true explanation was given over a century later by **Pierre Simon Laplace** (1749–1827). Newton failed to take into account the changes of elasticity due to the heat of compression and the cold of rarefaction. His expression amounts to $v = \sqrt{\dfrac{p}{d}}$; Laplace's correction makes it $v = \sqrt{\dfrac{1.41\,p}{d}}$, where p is the pressure of the air and d its density.

THE EIGHTEENTH CENTURY

THE progress of physics during the first eighty years of the seventeenth century was truly extraordinary. Nothing like it is seen during the earlier epochs of human history; nothing like it is exhibited during the eighteenth century. The names of Galileo, Guericke, Boyle, and Newton adorn the period when experiment assumed a place of supreme authority. In the eighteenth century there comes a reaction. On the whole, speculation is less effectively restrained and guided by experiment.

Another important cause makes the period less brilliant. It brought forth few great experimental physicists—none of such transcendent genius as Galileo, Huygens, Newton. Mathematics and mathematical astronomy were enriched during the eightenth century by the remarkable researches of the Bernoullis, Euler, Clairaut, D'Alembert, Lagrange, Laplace, but physics proper was cultivated by men of more limited powers.

The eightenth century has been characterized as a materialistic age in science. The concept of energy was unknown to that time. Forces were properties of matter. It was an age which sought to explain the hidden phenomena in physics and chemistry by the assumption of the existence of "imponderables" which were very subtle, attenuated forms of matter not capable of being weighed. The term was used in distinction to ordinary or ponderable matter. The eighteenth century had some seven such substances, three of which it inherited from the seventeenth and earlier centuries. They were not always assumed to be without weight. In that respect, considerable diversity prevailed among different writers.

The oldest of the imponderables was *caloric*, the stuff called heat. It goes back to Roman and Greek time, although the name "caloric" is comparatively recent; it was introduced by the chemist Lavoisier in his *Traité élémentaire de chimie*, in 1789. In the seventeenth century many leaders of science looked upon heat as a form of motion. It was in the eighteenth century that heat as a substance took firm hold of the minds of scientists, and continued to do so until nearly the middle of the nineteenth century.

The substance which Descartes in 1644 assumed to fill interstellar space and which moved in great *vortices* maintained its place in the thought of continental Europe until nearly the middle of the eighteenth century. This substance was imponderable and globular in form. Descartes assumed also two ponderable forms of matter, the luminous matter of the sun and the opaque matter of the earth.[1]

As we have already seen, Huygens and Hooke, and also Newton, postulated the existence of a luminiferous ether. In the eighteenth century only very few scientists felt the need of this substance. On the other hand, the corpuscles of Newton's emission theory of light were indispensable. Except for these flying bullets, interstellar space was empty in this century, after the disappearance of Descartes's vortices.

The beginning of the eighteenth century witnessed the creation of the famous *phlogiston* theory by the Bavarian chemist Georg Ernst Stahl. He had imbibed preliminary ideas of such a doctrine from his teacher, Iohann J. Becher. It was intended to explain what is now called oxidation. It held its place until overthrown by Lavoisier, about 1789. What escapes from bodies and from metals when they are calcined or oxidized is what Stahl called phlogiston. Whether he considered it ponderable or imponderable does not appear clearly; it was probably ponderable. Oxidizing of metals was with Stahl a process of *decomposition*. Phlogiston was driven out of the metal regarded as a compound, leaving behind the more primitive earths. Stahl and many contemporary chemists

[1] See E. T. Whittaker, *A History of the Theories of Aether and Electricity from the Age of Descartes to the Close of the Nineteenth Century*. London, 1910.

made only slight use of the balance. Otherwise they would have been haunted by the fact that driving phlogiston out of wood leaves ashes weighing less than the wood, while driving phlogiston out of metal leaves a residue weighing more than the original metal. The phlogiston and the caloric theory sometimes came in conflict with each other. The increase in weight in the oxidation of metals was explained by some writers, by the aid of a ponderable heat substance, as a *synthetic* process, not a decomposition. Caloric entered the substance during the process. After Lavoisier overthrew phlogiston, caloric had no rival and ruled supreme for about half a century.

In electricity we shall see that Du Fay and Symmer felt the need of assuming two imponderable fluids, while Franklin postulated only one. Franklin assumed electricity to be granular in structure, which is in harmony with modern notions. Magnetism, too, was explained by some as due to imponderable fluids. Euler used one magnetic fluid, Coulomb used two. They must be very fine to be able to pass through glass and affect a magnetic needle on the other side. The eighteenth century was truly materialistic.

MECHANICS

The mechanical principles, as stated by Newton, suffice to explain any ordinary practical problem, whether in statics or dynamics. Nevertheless, it has been found convenient to deduce particular laws by which certain groups of problems may be treated by routine. As examples, we cite "D'Alembert's Principle" and the laws of the "Conservation of Momentum," "Conservation of the Centre of Gravity," "Conservation of Areas." The eighteenth century has contributed much toward the development of these principles, enabling mechanical phenomena to be viewed from new standpoints. But their subjects, together with the analytical development of mechanics, lie outside the scope of this work.[1]

[1] The reader may consult E. Mach, *The Science of Mechanics*, trans. by T. J. McCormack, Chicago, 1893; E. Dühring, *Krit. Gesch. d. allgem. Princ. d. Mechanik*, Leipzig, 1887.

Mention must be made of the new contrivance invented by **George Atwood** (1746–1807), for the study of the laws of falling bodies. Galileo had retarded the velocity of falling bodies by means of the inclined gutter, and thereby facilitated experimentation. Atwood accomplished this end by suspending two weights by a thread over an easily running pulley. Atwood was a fellow and tutor of Trinity College, Cambridge, where his public lectures in experimental philosophy were remarkable both for the fluent ease of delivery and for the ingenuity of their experimental illustrations.[1] He published a description of his machine in 1784 in a treatise *On the Rectilinear Motion and Rotation of Bodies.*

LIGHT

Wave Theory Abandoned

During the seventeenth century we have witnessed a conflict between two theories of light. We have seen how Newton, from the facts then known, balanced the arguments for and against each theory and hesitatingly decided in favor of the emission theory, while on the continent his great contemporary, Huygens, advocated the wave theory. A nineteenth century view of eighteenth century science is found in an address delivered in 1888 by S. P. Langley: "These two great men, then, each looked around in the darkness as far as his light carried him. All beyond that was chance to each; and fate willed that Newton, whose light shone farther than his rival's, found it extend just far enough to show the entrance to the wrong way. He reaches the conclusion that we all know; one not only wrong in regard to light, but which bears pernicious results on the whole theory of heat, since light, being conceded to be material, radiant heat, if affiliated to light, must be regarded as material too; and Newton's influence is so permanent, that we shall see this strange conclusion drawn by the contemporaries of Herschel from his

[1] *Dic. Nat. Biog.* See also T. Young's *Misc. Works,* Vol. II., pp. 617–623.

experiments made a hundred years later. It would seem then that the result of this unhappy corpuscular theory was more far-reaching than we commonly suppose.''[1]

The only prominent writers of the eighteenth century who advocated the undulatory theory were **Leonard Euler** (1707–1783) [2] and Benjamin Franklin. They advanced only theoretical considerations in its favor, and convinced no one. In 1750 Euler published his *Lettrés à une Princesse d'Allemagne sur quelques sujets de physique*. The German translator of this work thought it necessary to interpolate explanations, lest some innocent reader might be led to believe in a theory which was not held now (1792) ''by a single physicist of prominence.''[3] Euler explained diversity in colors by the difference in duration of vibrations. He made the conjecture that the different media of the eye had the property of preventing the dispersion of colors, and suggested that lenses be prepared out of two different substances, with the view of removing chromatic defects. He had a theory as to how this might be done, but was not able actually to produce a lens free from color. This failure he attributed to the difficulty of accurate construction.

Invention of the Achromatic Lens

Euler's speculations excited the curiosity of Samuel Klingenstierna, professor at Upsala, who began to repeat Newton's experiments on achromatism and arrived at results at variance with Newton's. At this stage, **John Dollond,** a London optician, began a series of tests. They, too, went contrary to Newton's. Dollond then tested different kinds of glass, and in 1757 wrote a letter to Klingenstierna, in which he points out that the ratio of the sine of incidence to the sine of the mean angle of refraction is 1.53 for crown glass and 1.583 for

[1] S. P. Langley, *The History of a Doctrine,* 1888, p. 4, delivered at the Cleveland meeting of the A. A. A. S.

[2] Papers thereon appear in *Memoiren der Berliner Akademie,* 1746, 1752.

[3] Rosenberger, *I. Newton u. s. Physik. Princ.,* 1895, p. 332.

flint glass.[1] Hence he concluded that achromatism must be possible in lenses. The practical realization of this idea proved to be difficult and required (to use his own words) "a resolute perseverance."[2] In 1758 he at last succeeded, and presented an achromatic telescope to the Royal Society. It created a sensation throughout Europe. Dollond's success seemed to disprove Euler's theory of dispersion and caused him much embarrassment.

After Dollond's death, in 1761, his son, Peter Dollond, manufactured (in partnership with the mechanic Ramsden) refractors of great merit. After repeated failures, achromatic lenses came to be applied successfully also to microscopes.

The achromatic telescope greatly facilitated the growth of modern astronomy. How great an advantage was secured becomes the more apparent when we remember that Huygens's method of removing color effects by the use of lenses of great focal length led to the construction by him of very long tubeless refractors (the objectives being mounted on high poles). which were exceedingly clumsy and at the same time yielded inferior optical results. One object lens presented by him to the Royal Society had a focal length of 123 feet.

When Dollond's telescopes had become famous, the claims of another man were laid before the public. As early as 1729 Chester More Hall, of More Hall in Essex, while studying the mechanism of the human eye, was led to the design of lenses without color. He employed several working opticians to grind his lenses, and several object-glasses were completed. But he never published any account of his labors. Dollond's work was independent of Hall's.[3]

---

[1] H. Servus, *Geschichte des Fernrohrs*, 1886, p. 83.

[2] Consult *Phil. Trans.*, Vol. 50, 1758, p. 733.

[3] D. Brewster, *Life of Sir I. Newton*, New York, 1831, pp. 64–67. For further details on Hall and achromatism, consult the article "Telescope" in the *Encyclopædia Britannica*, 9th ed., and the article "Optics" in the *Edinburgh Encyclopædia*, p. 607, note.

Rivalry of Reflecting and Refracting Telescopes

Contemporaneous with the early development of the achromatic telescope is the construction of large reflecting telescopes. Again England displayed superior skill. In 1723, about half a century after Newton made his reflectors, **John Hadley** presented to the Royal Society an instrument six feet long. It equalled in performance the Huygenian refractor 123 feet in length! Further progress in the design of concave mirrors was made by James Short of Edinburgh, and especially by **William Herschel** (1738–1822). To improve the "space-penetrating power" Herschel increased the light-gathering power by the use of larger mirrors. He experimented in the shaping and polishing of concave mirrors with an enthusiasm and skill never surpassed. Mirrors of 10, 20, 30 feet, and finally one of 40 feet focal length, left his hands. The last, completed in 1789, was four feet in diameter and weighed 2500 pounds. The telescope led to Herschel's discovery of the two Saturnian satellites nearest to the ring. In 1745 was completed by Lord Rosse at Parsonstown in Ireland a gigantic reflector, with a mirror six feet across and a tube 58 feet long and seven feet in diameter. So large was this tube that Dean Peacock walked through it once with uplifted umbrella.[1] This "light-grasper" displayed celestial objects with extraordinary splendor. "Never in my life," exclaims Sir James South, "did I see such glorious sidereal pictures!" This was the largest reflecting telescope constructed preceding the twentieth century. The more prominent of recent reflectors are the Crossley and Mills reflectors of the Lick Observatory in California; the great 72-inch reflector at the Dominion Observatory in Canada, and the 100-inch Hooker reflector of the Mount Wilson Observatory in California. George E. Hale[2] states that silvered glass has been found superior to metals for telescope mirrors, "chiefly because of the perfection with which glass can be ground and polished,

[1] A. M. Clerke, *A Popular History of Astronomy*, New York, 1893, pp. 145, 147.
[2] George Ellery Hale, *The New Heavens*, New York, 1922, p. 16.

and the ease of renewing its silvered surface when tarnished.''
The coat of pure silver must be ''renewed several times a
year and always kept highly burnished.'' Hale adds further:
''It would be interesting to trace the long contest for su-
premacy between refracting and reflecting telescopes, each of
which, at certain stages in its development, appeared to be un-
rivalled. In modern observatories both types are used, each
for the purpose for which it is best adapted. For the photography of nebulæ and the study of the fainter stars, the reflector has special advantages.'' [1]

HEAT

AMONTONS'S AIR THERMOMETER

Guillaume Amontons (1663–1705) effected in 1702 an improvement of Galileo's air thermometer. In his youth Amontons became deaf; but this was not regarded by him as an
affliction, since it permitted scientific pursuits with less moles-
tation from the outer world. He held a government position
in Paris. His air thermometer was of constant volume and
consisted of a U-shaped tube with the shorter arm ending in
a bulb and the longer measuring 45 inches. Degrees of temperature were indicated by the height (in inches) of the mercury column in the longer arm necessary to keep the volume
constant. The instrument was intended as a standard, by
which a mercury thermometer in Paris, say, could be compared with one in St. Petersburg without the necessity of
transmitting thermometers, from one place to the other. But
the invention met with little favor. He chose the boiling-
point of water as a fixed point, but, being unaware of the dependence of the boiling-point upon air pressure, he could not

[1] Consult further the history of the telescope by C. S. Hastings
in *Smithsonian Report*, 1892; also George E. Hale, ''On the Comparative Value of Refracting and Reflecting Telescopes for Astrophysical
Investigations,'' *Astrophysical Journal*, Vol. V., 1897, pp. 119–131.
Students interested in the history of *anamorphosis* during the sixteenth
and seventeeth centuries may consult H. Ruoss, ''Geschichte der optischen und katoptrischen anamorphosen,'' *Zeitsch. d. Math. u. Phys.*,
Vol. 39, 1894, His. Lit. Abth., p. 1.

attain extreme accuracy.[1] It is an interesting fact that Amontons's researches amount to an experimental proof of the law
of gases now named after Charles and Gay-Lussac, and that
he first arrived at the notion of absolute temperature. "It
appears," says he, "that the extreme cold of this thermometer
is that which would reduce the air by its spring to sustain no
load at all, which would be a degree of cold much more considerable than what is esteemed very cold." From Amontons's
data the absolute zero in our centigrade scale is found to be
— 239.5°. Lambert, who repeated Amontons's experiments
with greater accuracy,[2] obtained data yielding — 270.3°. The
value now accepted is — 273.1°.[2] Lambert uses this language:
"Now a degree of heat equal to zero is really what may be
called absolute cold. Hence at absolute cold the volume of the
air is zero, or as good as zero. That is to say, at absolute cold
the air falls together so compactly that its parts absolutely
touch, that it becomes, so to speak, water-proof."

THE FAHRENHEIT THERMOMETER

Stimulated by Amontons's researches **Gabriel Daniel Fahrenheit** (1686–1736) began to study the accurate construction
of thermometers. He was a native of Danzig, but went to
Amsterdam to secure a business education; he became interested in physics, and travelled in England, Denmark, and
Sweden. He was a manufacturer of meteorological instruments. That he attained considerable celebrity is evident
from his election to the Royal Society of London in 1724.
The same year he contributed to the *Philosophical Transactions* five short papers in Latin. Therein he revealed for the
first time his process of making thermometers.[3] Fahrenheit

[1] E. Gerland, "Ueber Amontons' und Lambert's Verdienste um die
Thermometrie," *Zeitsch. f. Instrumentenkunde*, Vol. VIII., 1888, pp.
319–322. Abstract given in Poske's *Zeitschrift*, Vol. II., 1899, pp. 142,
143.

[2] Lambert, *Pyrometrie*, Berlin, 1779, p. 29; E. Gerland, *Instrumentenkunde*, Vol. VIII., p. 322.

[3] The five papers, together with articles on thermometry by Réaumur
and Celsius, are brought out in German translation in *Ostwald's Klassiker*, No. 57, Leipzig, 1894.

was in communication with Olaf Römer, whom he probably visited in Copenhagen. During the cold winter of 1709 both are said to have taken records of temperatures.

Fahrenheit was greatly interested in Amontons's observations of the constancy of the boiling-point (previously observed by Huygens, Newton, and Halley). Curious to know how other liquids would behave, he made a series of tests, and found that, like water, each had a fixed boiling-point.[1] Later he noticed that the boiling-point varied with a change in atmospheric pressure.[2] Attention to this fact contributed vastly towards exact thermometry. Fahrenheit deserves great credit for first bringing about the general use of mercury in thermometers. (The earliest mercury-in-glass thermometer, it will be remembered, is due to Ismaël Boulliau, 1659.) The success of Fahrenheit's mercury thermometers was largely due to a method which he invented for cleaning the mercury.

Fahrenheit made two kinds of thermometers,—the one filled with spirit of wine, the other with mercury. From his first paper published in 1724, it appears that the two fixed points chosen for the thermometers he then used, were an ice-water-salt mixture and the blood temperature of the human body, and that the interval between them was divided into 96 steps. From his second paper of 1724, it appears that he used also a third point, determined by an ice-water mixture. We quote from that paper: "The scale of those thermometers which are used only in meteorological observations begins with 0 and ends with 96. This scale depends upon the determination of three fixed points, which are obtained as follows: the first, the lowest, . . . is found by a mixture of ice, water, and sal-ammoniac or sea salt, if the thermometer is dipped in this mixture, then the liquid falls to the point marked 0. This experiment succeeds better in winter than in summer. The second point is obtained, if water and ice are mixed without the salts just mentioned; if the thermometer is dipped in this

---

[1] *Phil. Trans.*, Vol. 30, 1724, pp. 1–3; *Ostwald's Klass.*, No. 57, p. 3.
[2] *Phil. Trans.*, Vol. 33, pp. 179, 180; *Ostwald's Klass.*, No. 57, p. 17.

mixture, it will stand at 32° . . . ; the third point is at the 96th degree, and the alcohol expands to that point if the thermometer be held in the mouth or armpit of a healthy person."[1]

In his fifth paper he says: "In my account of experiments on the boiling-point of several liquids, I mentioned that at that time the boiling-point of water was found to be 212°; later I recognized through various observations and experiments that this point is fixed for one and the same weight of the atmosphere, but that for different weights of the atmosphere, it may vary either way." From this it appears that in 1724 the number 212 was not pre-arranged; boiling water simply *happened* to raise the mercury column to that point. If our interpretation of Fahrenheit's papers of 1724 is correct, then it was equally a matter of chance that 32° came to mark the freezing temperature of water and that 180 came to stand for the number of degrees between the freezing and boiling points of water. We would expect that in his later practice, Fahrenheit would profit by the results of his experimentation, that he would discard the two fixed points mentioned in his first paper and choose the freezing and boiling temperatures of water as more convenient fixed points. But we possess no direct and reliable information that either he or his Amsterdam partner actually took this step. A description in the *Acta eruditorum* of 1714 of two thermometers which Fahrenheit donated to Christian Wolf indicates that the interval from ice-water-salt to blood temperature was first subdivided into 24 parts, then each of these into four smaller subdivisions, making 96 parts in all.

While the Fahrenheit thermometers were adopted by the Dutch and English, other nations were slow to appreciate their value. In France Réaumur designed thermometers. **René Antoine Ferchault, Seigneur Réaumur, des Angles et de la Bermodière** (1683–1757), is known for his researches in zoölogy, botany, and physics He was not familiar with Fahrenheit's achievements. Dissatisfied with Amontons's air

[1] *Ostwald's Klassiker*, No. 57, pp. 6, 7.

thermometer (the only thermometer which he considered at all fit for use) and strongly opposed to the use of mercury on account of its small coefficient of expansion, he endeavored to construct instruments with spirit of wine which should be convenient and yet reach the desired degree of accuracy. His experiments accidentally led to the beautiful observation of the contraction in volume which may result on the mixing of liquids.[1] He found that spirit of wine (mixed with 1/5 water) expanded between the freezing and the boiling temperatures of water from 1000 to 1080 volumes; so he divided the intervening distance on the stem into 80 parts. But Réaumur's thermometers did not turn out well. All sorts of incredible readings were reported, and different instruments did not agree. **Jean André Deluc** (1727–1817) of Geneva returned to the use of mercury, and emphasized its advantages by arguments so powerful, that a physicist enthusiastically exclaimed, "Surely nature has given us this mineral for the making of thermometers."[2]

On the other hand Micheli du Crest, another scientist of Geneva, had no use for mercury, except to *calibrate* capillary tubes. He and De l'Isle in St. Petersburg introduced this process about the same time.[3] Rejecting the temperature of freezing water as a fixed point, Du Crest chose the temperature of the earth as determined in the cellar at the Paris Observatory, 84 feet deep. This was not a new idea with him. Boyle and others referred to the constancy of temperature in deep cellars. Du Crest divided the interval between this and the boiling-point into 100 steps, and thereby obtained degrees agreeing closely with Réaumur's. Part of his physical researches was carried on during his twenty years of political imprisonment.

[1] *Ostwald's Klassiker*, No. 57, pp. 100–116, 127. Réaumur's three articles on thermometers appear in German translation on pages 19–116.
[2] Deluc, *Recherches sur les Modifications de l'Atmosphère, Genève*, 1772, p. 330. E. Gerland, *op. cit.*, p. 20.
[3] J. H. Graf, *Das Leben und Wirken des Physikers und Geodäten Jacques Barthélemy Micheli du Crest*, Bern, 1890, p. 114.

Introduction of the Centigrade Scale

Centigrade scales were adopted after Du Crest by the botanist Linné and the astronomers Celsius and Strömer, all of Upsala. Linné exhibits on an engraved title page of his *Hortus,* Amsterdam, 1737, a thermometer with the middle of the stem marked 1, and the graduation proceeding both ways, up and down, to 100. **Andreas Celsius** in 1742 [1] marked the boiling-point 0° and the freezing 100°. The inverted scale, with the freezing-point 0° was introduced eight years later by Märten Strömer, a colleague of Celsius. The final form of our modern centigrade scale is, therefore, not that of Celsius, but that of Strömer.[2]

The number of different thermometric scales in actual use in the eighteenth century increased greatly. George Martine in 1740 mentions 13 of them; **J. H. Lambert** in 1779 enumerates 19.[3] All but three of them have passed into oblivion. Would that the centigrade scale were the sole survivor! In England and America the Fahrenheit scale predominates; in Germany the Réaumur; in France the Celsius. Among scientific men the last has found almost universal acceptance.

The earliest thermometer depending on the expansion and contraction of metallic rods was invented about 1747 by Pieter van Musschenbroek of Leyden. It was improved by **Jean Théophile Desaguliers.** About thirty-five years later came the Pyrometer of Josiah Wedgwood,[4] by which the high temperatures of a furnace were measured by the diminution in

---

[1] *Abhandl. d. schwedisch Akademie,* Vol. IV., pp. 197–205; trans. in *Ostwald's Klassiker,* No. 57, pp. 117–124.

[2] Unless indeed the credit of inversion be given also to Christin, a professor in Lyons. See *Poggendorff's Annalen,* Vol. 157, 1876, p. 352. Celsius and Strömer may have been prompted to make their improvements in thermometry by the botanist *Linné,* who once wrote in a letter, "I was the first who planned to make our thermometers in which 0 is the freezing-point and 100 the degree of boiling water." *Comptes Rendus,* Vol. 18, p. 1063. It will be remembered that the earliest suggestion of the use of these temperatures as fixed points was made by Huygens.

[3] Martine, *Essays medical and philosophical,* London, 1740; Lambert, *Pyrometrie,* Berlin, 1779.

[4] *Phil. Trans.,* Vol. 72, 1782; Vol. 74, 1784.

bulk of a block prepared from a pure fire-clay according to certain directions.[1]

EARLY DEVELOPMENT OF THE STEAM ENGINE

In 1705 there was invented the first important device for the practical application of steam power. For over 1000 years after Heron's eolipile no progress had been made. During the seventeenth century steam-fountains were designed, but they were merley modifications of Heron's engine, and were probably applied only for ornamental purposes.[2] Some effort was also made by Morland, Papin, and Savery to construct practical machines for the raising of water or driving of mill-works. The first successful attempt to combine the principles and forms of mechanism then known into an economical and convenient machine was made by **Thomas Newcomen**, a blacksmith of Dartmouth, England. It is probable that he knew of Savery's engine; Savery lived only fifteen miles from the residence of Newcomen. Assisted by John Calley, Newcomen constructed an engine—an "atmospheric steam-engine." A patent was secured in 1705. In 1711 such a machine was set up at Wolverhampton for the raising of water. Steam passing from the boiler into the cylinder held the piston up against the external atmospheric pressure until the passage between the cylinder and boiler was closed by a cock. Then the steam in the cylinder was condensed by a jet of water. A partial vacuum was formed and the air above pressed the piston down. This piston was suspended from one end of an overhead beam, the other end of the beam carrying the pump-rod. Desaguliers tells the story that a boy, Humphrey Potter, who was charged with the duty of opening and closing the stop-cock between the boiler and cylinder for every stroke, contrived by catches and strings an automatic motion of the

[1] G. T. Halloway, "The Evolution of the Thermometer," *Science Progress*, Vol. IV., 1895–1896, p. 417.

[2] R. H. Thurston, *A History of the Growth of the Steam-engine*, New York, 1893, p. 20.

cock.[1] The fly-wheel was introduced in 1736 by Jonathan
Hulls. The next great improvements were introduced in Scotland by **James Watt** (1736–1819). He was educated as a
mathematical instrument maker. In 1760 he opened a shop in
Glasgow. Becoming interested in the steam-engine and its history, he began to experiment in a scientific manner. He took
up chemistry and was assisted in his studies by Dr. Black, the
discoverer of "latent heat."[2] Observing the great loss of
heat in the Newcomen engine due to the cooling of the
cylinder by the jet of water at every stroke, he began to think
of means to keep the cylinder "always as hot as the steam that
entered it." He has told us how, finally, the happy thought
securing this end occurred to him: "I had gone to take a walk
on a fine Sabbath afternoon. I had entered the Green by the
gate at the foot of Charlotte Street, and had passed the old
washing-house. I was thinking upon the engine at the time,
and had gone as far as the herd's house, when the idea came
into my mind that, as steam was an elastic body, it would
rush into a vacuum, and, if a communication were made between the cylinder and an exhausted vessel, it would rush
into it, and might be there condensed without cooling the
cylinder."[3] The piston was now moved by the expansion of
steam, not by air pressure, as in Newcomen's engine. Watt
introduced a separate condenser, a steam-jacket, and other
improvements. He deservedly commands a preëminent place
among those who took part in the development of the steam-
engine.

The Caloric Theory of Heat

During the previous century the leading scientists saw more
or less clearly that heat was due to molecular motion. But
this correct view was finally abandoned in the eighteenth
century in favor of a materialistic theory. We have here a
good illustration of the fact that the path of science is not

---

[1] Thurston, *op. cit.*, p. 61.
[2] Thurston, *op. cit.*, p. 83. Then, and for a long time after, the study
of heat was taken up in chemistry, not in physics.
[3] Thurston, *op. cit.*, p. 87.

always in a forward direction—not always like the march of an army toward some definite end. Says Langley, "I believe this comparison of the progress of science to that of an army, which obeys an impulse from one head, has more error than truth in it; and though all similes are more or less misleading, I would prefer to ask you to think rather of a moving crowd, where the direction of the whole comes somehow from the independent impulses of its individual members; not wholly unlike a pack of hounds, which, in the long run, perhaps, catches its game, but where, nevertheless, when at fault, each individual goes his own way, by scent, not by sight, some running back and some forward; where the louder-voiced bring many to follow them, nearly as often in the wrong path as in the right one; where the entire pack even has been known to move off bodily on a false scent." [1]

The earliest traces of the theory that heat is matter are found in ancient Greece among Democritus, Epicurus and Lucretius. In modern times it was advocated by **Pierre Gassendi** (1592–1655), who was at one time professor of mathematics at the *Collège Royal* in Paris. He was a man of ability, but in physics his efforts were speculative rather than experimental.[2] The acceptance of the theory that heat is a material agent was facilitated through the previous introduction by **Georg Ernst Stahl** (1660–1734), professor at the University of Halle, of the erroneous theory of combustion, according to which a burning body gave off a substance called "phlogiston." One such agent paved the way for the other. In 1738 the French Academy of Sciences offered a prize question on the nature of heat. The winners of the prize (Euler was one of the three) favored the materialistic theory.[3] At first the only properties postulated for this material agent, called heat, were that it was highly elastic and that its particles repelled each other. By this repulsion the fact that hot bodies give

[1] S. P. Langley, *op. cit.*, p. 2.
[2] G. Berthold, *Rumford und d. Mech. Wärmetheorie*, Heidelberg, 1875, pp. 2–5.
[3] Berthold, *op. cit.*, p. 6.

off heat could be explained. Later it was assumed that the heat particles attracted ordinary matter, and that this heat was distributed among bodies in quantities proportional to their mutual attractions (or their capacities for heat). By the close of the eighteenth century this theory met with almost universal acceptance. Marat, afterwards famous as a leader in the French Revolution, gave in 1780 an exposition of this theory by starting from Newton's corpuscular theory of light. It was first vigorously attacked by an American, Count Rumford, but as late as 1856 it received preference over the dynamic theory in the article "Heat" in the *Encyclopædia Britannica* (8th edition).

Earliest Measurements of Heat

In spite of erroneous theories some new facts were found out regarding heat. Black discovered what he termed "latent heat" and "capacity for heat" (specific heat). **Joseph Black** (1728–1799) was born at Bordeaux, where his father, a native of Belfast, was settled as a wine merchant. He was professor at Glasgow, and at Edinburgh after 1766. He is well known as the founder of pneumatic chemistry.

In 1756 he began to meditate over the perplexing slowness with which ice melts and water is dissipated in boiling. He finally concluded that a large quantity of heat is consumed simply in bringing about these changes of state, without even the least alteration in temperature, and that the cause of this disappearance is a quasi-chemical combination between the particles of the substance and the subtle fluid called heat. According to his view this heat was "latent"; according to the modern view there is no "latent heat," but a transformation of energy takes place, the energy in form of heat becoming potential energy conferred on the material particles. Modern students need not feel disheartened over their failure to obtain at once accurate values for the heat of vaporization of water. The famous Black and his pupil, Irvine, obtained 417, later 450; the true value (at standard atmospheric pres-

sure) being 536. For the heat of fusion he obtained by the
method of mixtures 77.8, the more accurate value being 80.03
(Bunsen).

During Black's lifetime his great discoveries on heat remained unpublished, but after 1761 he explained them in his
lectures, dwelling with sedate eloquence on the beneficent
effects of the arrangement in checking and regulating the
processes of nature.[1] His discoveries not only formed the
basis of calorimetry, but they gave the first impulse to Watt's
improvements in the steam-engine.

Disliking the publicity of authorship, Black did not vindi-
cate his claims to priority. As might be expected, the same
ideas were worked out by others. Jean André Deluc in Paris
and Johann Karl Wilke in Sweden worked along the same
lines.

The great chemist, **Antoine Laurent Lavoisier** (1743–1794),
guillotined during the French Revolution, may be regarded
as a disciple of Black. In conjunction with **Pierre Simon
Laplace** (1749–1827), Lavoisier determined, about 1783, the
specific heats of a number of substances. They designed the
instrument now known as Laplace's ice calorimeter, but Black
and Wilke had employed the method of the ice calorimeter
before them.[2]

ELECTRICITY AND MAGNETISM

ELECTRIC SPARKS. INVENTION OF THE LEYDEN JAR

No branch of physics was cultivated during the eighteenth
century so successfully as electricity. Research was confined
to electro-statics until about 1790, when the study of current
electricity began.

Stephen Gray (?–1736), a pensioner at the Charterhouse,
England, discovered that the difference in electric conduc-

---

[1] *Dic. Nat. Biog.*

[2] Lavoisier and Laplace's joint papers appear in *Mémoires de l'Acadé-
mie,* 1780, p. 355 (actually printed three or four years after this date).
They are reprinted in German translation in *Ostwald's Klassiker,* No. 40.
The reference to Wilke is on p. 22 of this reprint.

tivity depends, not upon the color of objects or some similar quality, but on the material of which bodies are composed. Thus, metal wire conducts; silk does not. He demonstrated that the human body is a conductor, and was the first to electrify a human being (1730). A boy was suspended in the air by silken strings. Later Gray observed that conductors can be insulated by placing them on cakes of resin.

In France, Gray's experiments attracted the attention of **Charles François de Cisternay du Fay** (1698–1739), who had been educated as a soldier but devoted his maturer years to scientific pursuits. Experimentation led him to the unexpected conclusion that all bodies admit of being electrified; in other words, that all bodies possess the property which for ages was supposed to be peculiar to amber. Hence the classification of bodies (introduced by Gilbert) into "electrics" (capable of being electrified by friction) and "non-electrics" (not possessing this property) was found to have no foundation in fact. Du Fay noticed the discharging power of flames. Suspending himself by silk cords, in the manner taught by Gray, he observed that when he was electrified and another person came near, there issued from his body pricking shoots, making a crackling noise. In the dark these shoots were so many sparks of fire. "The Abbé Nollet says he shall never forget the surprise which the first electrical spark which was ever drawn from the human body excited, both in Mr. Du Fay and in himself." [1]

Du Fay discovered that there are two kinds of electricity, which he named the *vitreous* and the *resinous*. Later the same observation was made independently by Ebenezer Kinnersley of Philadelphia. To explain electric attraction and repulsion Du Fay postulated the existence of two fluids which are separated by friction and which neutralize each other when they combine. This is the earliest important attempt at a theory of electric phenomena. It was elaborated more fully

[1] Priestley, *Hist. of Elect.*, London, 1775, p. 47.

as a rival of Franklin's one-fluid theory by the Englishman **Robert Symmer.**

Considerable attention was paid at this time to the perfection of the electric friction machine. It assumed a supreme importance in laboratories, until finally it was supplanted by the influence machines of Holtz and Töpler. For Hauksbee's glass globe, Andrew Gordon in Erfurt substituted a glass cylinder. Martin Planta of Grisons, Switzerland, and later the optician Jesse Ramsden, of London, introduced circular glass plates. In place of the dry palm of the hand, held against the rotating glass, Johann Heinrich Winkler of Leipzig prepared a leather cushion rubber, which was pressed against the glass by a spring. John Canton, in 1762, secured still better results by applying tin amalgam to the rubber.[1]

About 1745 electric experimentation became so popular that in Holland and Germany public exhibitions were given. Many persons experimented for their own amusement. Among these was **Ewald Georg von Kleist** (died 1748), dean of the cathedral in Camin, Pomerania. Once, in 1745, he endeavored to charge a bottle by conduction. He observed that, when he held in his hand a small phial with a nail in it and electrified the nail by contact with the conductor of a machine, the nail became so strongly electrified that by touching it with the other hand he received a shock which stunned his arms and shoulders. The same discovery was made in 1746 in a similar manner at Leyden, Holland. **Pieter van Musschenbroek** (1692–1761), in his day a renowned physicist, attempted to electrify water in a bottle. At a trial, one of his friends held the bottle in one hand, and after a while proceeded with the other hand to remove the wire connecting the water to the prime conductor. He was surprised by a sudden shock in his arms and breast. Thus was discovered what we now call the "Leyden jar." Musschenbroek repeated the experiment and then wrote to Réaumur "that he would not take another shock for the kingdom of France." More heroic sentiments

[1] For drawings of various machines, see G. Albrecht, *Gesch. d. Electricität*, 1885, pp. 20–30; Priestley, *Hist. of Elect.*, Plates IV.–VIII.

were expressed by Professor Bose of Wittenberg. He wished he might die by the electric shock, that the account of his death might furnish an article for the memoirs of the French Academy of Sciences.[1]

The invention of the Leyden jar gave still greater *éclat* to electricity. In almost every country in Europe numbers of persons gained a livelihood by going about and showing the experiments. Winkler of Leipzig proved that Von Kleist was wrong in supposing that the human body played an essential part in the discharge of the jar. He pointed out that any conductor connecting the inside coating to the outside fully answered the purpose.

Musschenbroek's letter to Réaumur did not deter French philosophers from experimentation. **Abbé Nollet**, who in France was even more celebrated than was Musschenbroek in Holland, repeated the Leyden jar experiments on himself. He then, in the King's presence, passed the discharge through 180 guards. Later the Carthusian monks at the convent in Paris were formed into a line 900 feet long, by means of iron wires between every two persons, and the whole company, upon the discharge of the jar, gave a sudden spring at the same instant. This behavior of the austere monks must have been ludicrous in the extreme. Experimenters in France and elsewhere killed birds and other animals by the discharge of the Leyden jar; they passed the discharge long distances through water across rivers and lakes; they magnetized needles by it and melted thin wire. The discovery of the Leyden jar was hailed as a great advance in science.

Experiments in America

Some of the boldest researches and profoundest theories of the eighteenth century were soon to be advanced in far-off America by **Benjamin Franklin** (1706–1790). Although in his youth only a printer's apprentice, he developed into a man of unusual powers, not only in the fields of politics and diplo-

[1] Priestley, *op. cit.*, p. 86.

macy, but also in physical research. At the age of forty he happened to see Dr. Spence from Scotland perform some electrical experiments at Boston. The subject was new to him. After his return to Philadelphia the Library Company in that city received from Peter Collinson, a London merchant and member of the Royal Society, a glass tube, with instructions how to use it in electrical experiments. Franklin's curiosity having been excited, he began to study this subject, and also to experiment for himself.[1] In his first letter to Collinson, March 28, 1747, he expresses thanks for the "electric tube," and says: "I never was before engaged in any study that so totally engaged my attention and my time as this has lately done."[2] His home came to be frequented by curiosity seekers. There was formed a small group of investigators, consisting of Franklin, Ebenezer Kinnersley, Thomas Hopkinson, and Philip Sing. In the next letter to Collinson, July 11, 1747, Franklin describes the "wonderful effect of pointed bodies, both in drawing off and throwing off the electrical fire" This action of points had been observed by others, but Frankin was the first fully to realize its importance and to put it to use.

This same letter contains Franklin's theory of electricity, which explained phenomena more satisfactorily than any other proposed up to that time. He supposed that "electric fire is a common element," existing in all bodies. If a body acquired more than its normal share, it was called "plus"; if less, it was designated "minus." Thus, instead of Du Fay's two-fluid theory, Franklin advocated a one-fluid theory. To him we owe the terms "plus" and "minus," or "positive" and "negative" electricity. This material theory held its own until the times of Faraday and Maxwell. Franklin explained the charged Leyden jar as containing on one coating an excess of the fluid, "a plenum of electrical fire," and on the

---

[1] *Works of Benjamin Franklin,* edited by Jared Sparks, Boston, 1837, Vol. V., pp. 173–180. This volume contains Franklin's famous letters on electricity; also an appendix containing letters by various scientific men respecting Franklin's discoveries.

[2] *Works,* (Ed. of J. Sparks), Vol. V., p. 181.

other a "vacuum of the same fire," but really containing no more electricity than before charging.[1] He showed experimentally that "the whole force of the bottle and power of giving a shock is in the glass itself" (p. 201).

In 1748 Franklin sold his printing house, newspaper, and almanac, with the view of retiring from business and devoting all his time to electrical experiments. He equipped himself with new apparatus. His friend Kinnersley proved that the Leyden phial can be as easily electrified by sparks passing to the outside as to the inside (p. 197). In 1749 Franklin states in a letter to Collinson that "hot weather is coming on, when electrical experiments are not so agreeable," and he proposed to end the season with an electric party. "A turkey is to be killed for our dinner by the electrical shock, and roasted by the electrical jack, before a fire kindled by the electrified bottle" (p. 211). But before the summer of 1749 he entered upon more serious reflections.

LIGHTNING AN ELECTRIC PHENOMENON

At this time Franklin first suggested the idea of explaining lightning on electrical principles. The conjecture that the nature of lightning was the same as that of the electric spark had been made before. Gray, Wall, Nollet, Freke, Winkler, had all expressed this thought.[2] Franklin probably did not know of these conjectures. Though contrary to the then prevalent theory of lightning it certainly warranted some one in making an experimental test. Thunder and lightning were generally believed to be due to exploding gases, though opinions differed as to the nature of the gases. In 1737 Franklin believed lightning to be due to "the inflammable breath of the Pyrites, which is a subtle sulphur, and takes fire of itself." As already stated, in the early summer of 1749, he advanced the electrical theory, and conceived bold plans for experimentation. The heat of summer did not deter him and Kin-

[1] *Ibidem*, p. 191.
[2] Benjamin, p. 575.

nersley from experimentation. Under the date of November 7, 1749, the following passage is found in his note-book: "Electrical fluid agrees with lightning in these particulars: (1) Giving light; (2) color of the light; (3) crooked direction; (4) swift motion; (5) being conducted by metals; (6) crack or noise in exploding; (7) subsisting in water or ice; (8) rending bodies it passes through; (9) destroying animals; (10) melting metals; (11) firing inflammable substances; (12) sulphurous smell." Will lightning be attracted and drawn off by points like the electric fluid in his jars? "Since they agree in all the particulars wherein we can already compare them, is it not probable that they agree likewise in this? Let the experiment be made." By the action of points he proposed to draw down the lightning. "On the top of some high tower or steeple, place a kind of sentry-box (as in Fig. 16), big enough to contain a man and an electrical stand. From the middle of the stand let an iron rod rise and pass, bending out of the door, and then upright twenty or thirty feet, pointed very sharp at the end. If the electrical stand be kept clean and dry, a man standing on it, when such clouds are passing low, might be electrified and afford sparks, the rod drawing fire to him from a cloud." "If these things are so, may not the knowledge of this power of points be of use to mankind in preserving houses, churches, ships, etc., from the stroke of lightning? . . . "[1]

FIG. 16.

Such are the thoughts communicated in a letter to Collinson in July, 1750, and submitted by him to the Royal Society. That body at first received the new ideas with derision. The plans seemed visionary.[2] As the Royal Society failed to pub-

[1] *Works,* Vol. V., pp. 236, 237.
[2] Three years later (1753), after Franklin's researches had met with enthusiastic appreciation on the part of French scientists and the French king, the Royal Society awarded him the Copley Medal. The president's address on the occasion of the award is given in Franklin's *Works,* Vol. V., pp. 499–504. In 1756 Franklin was elected member of the Royal Society.

lish anything but a brief notice of Franklin's researches, Collinson determined to bring out the letters without its imprint. By the additional letters that arrived later, they swelled to a quarto volume which passed through five editions. Seventeen years after the first publication, Priestly wrote: "Nothing was ever written upon the subject of electricity which was more generally read and admired in all parts of Europe than these letters. There is hardly any European language into which they have not been translated; and, as if this were not sufficient to make them properly known, a translation of them has lately been made in Latin."[1]

In America popular curiosity ran high. Kinnersley started on a lecturing tour, showing electric experiments and winning applause. In New York, Newport, and Boston these lectures produced a genuine sensation. "Faneuil Hall resounded with the cracks and snaps of his jars and globes, long before it echoed the impassioned eloquence of the orators of the Revolution."[2]

Franklin was of the opinion that no building in Philadelphia or hill near by was high enough to enable him to perform the experiment with the sentry-box. While he was endeavoring to raise money by means of a lottery for the erection of a spire of sufficient height, news came that the experiment had been tried successfully at Marly-la-Ville, near Paris, by Dalibard, under the auspices of the French king. How was it done? Simply by a rod 13 metres (40 feet) high, insulated at its base, and resting upon a small table within a small cabin. Dalibard instructed an old dragoon to watch for clouds. A brass wire mounted in a glass bottle was gotten ready for the purpose of drawing off sparks from the rod. After several days' waiting, a thunder-cloud appeared on May 10, 1752. The dragoon approached the wire to the rod, and there was a lively crackling of sparks. The flame and sulphurous odor were evidently infernal. The terrified dragoon dropped the

[1] Priestley, *Hist. of Elect.*, p. 154.
[2] Benjamin, p. 585.

wire and shouted to his neighbors to send for the village priest. The latter was braver than the dragoon. He began to experiment for himself and drew sparks from the rod. He communicated the results to Dalibard.[1] "Franklin's idea ceases to be a conjecture," writes Dalibard; "here it has become a reality." A week later Delor in Paris repeated the experiment with a rod 32 metres (99 feet) high.

Franklin himself did not regard the tests in Paris conclusive. He was not fully convinced that the Frenchmen's rods had become electrified by lightning. The rods did not reach up into the clouds. A new idea flashed into his mind. Why not send a kite up into the very interior of the cloud, and conduct the lightning down on its cord? Abandoning the plan of erecting a sentry-box, he prepared a kite. "Make a small cross," he writes afterwards to Collinson, "of two light strips of cedar, the arms so long as to reach to the four corners of a large thin silk handkerchief when extended; tie the corners of the handkerchief to the extremities of the cross, so you have the body of a kite; . . . to the top of the upright stick of the cross is to be fixed a very sharp-pointed wire, rising a foot or more above the wood. To the end of the twine next the hand is to be tied a silk ribbon, and where the silk and twine join, a key may be fastened."[2] With this apparatus he went out on the common, accompanied only by his son. He placed himself under a shed to avoid the rain, and raised the kite. A thunder-cloud passed, but as yet there was no sign of electricity. He almost despaired of success, when suddenly he observed the loose fibres of the string erect themselves. He now presented a knuckle to the key, and received a strong spark.[3] What exquisite pleasure that spark must have given him! More sparks were obtained; a Leyden jar was charged, a shock given, etc. He had demonstrated that lightning is an electric phenomenon.

[1] The priest's letter, as also Dalibard's communication to the French Academy, are given in Franklin's *Works*, Vol. V., 288–293. See also Benjamin, p. 588.
[2] Franklin's *Works*, Vol. V., p. 295.
[3] Franklin's *Works*, Vol. V., p. 175.

"In September, 1752," says Franklin, "I erected an iron rod to draw the lightning down into my house, in order to make some experiments on it, with two bells to give notice when the rod should be electrified."[1] He then concluded from a number of experiments "that the clouds of thunder-gust are most commonly in a negative state of electricity, but sometimes in a positive state" (p. 304).[2] Hence, "for the most part, in thunder-strokes it is the earth that strikes into the clouds, and not the clouds that strike into the earth" (p. 305).

Franklin's experiments on atmospheric electricity were repeated everywhere. The French physician, Louis Guillaume Lemonnier, found that the atmosphere is always electric, even when no clouds are in sight. Georg Wilhelm Richmann, of St. Petersburg, was struck dead while experimenting with lightning in 1753. Detailed reports of the effect on the various organs of his body were published by scientific societies. Says Priestly,[3] "It is not given to every electrician to die in so glorious a manner as the justly envied Richmann."

FRANKLIN'S LIGHTNING RODS

Franklin's suggestion to protect buildings by lightning-rods was first carried out in 1754 by Procopius Divisch, a cleryman at Prenditz, in Mähren. In 1760 Franklin erected one on a building in Philadelphia. William Watson erected the first lightning-rod in England in 1762. In 1782 there were about 400 rods in Philadelphia. At first some opposition to their erection was made by certain theologians. It was argued that as thunder and lightning were tokens of divine wrath, it was impious to interfere with their power of destruction.[4] To this argument **John Winthrop,** the first professor of physics at Harvard College, gave the common-sense reply: "It is as much our duty to secure ourselves against the effects of light-

[1] *Ibidem,* p. 301.
[2] That atmospheric electricity may vary in sign had been noticed before this by John Canton.
[3] *Hist. of Elect.,* p. 86.
[4] A. D. White, *Warfare of Science with Theology,* 1896, Vol. I., p. 366.

ning as against those of rain, snow, and wind, by the means God has put into our hands." [1]

Experience soon proved that rods were not an absolute protection against lightning. Failure to protect was then and long afterwards attributed either to bad earth connection or to dull points. Various improvements in construction were suggested.[2] But the real difficulty was not recognized until nearly a century later. Franklin's theory of the action of the rod was incomplete. We now begin to see that the failure of carefully erected rods to protect is due to the fact that the discharge may be oscillatory.[3]

In 1703 Dutch travellers brought tourmaline from Ceylon. They observed that it was capable of attracting the light ashes on glowing peat. Its properties were examined by Franz Ulrich Theodor Æpinus and Johann Karl Wilke, who concluded that it became electrified by heating, its ends carrying charges of opposite sign. Torbern Olof Bergman showed in 1766 that it was not so much the heat that produced electricity as it was the difference in temperature between its parts; that on cooling the charge at each end is reversed. Benjamin

[1] For an account of John Winthrop, see W. J. Youmans, *Pioneers of Science in America,* New York, 1896.

[2] See, for instance, a paper by Robert Patterson of Philadelphia in *Trans. Am. Philos. Society,* Vol. III., 1793, pp. 122, 321.

[3] Franklin supplied Harvard College with electrical apparatus. In a letter of 1753 he speaks of the shipment of Leyden jars. Before this time the instruction in electricity at Harvard must have been quite meagre. Among manuscript notes of excellent lectures on astronomy, and a few on light and electricity, prepared by John Winthrop in 1750, there is only one lecture on electricity and magnetism. Trowbridge gives part of these notes as follows: "If a flaxen string be extended and supported, and at one end an excited tube be applied, light bodies will be attracted, and that at the distance of 1200 feet at the other end. This electricity since the year 1743 has made a considerable noise in the world, upon which it is supposed several of the (at present) hidden phenomena, of nature depend. . . . Men have been so electrized as to have considerable light round their heads and bodies, not unlike the light represented around the heads of saints by painters." Trowbridge adds that "the entire apparatus to illustrate the subject of electricity and magnetism in Harvard University until 1820 consisted merely of two Franklin electrical machines, a collection of Leyden jars, and small apparatus to illustrate the effects of electrical attractions and repulsions shown by electrified pith balls or similar light objects." See John Trowbridge, *What is Electricity?* 1897, p. 26.

Wilson and John Canton found that the electric property of tourmaline was shared by other crystals.

CAVENDISH'S MEASUREMENTS IN STATIC ELECTRICITY

During the latter part of the eighteenth century the first important steps were taken in the way of exact measurements in static electricity. In this field of research we meet two great names, Cavendish and Coulomb. **Henry Cavendish** [1] (1731–1810) attended Peterhouse College, Cambridge, and afterward lived chiefly in London. The great obscurity hanging over his private history has rendered it impossible to ascertain what influences induced him to devote himself to experimental science. He experimented in chemistry, heat, electricity, but he took little pains to publish his results and to secure priority of discovery. He lived a strangely retired life. Being of frugal habits, he allowed his large income to accumulate. "He received no stranger at his residence; he ordered his dinner daily by a note left on the hall table, and from his morbid shyness he objected to any communication with his female domestics." [2] "He probably uttered fewer words in the course of his life than any man who ever lived to fourscore years, not at all excepting the monks of La Trappe." [3] Cavendish's whole existence was in his laboratory and his library. [4] His experiments on electrostatics were completed before the end of the year 1773, but remained unpublished. He printed only two electric papers, and these contained matter of secondary importance. About a century later, in 1879, James Clerk

[1] *Dic. Nat. Biog.*
[2] *Dic. Nat. Biog.*
[3] Lord Brougham, *Lives of Philosophers*, London, 1855, p. 106.
[4] Henry Cavendish happened once at a dinner to sit next to William Herschel, who had been constructing telescopes of such unheard-of magnitude and accuracy of figure that a star could be seen without "rays." Cavendish slowly addressed the astronomer with, "Is it true, Dr. Herschel, that you see the stars round?" "Round as a button," exclaimed the doctor, when the conversation dropped, till at the close of dinner, Cavendish repeated interrogatively, "Round as a button?" "Round as a button," briskly rejoined the doctor and no more was said. From article "Herschel, Sir William," in *Dic. Nat. Biog.*

Maxwell published a book under the title, *Electrical Researches of the Honourable Henry Cavendish,* written between 1771 and 1781. ''These papers,'' says Maxwell, ''prove that Cavendish had anticipated nearly all those great facts in electricity which at a later period were made known to the scientific world through the writings of Coulomb and the French philosophers.'' Cavendish made the capacity of condensers a subject of investigation, and constructed for himself a complete set of condensers of known capacity, by which he measured the capacity of various pieces of apparatus. A battery of 49 jars was found to contain 321,000 ''inches of electricity'' (about $\frac{1}{2}$ microfarad). His ''inches of electricity'' express the diameter of the sphere of equivalent capacity. Our modern electrostatic measurements of capacity differ from this simply in the use of ''centimeters'' and ''radius'' in place of ''inches'' and ''diameter.'' Cavendish anticipated Faraday in the discovery of specific inductive capacity of different substances, and measured this quantity for several substances. For paraffin he found the values 1.81 to 2.47, while more recently Boltzmann has given 2.32, Wüllner 1.96 Gordon 1.994.[1] The preceding ideas presuppose the notion of potential. This was introduced by Cavendish under the name ''degree of electrification.'' He proved that static charges reside on the surfaces of conductors and that the electric force varies inversely as the square of the distance, or at least cannot differ from that ratio by more than 1/50 part. In 1781 he completed an inquiry which amounts to an anticipation of Ohm's Law.[2]

It is a matter of regret that Cavendish did not give scientists of his day the benefit of his far-reaching results. It is remarkable that, while Cavendish originated new concepts, and engaged largely in electric measurements, he was no inventor of new apparatus. Coulomb invented the torsion electrometer; Abraham Bennet, in 1786, brought forth the

[1] Maxwell, *Elect. Researches of the Hon. H. Cavendish,* p. liii.
[2] *Ibidem,* pp. lix., §§ 574, 575, 629, 686. The law is not worked out by him as carefully and systematically as by Ohm over forty years later.

gold-leaf electroscope; but Cavendish designed no similar instruments. He used the pith-ball electrometer.

Coulomb's Proof of the Law of Inverse Squares

Charles Augustin Coulomb (1736–1806) was born at Angoulême, studied in Paris, and at an early age entered the army. After several years' service in the West Indies, he returned to Paris and served as engineer. He engaged at the same time in scientific research. When a project of navigable canals in Bretagne was under consideration, Coulomb was appointed by the minister of marine to examine the ground. His report was unfavorable. This displeased some influential persons, and under the pretext that he had no orders from the minister of war, they placed him in confinement. Later the government of Bretagne saw its error, and offered Coulomb a large recompense, but he accepted only a seconds watch, which he afterwards used in experimentation. Says Thomas Young: "His moral character is said to have been as correct as his mathematical investigations." [1]

Coulomb entered upon researches on the torsional elasticity of hairs and wires. This led in 1777 to the torsion balance, or "balance de torsion." Some similar device had been previously suggested in England by John Mitchell.[2] The torsion balance has held its place in texts on electricity for a century, though now the instrument is no longer used in the laboratory. Coulomb experimented with great ingenuity and accuracy, and proved with it that Newton's law of inverse squares holds also in electric and in magnetic attraction and repulsion.[3] He proved that the action varies as the product of the quantities of electricity; he showed also that electric charges exist on the surfaces of conductors and compared the surface charges on various parts of a conductor. Coulomb was an advocate of

[1] *Misc. Works*, Vol. II., p. 540.
[2] Heller, Vol. II., p. 499.
[3] That magnetic action follows the law of inverse squares was shown before this (about 1760) by Tobias Mayer of Göttingen. See Albrecht, *Gesch. d'Elect.*, p. 75.

the two-fluid theory and believed that attraction and repulsion take place by an "actio in distans," without an intervening medium. His electrical memoirs, which appeared between 1785 and 1789, furnished the data on which Poisson later founded his mathematical theory of electricity.[1]

ANIMAL ELECTRICITY

From very early times it was known that certain species of water-animals are capable of giving shocks. After the invention of the Leyden jar, men began to ponder over the similarity in the physiological effect of its discharge to that of shocks given by these animals. John Walsh made the first thorough investigation of this subject at La Rochelle and proved that the shocks imparted by the fishes are electrical. Connecting the back and under side of the fish with a conductor, a discharge took place.[2]

DISCOVERY OF CURRENT ELECTRICITY

Among those interested in animal electricity was **Aloisio Galvani** (1737–1798), a physician and professor of anatomy in Bologna. By accident he was led to the great discovery of current electricity or "galvanism." The story goes that his wife was in poor health and was ordered to eat frogs' legs. Galvani prepared them himself. When he had taken off their skins, he laid them on a table near the conductor of a charged electric machine and left the room. His wife chanced to hold the scalpel near the machine while at the same time the scalpel's point touched the exposed crural nerve of a frog's leg. A spark passed and the leg convulsed violently. She acquainted her husband of this, and he repeated the experiment. This occurred on November 6, 1780. Galvani's own

[1] Coulomb's seven papers appeared originally in the *Mémoires de l'Académie royale des sciences*, 1785 and 1786. The first four are printed in German translation in *Ostwald's Klassiker*, No. 13.
[2] His papers appeared in the *Phil. Trans.* for 1773 and 1774.

account is more prosaic.[1] His wife plays no rôle in the discovery; only one frog is dissected; an assistant first notices the twitching.

Galvani set about to discover the cause. It seemed necessary to touch a nerve and to have a spark. The effect was the same when the legs were placed in a vacuum. The question arose, will atmospheric electricity serve as well as that from the machine? He suspended frogs' legs by iron hooks from an iron trellis in the garden. The legs exhibited motion. It was violent when storm-clouds passed, but could be seen at times during a clear sky. At first he attributed the twitching to changes in atmospheric electricity. He abandoned this view after he succeeded in producing the same effects indoors by placing the frogs' legs on a metallic plate and allowing the wire piercing the crural nerve to touch the plate. The cause must lie in the leg, the plate, or the wire. Galvani placed the leg on glass and touched the crural nerve and a muscle of the foot, both at the same time, with the ends of a bent rod. If the rod was of glass, no effect was seen; if it was of copper and iron, or copper and silver, then prolonged convulsions followed. The fact that a rod of iron alone produced motion, though it was not so continuous and pronounced as when it consisted of two metals, led Galvani to the conclusion that the rod served merely as a conductor. Further tests seemed to him to locate the source of electricity in the nerve.

Galvani's observations were of startling novelty and astonished scientific men everywhere. More profound than his own was the reasoning on this subject by his countryman, **Alessandro Volta** (1745–1827), who occupied the chair of physics for five years at the gymnasium of his native town, Como, and after 1779, for twenty-five years, the chair of physics at the university of Pavia. He had been a diligent experimenter in electricity and in 1775 had invented the electrophorus. He found that the electric discharge through a nerve could pro-

---

[1] See *Ostwald's Klassiker*, No. 52, p. 4. This number is a German translation of Galvani's article, ''De viribus electricitatis in moto musculari commentarius,'' in *Comment. Acad. scient. Bonon.*, 1791.

duce other effects than motion. If a bent rod of two metals touched the eye above, while the other end was held in his mouth, a sensation of light followed at the moment of making contact. A silver and a gold coin held against the tongue produced a bitter taste as soon as the coins were connected by a wire.[1] Thus, the electricity was able not only to produce motion, but to affect the nerves of vision and taste. Volta conjectured that the essential thing in all these experiments was the contact of different metals. After 1794 he set about to prove this hypothesis. If Galvani was right in placing the seat of electricity in the frog's leg and in attributing to the metal rod merely the function of discharger, as in the Leyden jar, then one metal should produce twitching as easily as two. If the ends of a wire of one metal are at different temperatures, then vigorous convulsions follow; they disappear almost entirely on equalization of temperature. Hence Volta concluded that slight effects due to a wire of a single metal are due to slight difference in its condition. This new electricity, declared Volta, might as well be called "metallic" as "animal." The strongest proof of his contact theory was given by means of his condensing electroscope. This was a gold-leaf electroscope combined with a small condenser. A feeble source, like that in a compound bar of two dissimilar metals, could supply considerable electricity to the condenser without materially raising its potential. But when the upper plate of the condenser was removed, the potential rose and the leaves diverged. This experiment seemed to prove that electricity was generated at the contact of the two different metals, one metal becoming positively charged, the other negatively.

Volta's Pile in England

On March 20, 1800, Volta wrote a letter to Joseph Banks, then president of the Royal Society of London, in which he describes the voltaic pile, called by him "organe électrique

[1] This bitter taste had been observed previously in Germany by Johann Georg Sulzer. See Edm. Hoppe, *Gesch. d. Elect.*, Leipzig, 1884, p. 128.

artificiel" in distinction to the "organe électrique naturel" of the torpedo.[1] Two dissimilar plates, say zinc and copper, were placed in contact. Over this went a piece of flannel or blotting paper moistened with water or brine. Then followed another pair of zinc and copper plates, and so on, each pair of plates being separated by a moist conductor. Such a pile, consisting of a dozen or more pairs of plates, multiplied the effect of a single pair. In the same letter Volta explains the "couronne de tasses" or "crown of cups." It consisted of cups containing brine or dilute acid, into which dipped strips half zinc and half copper. The zinc end of one strip dipped into one cup, the copper end into another. This is the first voltaic cell.

Six weeks after Volta had written that memorable letter, the first pile was constructed in England by **William Nicholson** and **Sir Anthony Carlisle**, and on May 2, the decomposition of water by it was observed. This experiment was the foundation of electro-chemistry. It was described in *Nicholson's Journal* for July, 1800, and appeared before Volta's own account of the voltaic pile was printed in the *Philosophical Transactions*.[2] Volta's researches met with immediate appreciation. As early as 1791 he was elected member of the Royal Society of London. In 1801 Napoleon called him to Paris to perform before the Institute his experiments on the pile. The French awarded him a gold medal.

The controversy between Volta and Galvani divided electricians into two hostile parties. The most prominent of Galvani's supporters was Alexander von Humboldt in Germany; the most prominent of Volta's were Coulomb and other French physicists. The contact theory was applied to the explanation of the voltaic cell. This theory has been a bone of contention from that time to the present. Only in very

[1] *Phil. Trans.*, 1800, p. 405.

[2] The electric decomposition of water was accomplished at an earlier date by Dr. Ash at Oxford, Fabbroni in Florence, Crève in Mainz, but Nicholson and Carlisle were the first to systematically study the phenomenon and to prove that the separated gases actually were hydrogen and oxygen. See Hoppe, *op. cit.*, pp. 132–139.

recent years has it finally succumbed to a modern chemical theory.

SOUND

Joseph Sauveur (1653–1716) carried on important researches in acoustics. He was born at La Flêche. At the age of seventeen he travelled on foot to Paris to seek his fortune. In 1686 he became professor of mathematics at the Collège Royal. He was a stammerer and had such a poor ear for music that he could compare pitches only with the assistance of musicians.[1] Yet his papers on acoustics, published in the Memoirs of the Academy, 1700–1703, are very important. Independently of Noble and Pigott, he discovered overtones in strings. He used paper riders to locate nodes and anti-nodes. He observed sympathetic vibrations and gave a correct explanation of beats. He tuned two organ pipes in the ratio 24:25, and observed four beats per second. From this he concluded that the pipe of higher pitch made 100 vibrations per second. He determined rates of vibration with considerable precision.[2] Vittorio Francesco Stancari of Bologna made such measurements by the use of toothed wheels.[3]

The early development of the siren took place in England. The experiments of Robert Hooke were continued between 1793 and 1801 by John Robison, professor of physics at the University of Edinburgh. A wheel was made to strike in rapid succession the teeth of a pinion, so as to force out a portion of air from between them; or a pipe through which air was passing was alternately opened and shut by the revolution of a stopcock or valve.[4]

[1] Rosenberger, Part II., p. 269.

[2] Consult further E. Mach on Joseph Sauveur in *Mittheil. d. deutsch. math. Ges. zu Prag*, 1892; abstracted in *Poske's Zeitschr.*, Vol. VI., pp. 39–41.

[3] Ernst Robel, *Die Sirenen, Ein Beitrag zur Entwickelungsgeschichte der Akustik*, Berlin, 1891, Theil I., p. 5.

[4] *Ibidem*, pp. 7–10. Consult also Robison, "Temperament of the Scale of Music" in third edition of the *Encyclopædia Britannica;* Thomas Young, *Lectures on Nat. Phil.*, London, 1807, Vol. I., p. 378.

THE NINETEENTH CENTURY

In physical speculation the nineteenth century overthrew the leading theories of the previous one hundred years, and largely built anew on the older foundations laid during the seventeenth century. The emission theory of light gave way to the wave theory; the substance called "caloric" was set aside, and the fact was established that heat is due to molecular motion. The imponderables, assumed to exist by the advocates of the one-fluid and the two-fluid theories of electricity, were discarded in favor of the view that the phenomena of electricity and magnetism are to be explained, in some way, by the existence of pulsations and strains in the luminiferous ether. The effluvia of a magnet, capable of passing through glass without resistance, are of interest now only to the historian. The chemical substance phlogiston is no more. Of the seven imponderables of the eighteenth century, none remained, but the luminiferous ether of the seventeenth century was readmitted and assigned a place of prime importance in physical speculation. By it two great branches of physics, light and electro-magnetism became practically one. Notwithstanding the enormous multiplication of observed phenomena, there was a simplifying of the interpretation of them by bringing into consistent and comprehensive order that which formerly seemed to be capricious and isolated. The very fact that intimate relations were perceived to exist between wide realms of physics, once thought to be perfectly distinct, seemed to show that the movement was in the right direction. The concept of energy, unknown to the eighteenth century, was introduced. Radiant energy developed into a subject of central importance.

Stimulated and aided by the progress of its sister science chemistry, physics made marvellous progress during the past one hundred years. At the beginning of the century the chemist with his balance had established the law of the Conservation of Mass. Then came the physicist and set forth in bold relief the all-embracing principle of the Conservation of Energy. The nineteenth century has been truly characterized as an *age of correlation* [1] in science.

No previous epoch had seen such a vast army of scientific workers, or beheld the acquisition of such extensive experimental knowledge of all physical subjects. Theory and practice went hand in hand. Steam and electricity were made to minister to the needs and comfort of mankind.

To this scientific advance all leading European nations have contributed. In Great Britain the new period of productiveness was ushered in when the doting attitude of Englishmen toward Newton was changed, and the truth was perceived that no human mind, however great, can be infallible on all points. Among the earlier scientists of this time are the Herschels, Thomas Young, Sir Humphry Davy, and Sir David Brewster.

Germany, impoverished, devastated, and politically shattered by religious struggles, began after the Napoleonic wars to recover and to put forth extraordinary scientific effort. The attitude of German physicists of the early part of this century toward philosophers and mathematicians was grotesque. The obscure and undemonstrated assertions of the philosophers Hegel and Schelling worked injuriously upon science. [2] But a reaction set in. There arose in Berlin an empirical school of scientists, comprising Poggendorff, Riess, Dove, H. G. Magnus. They looked with contempt upon metaphysical obscu

---

[1] Paul R. Heyl, *The Fundamental Concepts of Physics in the Light of Modern Discovery*, Baltimore, 1926, p. 28.

[2] Helmholtz in *Wiedemann's Annalen*, Neue Folge, Vol. 54, 1895, pp. 2 *et seq.* Helmholtz says in his lecture, "On the relation of natural science to general science," *Popular Lectures*, transl. by E. Atkinson, London, 1873, p. 7: "Hegel . . . launched out, with unusual vehemence and acrimony, against the natural philosophers and especially against Sir Isaac Newton, as the first and greatest representative of physical investigation. The philosophers accused the scientific men of narrowness; the scientific men retorted that the philosophers were crazy." Consult also Rudolph Virchow, "Transition from the Philosophic to the Scientific Age," *Smithsonian Report*, 1894, pp. 681-695.

rantism. Magnus, the leader of this school, did much toward the evolution of the modern physical laboratory.

Strange to say, Magnus would have nothing to do with mathematics. This one-sided and ill-founded conception of the use of mathematics in physical research was not shared by his great pupils Krönig, Clausius, and Helmholtz. Nor did all German contemporaries of Magnus shun mathematical physics. This branch was cultivated at Göttingen by Gauss and Wilhelm Weber, and at Königsberg by Ernst Franz Neumann. The first movement toward unity of action among physical experimentalists and mathematicians took place in the organization at Berlin in 1844 of the Physical Society, which grew out of a physical "colloquium" held by Magnus.[1]

France, at the beginning of the nineteenth century, possessed an array of scientific men of unsurpassed brilliancy. We need mention only Lagrange, Laplace, Fresnel, Arago, Biot, Carnot, Fourier. Not till the middle of this century did some of the other countries equal her in scientific productiveness.

In the United States comparatively little was achieved before the last quarter of the century, and that little failed, at the time, to catch the eye of the scientific public abroad.

THE CONSTITUTION OF MATTER

ATOMIC THEORY

Immediately after the time of Dalton, atoms were commonly regarded as impenetrable, rigid solids. All atoms of any one chemical element were assumed to possess the same "weight"; any two atoms belonging to different elements possessed different "weights." A few scientists regarded the atom as elastic, which implied relative motion of its parts; this assumption was rejected by others as too complicated and incapable of meeting the demands made upon it. But in a

[1] G. Wiedemann in *Wiedemann's Annal.*, Vol. 39, 1890, "Vorwort."

collision between a pair of inelastic atoms there would be a loss of energy of motion, and the kinetic energy of an aggregation of atoms would therefore gradually diminish through internal collisions—a situation contrary to experience.

One mode of overcoming the consequences of the hypothesis of inelastic atoms, was to postulate, as Boscovich (1711–1787) had done in the eighteenth century, that atoms were mere centers of attractive and repulsive forces acting at a distance, and that there were actually no collisions of atoms. Ampère, Cauchy and Faraday regarded atoms as unextended, or as simple centers of force. But this hypothesis that the atom had no extension, but had mass and was acted upon by various forces was very involved and unimaginable.

MOLECULES

Another attempt to overcome the difficulties of inelastic atoms was the assumption that the smallest particle of matter was not the atom, but a group of atoms which came to be called a *molecule*. The eighteenth century use of the word "molecule" was vague. Dalton spoke of the molecules NO of nitric oxide as "atoms." Avogadro (1776–1856) in 1811 distinguished between "molecules intégrantes" (our modern molecule), and "molecules élémentaires" (our atom). V. Regnault[1] in 1859 used the words molecules and atoms synonymously and spoke of "simple" and "complex" molecules. Justus von Liebig[2] (1803–1873) used the terms "einfache Atome" and "zusammengesetzte Atome," meaning our atom and molecule respectively. In the English translation of Liebig's Letters on Chemistry, the editor, John Blyth, writes "compound atoms or molecules." In 1868, the chemist E. Roscoe[3] gives the definition: "A molecule is a group of atoms forming the smallest portion of a chemical substance,

---

[1] V. Regnault, *Cours élémentaire de chimie*, Paris, 1859, 5 Ed., p. 3.
[2] Justus von Liebig, *Chemische Briefe*, 4. Ed., 1859, p. 132, 224 (1. Ed., 1844).
[3] Henry E. Roscoe, *Lessons in Elementary Chemistry*, London, 1868, p. 114.

either simple or compound, that can be isolated, or that can exist alone. . . . A molecule of water H_2O contains two atoms of hydrogen." Clerk Maxwell, in his address of 1873 before the British Association, used the word "molecule" in the sense of "atom," as this word is employed by the chemist.[1] Being a physicist, Maxwell fixed his attention upon those small parts of matter "any further sub-division" of which "will deprive them of the properties" belonging to the substance.[2] Later he spoke of the "internal motion of each molecule consisting partly of rotation and partly of vibrations among the component parts of the molecule"; he looked upon the "molecule" as made up of "atoms"[3]—in fact, used the modern terminology.

Molecules were assumed to behave as if elastic, even though the atoms were taken to be inelastic. Both Clausius and Maxwell adopted this view. Lord Kelvin[4] said, "we are forbidden by the modern physical theory of the conservation of energy to assume inelasticity or anything short of perfect elasticity in ultimate molecules." Molecules, having impact with one another, like perfectly elastic spheres, came to play an important rôle in the kinetic theory of gases which was developed with great success by a succession of physicists: Joule in 1848, August Krönig[5] in 1856, Clausius[6] in 1857, Maxwell[7] in 1860, Boltzmann[8] and others of later date.

Vortex Atom

A third way of evading the difficulty of the inelastic atom was Lord Kelvin's *vortex atom*.[9] Helmholtz had shown that

[1] F. Soddy, *The Interpretation of Radium*, 4. Ed., New York, 1920, p. 158.
[2] C. Maxwell, *Theory of Heat*, 7. Ed., 1883, p. 305, 311, 312 (1 Ed., 1871.)
[3] C. Maxwell, Art., "Atom", *Encyclop. Britannica*, 9th Edition.
[4] *Phil. Mag.*, 4. S., Vol. 45, 1873, p. 329.
[5] *Poggendorff's Annalen*, Vol. 99, 1856, p. 315.
[6] *Loc. cit.*, Vol. 100, 1857, p. 353.
[7] *Phil. Mag.*, Vol. 19, 1860, p. 22.
[8] *Wiedemann's Annalen*, Vol. 24, 1885, p. 37.
[9] W. Thomson, "Vortex Atoms", *Proceed. Royal Soc. of Edinburgh*, Feb., 1867; *Popular Lectures and Addresses*, Vol. I., 1889, pp. 235-252.

in a homogeneous, incompressible, frictionless fluid, vortex tubes can exist in which the fluid is in permanent rotational motion and that such a tube can form a closed indestructible ring. Kelvin's hypothesis regarded such a ring as an atom and he found that such a vortex ring had more of the properties of an ideal atom than any of the earlier kinds of atoms. The original fluid possessed inertia but only the vortex ring had the character of matter. Maxwell pointed out the difficulty in explaining the inertia of what is only a mode of motion of a substance but is not a substance itself.

Opposition to the Atomic Theory

The ease with which able men may move in the wrong direction in the rejection or adoption of hypotheses is beautifully shown by the opposition which arose in the latter part of the nineteenth century to the atomic theory. The great prominence given to the atomic and molecular theories during the last quarter of the nineteenth century was deplored by some critics. Why, asked **E. Mach**[1] (1838–1916), should we conceive of the world as a mosaic, since we cannot examine its individual pieces of stone? Indeed, no expectation of actually seeing atoms or detect the effect of a single atom could be entertained, for Sir William Thomson had established in 1883 their extreme minuteness by four lines of reasoning which, being "founded respectively on the undulatory theory of light, on the phenomena of contact electricity, on capillary attraction, and on the kinetic theory of gases, agree in showing that the atoms or molecules of ordinary matter must be something like the 1/10,000,000th, or from the 1/10,000,000th to the 1/100,000,000th, of a centimeter in diameter."[2] The leader of the opposition to the atomic theory was Wilhelm Ostwald of Berlin. Idolizing the principle of the conservation of energy and regarding energy as the ultimate reality, Ost-

[1] See *Kultur der Gegenwart, Physik,* Berlin, 1915, p. 224.
[2] Sir William Thomson, *Popular Lectures and Addresses,* Vol. I., London, 1889, p. 148.

wald [1] endeavored to free science "from hypothetical conceptions which lead to no immediate, experimentally verifiable conclusions." He abandoned the atomic and molecular theories, "those pernicious hypotheses" placing "hooks and points upon the atoms." He took up the more direct study of experimental facts and of the resulting graphic charts. In 1897 L. Boltzmann [2] entered a protest to this attitude, in an article on the indispensability of atomism in natural science. Curiously the opposition to the atomic theory sprang up at the very time when the first experimental facts were being revealed which firmly and definitely established its validity.

LIGHT

Wave Theory

We are indebted to **Thomas Young** (1773–1829), a native of Milverton, Somersetshire, for the revival of the undulatory theory of light after a century of neglect. This great scientist had an extraordinary childhood. He could read with considerable fluency at the age of two. When four years old he had read the Bible twice through; when six he could repeat the whole of Goldsmith's Deserted Village. He devoured books, whether classical, literary, or scientific, in rapid succession; and, strange to say, he grew up with unimpaired physical and intellectual powers. At about sixteen he abstained from the use of sugar on account of his opposition to the slave-trade. At nineteen he entered upon a medical education, which was pursued first in London, then in Edinburgh, Göttingen, and finally at Cambridge. In 1800 he began medical practice in London. The year following he accepted the office of Professor of Natural Philosophy in the Royal Institution, the metropolitan school of science established in the year preceding by Count Rumford. He held this position two years. From

[1] Among Ostwald's later utterances on this subject, see his Faraday Lecture in *Nature*, Vol. 70, 1904, p. 15; Ostwald's *Uebber Katalyse*, 2. Ed., Leipzig, 1911, pp. 25, 26.
[2] *Wiedemann's Annalen*, Vol. 60, 1897, p. 311.

January to May, 1802, he delivered there a series of lectures. These and a later series were published in 1807 under the title, *Lectures on Natural Philosophy and the Mechanical Arts*, a treatise still worthy of perusal. In 1802 he was appointed Foreign Secretary of the Royal Society. This office he held for the remainder of his life.

Young's earliest researches were on the anatomical and optical properties of the eye. Then followed the first epoch of optical discovery, 1801–1804. His theory was laughed at, and he proceeded to other studies. The twelve succeeding years were given to medical practice and to the study of philology, especially the decipherment of hieroglyphic writing. But when Fresnel, in France, began to experiment on light and to bring into prominence the theory of Young, then the latter resumed his early studies, and entered upon his second epoch of optical investigation.

In 1801 Young read before the Royal Society a paper on the color of thin plates, in which he expressed himself strongly in favor of the undulatory theory of light. The great step taken in this article is the introduction of the *principle of interference*. "When two undulations, from different origins, coincide either perfectly or very nearly in direction, their joint effect is a combination of the motions belonging to each."[1] Imperfect hints of this principle occur in Robert Hooke's *Micrographia*, but Young was unaware of these until after he had arrived at the notion independently. Young was the first to make a thorough application of it to sound and light. By this principle he explained the colors of thin plates and the diffraction colors of scratched or "striated surfaces."[2] Young's observations were made with great exactness, but the mode of exposition in these as in most of his memoirs, was con-

[1] *Miscellaneous Works of the Late Thomas Young*, edited by George Peacock, London, 1855, Vol. I., p. 157. See also p. 170.

[2] The colors of scratches on polished surfaces were observed first by Robert Boyle. Later, examples of lines drawn on glass were produced by Mr. Barton, which, when transferred to steel—as in the case of the buttons which are known by his name—produce a very brilliant effect of coloration. George Peacock's *Life of Dr. Young*, 1855, p. 149.

densed and somewhat obscure. His papers, containing the great principle of interference, constituted by far the most important publication on physical optics issued since the time of Newton. Yet they made no impression upon the scientific public. They were attacked violently by **Lord Brougham** in Nos. II. and IX. of the *Edinburgh Review.* Young's articles were declared to contain "nothing which deserves the name either of experiment or discovery," to be "destitute of every species of merit." "We wish to raise our feeble voice," says Brougham, "against innovations that can have no other effect than to check the progress of science." After exposing the law of interference as "absurd" and "illogical," the reviewer says, "We now dismiss, for the present, the feeble lucubrations of this author, in which we have searched without success for some traces of learning, acuteness, and ingenuity, that might compensate his evident deficiency in the powers of solid thinking, calm and patient investigation, and successful development of the laws of nature, by steady and modest observation of her operations." [1] Young issued an able reply, published in the form of a pamphlet, which failed to turn public opinion in favor of his theory, because, as he said, "one copy only was sold." [2] Says Tyndall,[3] "For twenty years this man of genius was quenched—hidden from the appreciative intellect of his countrymen—deemed in fact a dreamer, through the vigorous sarcasm of a writer who had then possession of the public ear. . . . To the celebrated Frenchmen, Fresnel and Arago, he was first indebted for the restitution of his rights."

Augustin Jean Fresnel (1788–1827) was born at Broglie in Normandy. He advanced very slowly in his studies, being at eight years of age scarcely able to read.[4] The state of his health was always delicate. Unlike Thomas Young, he gave no promise of becoming a great savant. At

[1] *Edinburgh Review,* No. IX., 6th ed., Vol. V., p. 103; *Young's Works,* I., p. 193.
[2] *Ibidem,* I., 215.
[3] *Six Lectures on Light,* 2d ed., New York, 1877, p. 51.
[4] F. Arago, *Biographies,* 2d Series, Boston, 1859, p. 176.

the age of thirteen he went to the central school at Caen, at sixteen to the Polytechnic School in Paris, then to the *École des ponts et chaussées.* Then he served as government engineer for about eight years. He was a strong Royalist, and joined the army organized to oppose the return of Napoleon from Elba. As a result he was deprived of his office. On the reinstatement of Louis XVIII. Fresnel obtained a new position as engineer. He entered upon his experimental researches in 1815. A letter of December, 1814, contains the following: "I do not know what is meant by polarization of light." Within a year he transmitted to the Academy an important memoir on diffraction (October, 1815). Other memoirs followed in rapid succession.[1] By placing a wire in a beam of light diverging from a point, the distances of the resulting fringes from the axis of the beam were accurately measured. He noticed, as Young had done earlier, the disappearance of the bands within the shadow, when the light which passed on one side of the wire was cut off before it reached the screen. Fresnel was led to the discovery of the principle of interference, without being aware that Young had achieved this more than thirteen years before. Many physicists were not inclined to admit that the phenomena were due to interference. Diffraction fringes had been known since the time of Grimaldi, and had been explained on the emission-theory by means of hypothetical laws of attraction and repulsion between the light corpuscles and the edges of the object causing diffraction. To remove these objections Fresnel designed the memorable experiment which yielded two small sources of light, without resorting to apertures or edges of opaque obstacles. By the use of two plane metallic mirrors, forming with each other an angle of nearly 180°, he avoided diffraction, and yet with the reflected beams produced interference.

Arago and Poinsot were commissioned to report on Fresnel's first memoir. Arago entered upon the subject with zeal and

[1] Consult *Œuvres complètes d'Augustin Fresnel,* Paris, 1866, in three volumes, with introduction by Émile Verdet (1824–1866).

became the first convert in France to the undulatory theory. Some of Fresnel's mathematical assumptions were not satisfactory; hence Laplace, Poisson, and others belonging to the strictly mathematical school at first disdained to consider the theory. By their opposition Fresnel was spurred to greater exertion. Young had not verified his explanations by extensive numerical calculations. Fresnel applied mathematical analysis to a much greater extent, and the undulatory theory began to carry conviction to many minds. He gave a complete answer to the old objection against the wave theory, that the latter could not explain the existence of shadows or the approximate rectilinear propagation of light. The difference in interference phenomena of light and sound arises from the very much shorter wave lengths of light.

Unlike Young, Fresnel made extensive use of Huygens's principle of secondary waves, stated by Fresnel as follows: "The vibrations of a luminous wave at any one of its points may be considered as the sum of the elementary movements conveyed to it at the same moment, from the separate action of all the portions of the unobstructed wave considered in any one of its anterior positions." [1]

It was Arago who first drew Fresnel's attention to Young's researches, and who sent to the English physician the first memoir of the French savant. It is a pleasure to note the absence of bitter contests of priority. Fresnel writes Young in 1816: "But if anything could console me for not having the advantage of priority, it was for me to have met a savant who has enriched physics with so great a number of important discoveries, and has at the same time contributed greatly to strengthen my confidence in the theory that I have adopted." [2] Young writes to Fresnel, October 16, 1819: "I return a thousand thanks, Monsieur, for the gift of your admirable memoir, which surely merits a very high rank amongst

---

[1] G. Peacock, *Life of Thomas Young*, London, 1855, p. 167.
[2] *Young's Works*, Vol. I., p. 378.

the papers which have contributed most to the progress of optics." [1]

Let us proceed to double refraction and the polarization of light. Double refraction had been observed in Iceland spar by Erasmus Bartholinus. Polarization had been studied by Huygens and Newton. Huygens had stated the true law of extraordinary refraction in uniaxial crystals. The property of "two-sidedness" or "polarization" was known to them as an isolated fact observed only in connection with double refraction. A century elapsed and then Malus observed that polarization may accompany reflection. Thus light may be polarized in other ways than by the action of crystallized bodies.

Étienne Louis Malus (1775–1812) was born in Paris. He was educated as a military engineer and served in the French army in Germany and Egypt. Later, during his superintendence of the work then in progress at Antwerp and at Strassburg, he found time to undertake the investigation of a prize question proposed by the French Institute, calling for a mathematical theory of double refraction. By accident he was led to the discovery alluded to above. He looked through a piece of crystal at the image of the sun reflected from the windows of the Luxembourg Palace, to the house in the Rue d'Enfer, where he lived, and was much surprised to find one of the double images disappear for a certain position of the crystal.[2] He tried to explain the singular phenomenon by some modification of the light undergone in traversing the atmosphere. But when night came, he found that the light of a taper, falling upon the surface of water at an angle of 36°, acted similarly and, in fact, was polarized. Moreover, if the two rays from calc-spar fell simultaneously on the surface of water at an angle of 36°, and if the ordinary ray was partly reflected, then the extraordinary ray was not reflected at all, and *vice versa*. Thus, in one evening, Malus created a new branch of modern physics.

[1] *Ibidem,* Vol. I., p. 393.
[2] *Young's Works,* Vol. II., p. 593.

At this time no explanation of polarization had been given by the wave theory, which was in great danger of being overthrown by the new mass of evidence furnished by Malus. Thomas Young wrote in 1811 to Malus (who was a pronounced partisan of the emission theory): "Your experiments demonstrate the *insufficiency* of a theory (that of interferences), which I have adopted, but they do not prove its *falsity*." [1] As Whewell says,[2] this was without doubt "the darkest time of the history of the theory." Young did not conceal the difficulty; nor did he despair of reconciling a seeming contradiction. Six years passed, then light began to dawn. On January 12, 1817, Young wrote to Arago, "It is a principle in this theory, that all undulations are simply propagated through homogeneous mediums in concentric spherical surfaces like the undulations of sound, consisting simply in the direct and retrograde motions of the particles in the direction of the radius, with their concomitant condensations and rarefactions. And yet it is possible to explain in this theory a transverse vibration, propagated also in the direction of the radius, and with equal velocity, the motions of the particles being in a certain constant direction with respect to that radius; and this is a *polarization*." [3] This was a happy suggestion which made it possible to see how a ray could exhibit two-sidedness. Later, instead of the "constant direction" spoken of by Young, the particular direction *transverse to the ray* was fixed upon. Fresnel arrived at this mode of explanation independently, but its publication appeared after Young's. Some idea of the difficulty encountered in grasping the notion of transverse vibrations is obtained from Arago's narration to Whewell, "that when he [Arago] and Fresnel had obtained their joint experimental results of the non-interference of oppositely polarized pencils, and when Fresnel pointed out that transverse vibrations were the only possible translation of this fact into the undulatory theory, he himself protested that he had

[1] Arago's *Biographies*, 2d Series, 1859, p. 159.
[2] *Inductive Sciences*, New York, 1858, Vol. II., p. 100.
[3] *Young's Works*, Vol. I., p. 383.

not courage to publish such a conception; and, accordingly, the second part of the Memoir was published in Fresnel's name alone." [1] Fresnel advanced the whole subject of polarized light. The rich colors produced by polarized light passing through certain crystals were discovered by Arago in 1811. Partisans of the two rival optical theories hastened to find explanations of this phenomenon of depolarization. On the undulatory theory explanations were given first by Young, then more fully by Arago and Fresnel. On the corpuscular theory, the facts were accounted for by Biot in a complicated research of great mathematical elegance. This was received favorably by Laplace and other mathematicians, who found the speculations of Biot more congenial to their habits of thought than those of Fresnel. Arago entered the lists against Biot, and the discussion was carried on with such bitterness that the two physicists, once intimately associated, became wholly estranged. [2] About 1816 Biot discovered that plates of tourmaline show double refraction, but absorb the ordinary ray. This led him to the construction of the well-known tourmaline tongs for the study of polarization phenomena. He gave also the important laws of rotary polarization and their application to the analysis of various substances.

The phenomena of polarized light in crystals were examined with great success by **Sir David Brewster** (1781–1868). Although educated for the Church, he never engaged in its active duties. In 1799 he was induced by his fellow-student, Brougham, to repeat and study Newton's experiments on diffraction. From that time on Brewster was engaged almost continually in original research. He became professor of physics at St. Andrews, and later, principal of the University of Edinburgh. In 1819 he established, in connection with Jameson, the *Edinburgh Philosophical Journal.* He was the leading organizer of the British Association for the Advancement of Science, which held its first meeting at York in

[1] *Inductive Sciences*, Vol. II., p. 101.
[2] *Proceedings of the American Academy of Arts and Sciences*, Vol. VI., 1862–1865, p. 16 *et seq.*, "Jean Baptiste Biot."

1831. He became famous as the inventor of the kaleidoscope,
for which the demand in both England and America was
greater, for a time, than could be met. Brewster, like Biot,
was never friendly to the undulatory theory. "The discoverer of the law of polarization of biaxial crystals, of optical
mineralogy, and of double refraction by compression" was in
a frame of mind to assert, even after the maturer researches
of Young, Fresnel, and Arago had been given to the world,
that "his chief objection to the undulatory theory of light
was that he could not think the Creator guilty of so clumsy a
contrivance as the filling of space with ether in order to
produce light."[1]

VELOCITY OF LIGHT

After 1825 the emission theory, though still supported by
several scientists of prominence, was abandoned by the majority of physicists especially by the younger men. The
crucial test that was believed to destroy once for all the validity of the emission theory, was not performed until the middle
of the century. According to Newton's emission theory the
velocity of light is greater in an optically denser medium,
while, according to the undulatory theory, it is smaller.
Wheatstone, who as early as 1834 had been determining the
duration of the electric spark by aid of rotating mirrors, suggested that the same method might be used to ascertain the
velocity of light and to find out whether the speed was greater
in the more refracting medium. The idea was taken up by
Arago, but as his eyesight was poor, the undertaking was left
to younger men. The mechanical difficulites were great; a
mirror must be made to rotate at a speed of over one thousand
revolutions per second. By some, Arago's project was considered chimerical, because it was thought impossible for the
eye to seize the instantaneous image of a flash reflected from
a mirror rotating with such enormous speed. Bertrand remarked that "an attentive and assiduous observer may, according to computations of M. Babinet, hope to catch the ray

[1] Tyndall, *Six Lectures on Light*, 2d ed., New York, 1877, p. 49.

once in three years."[1] The experiment was undertaken by
Foucault. He adopted the combination of apparatus now
described in almost every general treatise on physics, by which
the difficulty mentioned above was removed.[2] The success of
his experiments was announced to the Academy of Sciences,
May 6, 1850. He found the velocity of light in water to be
less than in air; from that moment Newton's emission theory
was abandoned.

Jean Léon Foucault (1819–1868) was born in Paris. He
studied medicine, but between the years 1845 and 1849 entered
upon physical researches. At this time he worked in conjunction with Fizeau. After their separation, each made determinations of the velocity of light. Foucault's research on the
velocity in air relative to that in water, mentioned above, was
carried on at his pavilion in the Rue d'Assas, and was submitted by him in 1853 as a thesis for the degree of Doctor of
Science.[3] In 1851 Foucault presented a memoir giving his
famous demonstration of the rotation of the earth by means of
the pendulum.[4] The following year he invented that marvel-

[1] Ph. Gilbert, *Léon Foucault, sa vie et son œuvre scientifique.* Brux-
elles, 1879, p. 32.

[2] For details, see Delaunay, "Essay on the Velocity of Light,"
Smithsonian Report, 1864, pp. 135–165.

[3] Ph. Gilbert, *op. cit.*, p. 32.

[4] The experiment was made in four places. The first one was a cellar
two metres deep at his pavilion in the Rue d'Assas. A brass ball weighing five kilogrammes was suspended by a steel wire. The ball was drawn
aside, held in that position by a thread until it was at complete rest, then
set free by burning the thread. The pendulum began oscillating in a
fixed vertical plane, making thereby the fact of the earth's rotation
experimentally evident. To the eye the plane of oscillation seemed to
rotate and the earth to be at rest. Theory indicated that the angle of
this apparent motion in a given time was equal to the angle through
which the earth rotated in the same time, multiplied by the sine of the
angle of latitude of the place where the experiment was made. An
accurate verification of this law required more favorable conditions.
Arago offered Foucault the use of the observatory building, where a
pendulum eleven metres long enabled him to demonstrate the law with
exactitude. Through the favor of Napoleon III., the Pantheon was
chosen for the third test. A ball of twenty-eight kilogrammes was suspended there by a wire sixty-seven metres long and 1.4 millimetres thick.
The Pantheon was thronged with visitors. The fourth exhibition was
made at the Universal Exposition of 1855. These pendulum experiments
became very famous. The only previous record of similar observations

lous piece of mechanism, the gyroscope. In 1854 Napoleon III. secured a place for him at the Paris Observatory as physicist. Much was contributed by Foucault toward greater perfection of astronomical instruments.[1]

Foucault's early co-worker, **Hippolyte Louis Fizeau** (1819–1896),[2] was born in Paris. Being in possession of a fortune which left him free to follow his own inclinations, he devoted himself to physics. The means for his researches were largely supplied from his own private resources. In 1849 he made the earliest experimental determination of the absolute velocity of light. Römer's and Bradley's measurements had been based on astronomical observation. Fizeau rotated a toothed wheel, which intercepted light at regular intervals. The intermittent flashes were reflected from a distant fixed mirror. The research was carried on in the suburbs of Paris, between Suresnes and Montmartre, a distance of 8633 metres.[3] His article in the *Comptes Rendus* (Vol. 29, p. 90) appeared in 1849, the year before Foucault's paper on the relative velocity of light in air and water (Vol. 30, p. 551). In the year 1862 Foucault applied his method to the determination of the absolute velocity, and found values surpassing in accuracy all previous measurements.[4]

Fizeau made experiments on the relative motion of ether and matter, which he interpreted as showing that the ether within a transparent medium is carried forward by the moving medium, but with a velocity less than that of the medium.

dates from the time of the *Accademia del Cimento*. Viviani is credited with the statement, ''We have observed that all pendulums suspended by a single thread deviate from their primitive vertical plane and do so always in the same direction.'' See Ph. Gilbert, *op. cit.*, p. 55. But there is nothing to show that the Italian had divined the cause.

[1] Foucault possessed a poorly developed body. Says Lissajous: ''It seemed as if nature had undertaken to establish a striking contrast between Foucault's physique and his intellectual powers. Who could have divined the man of genius under this frail appearance?'' *Ibidem,* 13.

[2] *Nature,* Vol. 54, 1896, p. 523; P. Larousse, *Grand Dictionnaire Universel.*

[3] Ph. Gilbert, *op. cit.*, p. 36.

[4] *Comptes Rendus,* Vol. 55, 1862, pp. 501, 792.

These experiments were confirmed by Michelson and Morley,[1] and have been re-interpreted by Einstein.

Fizeau's method of finding the velocity of light was adopted with some modifications by **Marie Alfred Cornu** (1841–1902) in Paris and by James Young and George Forbes in England. In Cornu's experiments of 1874 the fixed mirror was at a distance of 23 kilometres.[2] Young and Forbes's measurements, published in 1882,[3] seemed to show that the blue rays travel about 1.8 per cent faster than the red. The correctness of this result has been doubted. If true, stars should appear colored just before and after an eclipse; moreover, Michelson, by Foucault's method, should have seen a spectral drawing out of the image of the slit, yielding a colored image ten millimetres in width.[4]

The best determinations of light-velocity have been made in the United States. In 1867 **Simon Newcomb** (1835–1909), then of the Naval Observatory, recommended the repetition of Foucault's experiment that closer values for the solar parallax might be obtained. A preliminary test was made in 1878 by **Albert A. Michelson** (born 1852) at the laboratory of the Naval Academy at Annapolis.[5] A gift of $2000 enabled him to continue experimentation. Measurements were taken in 1879. At Newcomb's request Michelson, in 1882, made a determination at the Case Institute in Cleveland, Ohio. The main difficulty in Foucault's experiments had been that the deflection was too small to be measured accurately. His distance between the fixed and the rotating mirror was only 4 metres (though, by using five fixed mirrors, this was virtually increased to 20 metres), and the displacement of the return image was only .7 millimetre. In Michelson's improved

---

[1] *Am. Jour. of Sci.* (3), Vol. 31, p. 377, 1886.

[2] *Annales de l'Observtoire de Paris* (*Mémoires,* Vol. 13, 1876).

[3] *Philos. Trans.,* Part I., 1882.

[4] A. A. Michelson, *Astr. Papers for the Am. Ephem. and Naut. Almanac,* Vol. II., Part IV., p. 237, 1885.

[5] Joseph Lovering, ''Address on Presentation of Rumford Medal to Prof. A. A. Michelson,'' in *Am. Acad. of Arts and Science,* New Series, Vol. 16, 1888–89, p. 384. We have taken several details from this source.

arrangement the return image was displaced through 133 millimetres, or nearly 200 times that obtained by Foucault.

In March, 1879, Congress voted an appropriation of $5000 for experiments to be made under the direction of Simon Newcomb. The movable mirror was mounted at Fort Meyer. The fixed mirror was placed at one time at the Naval Observatory (distance, 2550.95 metres), and at another time at Washington Monument (distance, 3721.21 metres). Michelson assisted in the operations until he removed to Cleveland in the autumn of 1880. Observations began in the summer of 1880, and were continued until the autumn of 1882, the most favorable days in spring, summer, and autumn being selected. Only during the hour after sunrise or the hour before sunset were the atmospheric conditions such that a steady image of the slit could be obtained. Altogether 504 sets of measurements were made; 276 by Newcomb, 140 by Michelson, 88 by Holcombe.[1]

The results in kilometres per second obtained for the velocity of light *in vacuo* are as follows: Fizeau, in 1849, 315,000; Foucault, in 1862, 298,000; Cornu, in 1874, 298,500; Cornu, in 1878, 300,400; Young and Forbes, in 1880–1881, 301,382; Michelson, in 1879, 299,910; Michelson, in 1882, 299,853; Newcomb, in 1882, 299,860, when using only results supposed free from constant error, and 299,810 when including all observations.[2] Cornu, Newcomb and Michelson modified their figures somewhat in later estimates. The velocity of light engrossed the attention of Michelson as a young man; it continued to do so in his later life. In 1926 he obtained for it a speed of 299,796 km. per second. This figure is less by 24 km. than his own best earlier determination in 1924,

[1] Consult S. Newcomb, *Astr. Papers for the Am. Ephem. and Naut. Alm.*, Vol. III., Part III., 1885.

[2] These figures and some other details have been taken from Preston, *Theory of Light*, Ch. XIX. For a fuller account of researches on light the reader is referred to R. T. Glazebrook, "Report on Optical Theories," in *Report of British Association*, 1885, abstracted in *Nature*, Vol. 48, pp. 473–477; Humphrey Lloyd, "Report on the Progress and Present State of Physical Optics," in *Report of British Association*, 1834.

64 km. less than that of Simon Newcomb, in 1885, 104 km. less than that of Joseph Perrotin (1845–1904) in 1900, and 154 km. less than the best result of Marie Alfred Cornu.[1] Michelson's figure was obtained at Mount Wilson, with Mount San Antonio 22 miles away as the distant station. A novel feature was the use of an octagonal revolving mirror which offered the possibility of receiving the return light on a succeeding face, thus eliminating the measurement of the angular deflection of the returned beam. The velocity of light has always been considered one of the most important of the constants in nature, but it has been assigned a still more fundamental place by the theory of relativity, which makes the velocity of light in a vacuum the highest speed possible in nature.

FIRST OBSERVATIONS OF SPECTRAL LINES

The first observations of spectral lines due to luminous gases were made by a Scotsman, Thomas Melvill,[2] in 1752, who died in 1753 at the age of twenty-seven. He was a student of divinity at Glasgow in 1748–9. His research marks the first step forward since Newton's studies of the spectrum. Melvill observed the spectrum of burning spirits into which were introduced successively sal ammoniac, potash, alum, nitre and sea-salt. ''Having placed a paste-board with a circular hole in it between my eye and the flame of spirits, in order to diminish and circumscribe my object, I examined the constitution of these different lights with a prism—and found that— when sal ammon., alum or potash fell into the spirits, all sorts of rays were emitted, but not in equal quantities; the yellow being vastly more copious than all the rest put together, and red more faint than the green and blue. . . . The bright yellow which prevails so much over the other colors, must be

[1] A. A. Michelson, *Science*, Vol. 60, 1924, p. 392; *Astrophysical Journal*, Vol. 65, 1927, p. 1.
[2] Melvill read two papers before the Medical Society of Edinburgh, which were printed in 1766, in a book *Physical and Literary Essays*, and are reprinted in the *Journal of the R. Astr. Soc. of Canada*, Vol. 8, 1914, pp. 231–272.

of one determined degree of refrangibility; and the transition from it to the fainter color adjoining, not gradual, but immediate.'' The ''bright yellow'' in question is of course the ''sodium line.'' Until recently Melvill's papers were overlooked, except in 1785 by a Rev. Mr. Morgan[1] who experimented with flames, but made no noteworthy contribution. Later **William Hyde Wollaston** (1766–1828), a London physician,[2] observed the bright spectral bands due to blue light at the base of a candle flame, which are now called the ''Swan spectrum''—this having been observed again by William Swan at St. Andrews and described in 1856. The next observer of bright lines was Fraunhofer.

We pause to note the first observation of the dark lines in the solar spectrum. They were seen by Wollaston who had the gift of originating important lines of research, but in each case he just fell short of making a distinct step. In 1802, he saw seven lines; the five most prominent ones were considered by him to be the natural boundaries or dividing lines of the pure simple colors of the spectrum.[3] His explanation is of interest, for it shows how a most plausible theory may be destitute of all truth. Says Wollaston: '' . . . The colors into which a beam of white light is separable by refrac-

[1] *Philosophical Transactions*, London, Vol. 75, 1785, p. 190.

[2] His invention of the process of rendering platinum malleable brought him a considerable annual royalty. He invented the *camera lucida* and cryophorus; he discovered palladium and rhodium.

[3] Mrs. Mary Somerville, the mathematician and physicist, gives the following recollections: ''One bright morning, Dr. Wollaston came to pay us a visit in Hanover Square, saying, 'I have discovered seven dark lines crossing the solar spectrum, which I wish to show you;' then, closing the window shutters so as to leave only a narrow line of light, he put a small glass prism into my hand, telling me how to hold it. I saw them distinctly. I was among the first, if not the very first, to whom he showed these lines, which were the origin of the most wonderful series of cosmical discoveries, and have proved that many of the substances of our globe are also constituents of the sun, the stars, and even the nebulæ. Dr. Wollaston gave me the little prism, which is doubly valuable, being of glass manufactured at Munich by Fraunhofer, whose table of dark lines has now become the standard of comparison in that marvellous science, the work of many illustrious men, brought to perfection by Bunsen and Kirchhoff.'' *Personal Recollections of Mary Somerville*, by her daughter Martha Somerville, Boston, 1874, p. 133.

tion, appear to me to be neither *seven*, as they usually are seen in the rainbow, nor reducible by any means (that I can find) to *three*, as some persons have conceived; but . . . *four* primary divisions of the prismatic spectrum may be seen, with a degree of distinctness that, I believe, has not been described nor observed before."[1]

The first great research on solar dark lines was made by Fraunhofer, who had no knowledge of Wollaston's discovery. **Joseph Fraunhofer** (1787–1826) was born at Straubing in Bavaria. He was the son of a poor glazier, and early in life began to assist his father in his trade. Skilled in glass-grinding, he secured a place in the optical institute of Utzschneider in the village of Benediktbeuern. In 1818 he took charge of the institute, which, soon after, was moved to Munich. Fraunhofer became a member of the Munich Academy of Sciences and conservator of its physical cabinet.[2]

In his optical work, Fraunhofer combined to a rare degree theoretic insight with practical skill. "By his invention of new and improved methods, machinery, and measuring instruments for grinding and polishing lenses, by his having the superintendence, after 1811, also of the work in glass-melting, enabling him to produce flint and crown glass in larger pieces, free of veins, but especially by his discovery of a method of computing accurately the forms of lenses, he has led practical optics into entirely new paths, and has raised the achromatic telescope to, until then, undreamed-of perfection."[3]

In the endeavor to determine indices of refraction of glass for particular colors, to be used in the design of more accurate achromatic lenses, Fraunhofer accidentally discovered in the spectrum of a lamp the double line in the orange, now known as the sodium line. In oil and tallow light and, in fact, in all firelight, he saw this sharply defined, bright, double line,

[1] *Philos. Trans.*, 1802, p. 378.
[2] Rosenberger, III., p. 189.
[3] E. Lommel in preface, p. vii., to *Joseph von Fraunhofer's Gesammelte Schriften*, München, 1888.

"exactly in the same place and consequently very useful" in the determination of indices. A ray from a narrow slit was allowed to fall upon a distant flint-glass prism, placed in the position of least deviation in front of the telescope of a theodolite. Fraunhofer proceeded to use sunlight. "I wished to find out," he says, "whether a similar bright line could be seen in the spectrum of sunlight as in the spectrum of lamplight, and I found, with the telescope, instead of this, an almost countless number of strong and feeble vertical lines, which, however, were darker than the other parts of the spectrum, some appearing to be almost perfectly black."[1] On examining other substances, like hydrogen, alcohol, sulphur, he found the bright line again. This must have been due, of course, to the presence of sodium as an impurity, the minutest quantity of which will exhibit its spectrum. Fraunhofer examined also starlight, and recognized in Venus some of the solar lines.[2]

He was the first to observe spectra due to gratings, and with them he made the earliest determination of wave-lengths. His gratings were of wire .04 to .6 mm. thick. The grating space varied from .0528 to .6866 mm. He made ten gratings and found the wave-length for D with each. The results ranged from .0005882 to .0005897, giving a mean value of .0005888 mm., which is remarkably accurate, if we consider the crudeness of his gratings.[3] A paper of 1823 contains experiments with two glass gratings having spaces of .0033 and .0160 mm., respectively.

Fraunhofer's publication of 1814 did not receive prompt recognition, nor did his papers of 1821 and 1823. Physicists

[1] *Gesammelte Schriften, op. cit.,* p. 10. Quoted from the memoir, "Bestimmung des Brechungs- und des Farbenzerstreuungs-Vermögens verschiedener Glasarten, in Bezug auf die Vervollkommnung achromatischer Fernröhre," which appeared first in *Denkschriften der Münchener Akad.,* Band V., 1814–1815.

[2] G. W. A. Kahlbaum, *Aus der Vorgeschichte der Spectralanalyse,* Basel, 1888, p. 12.

[3] See Fraunhofer, *Neue Modification des Lichtes,* 1821; also Louis Bell, "The Absolute Wave-Length of Light" in *Philos. Magazine* (5), Vol. 25, 1888, p. 245.

were fighting over the emission and wave theories of light. The attention of chemists was concentrated upon Dalton's atomic theory and the Berthollet-Proust controversy over the law of definite proportions. The full explanation of the new fact brought forth by Fraunhofer was not given for nearly forty years. He himself had failed to find the key to the hieroglyphics of the solar lines, the "Fraunhofer lines," nor had he clearly defined the rôle which the spectral lines were destined to play in chemical analysis.

After Fraunhofer, the first researches were made in England. J. F. W. Herschel examined bright-line spectra of several substances, stated that the colors of the bright lines were a means of detecting small quantities of a substance, and in 1827 touched on this subject in his work *On Light*. Charles Wheatstone published, in 1835, a paper on spectra of the electric arc passing between metals. **William Henry Fox Talbot** (1800–1877), a rich citizen, expressed the belief that every homogeneous ray, whatever its color, always indicates the presence of a definite chemical compound. Yet none of these investigators arrived at clear notions on the subject. Talbot, for instance, falls into an error which inexperienced students in our laboratories frequently commit: he looks upon certain bright-line spectra as being really dark-line spectra. "Copper-salts give spectra so covered with dark lines as to resemble the solar spectrum." [1] Kirchhoff points out that the English investigators did not establish the strict dependence of the spectral lines upon the particular element in the flame; [2] thus Talbot ascribes the *D* line to both sulphur and the salts of sodium. Sir David Brewster, in 1832, described dark-line spectra, formed by absorption of rays passing through colored glass and through certain gases. These spectra simulated the solar spectrum. In the fact that fuming nitric acid absorbs lines, while the liquid does not, Brewster saw an argument against the wave theory of light; for a gas ought to offer less

[1] Kahlbaum, *op. cit.*, p. 18.
[2] Kirchhoff, "Zur Geschichte der Spectralanalyse," *Gesammelte Abhandlungen*, Leipzig, 1882, pp. 625–641; Rosenberger, III., p. 313.

impedance to motion of the ether than its denser liquid. The exact coincidence of the bright lines of sodium with the dark *D* lines of the sun was established by William Allen Miller of Kings College, and by Foucault in Paris. The latter did this by introducing simultaneously into the spectroscope sunlight and the electric light displaying the sodium lines. The possible production of the Fraunhofer lines through absorption of certain rays by the solar atmosphere was then under consideration, but no definite conclusion was reached as to the validity of this explanation.

PHOTOGRAPHING SPECTRA

A great aid to the study of spectra was the discovery of the art of photography by **Joseph Nicephore Niepce** (1765–1833), who produced photographic pictures on metal in 1827. **Louis Jacques Mandé Daguerre** (1789–1851) was for some years Niepce's coadjutor, and subsequently improved the method of the latter, announcing in 1839 the new process known as the "daguerreotype." This famous process was at once taken up by J. W. Draper in New York, who was the first to apply it to individuals. In the first trials, "the face of the sitter . . . was dusted with white powder," and on a bright day a picture was taken in five or seven minutes. In 1840 Draper photographed the moon; in 1842 he photographed the Fraunhofer lines, only a few months after a similar achievement by **Edmond Becquerel** (1820–1891) in France. In 1843 Joseph Saxton, a mechanician of the United States mint in Philadelphia, ruled for Draper a diffraction grating of glass, and the latter photographed the diffraction spectrum. We will now sketch the life of this assiduous investigator.

John William Draper (1811–1882) was born at St. Helen's, near Liverpool, and studied at the London University. He came to the United States in 1833. After studying medicine at the University of Pennsylvania, he was chosen to the chair of chemistry and physiology at Hampden-Sidney College, Virginia, and later to the same chair at the University of New

York, where he remained until the end of his long life. For many years he dwelt in a quiet retreat at Hastings-on-the-Hudson, near New York, surrounded by everything which could minister to the tastes of a veteran in science.[1]

In 1847, Draper published an important memoir,[2] in which he concluded from experiment that all solid substances and probably liquids become incandescent at the same temperature, viz., red hot at 525° C.; that below 525° C. invisible rays are emitted, and as the temperature rises above 525°, rays of greater refrangibility are added successively and continuously; that all spectra of incandescent solids are continuous, that gases give continuous spectra too, but may have bright lines superposed. The last statement is incorrect. The error originated in his use of bright flames giving, in addition to the line spectrum of the salt placed in the flame, the continuous spectrum of solid carbon; a luminous gas ordinarily gives only bright lines.

Thirteen years later Draper's correct conclusions were deduced independently from theoretical considerations by Kirchhoff, who started out from the relation between emitting and absorbing powers possessed by different bodies for radiant energy. This relation had been established in 1854 by Ångström (and later by Balfour Stewart).

EXPLANATION OF THE HIEROGLYPHICS IN THE SOLAR SPECTRUM

An exhaustive account of spectrum analysis before Kirchhoff and Bunsen would call for further reference to researches made by Anders Ångström, Balfour Stewart, Sir David Brewster, J. H. Gladstone, Julius Plücker (the inventor of "Plücker tubes"), V. S. M. van der Willigen, Edmond Becquerel, and many others.[3]

[1] *Am. Jour. of Science* (3), Vol. 23, 1882, p. 163; see also *Nat. Acad. of Sciences, Biographical Memoirs*, Vol. II., 1886, p. 351.

[2] *Philos. Magazine*, May, 1847; J. W. Draper's *Scientific Memoirs*, New York, 1878, "Memoir I."; see also J. W. Draper, "Early Contributions to Spectrum Photography and Photo-Chemistry," *Nature*, Vol. X., 1874.

[3] Consult Kahlbaum, *op. cit.;* Kirchhoff, "Zur Geschichte der Spectralanalyse."

Gustav Kirchhoff (1824–1887) was born at Königsberg; he became privat-docent in Berlin, then extraordinary professor at Breslau, ordinary professor at Heidelberg in 1854, and professor in Berlin after 1875. The rich period of his life was the twenty years he taught at Heidelberg, where he worked conjointly with the great chemist, **Robert Wilhelm Bunsen** (1811–1899).[1] It was during the years 1859–1862 that these great investigators together made the great discoveries of spectrum analysis. At the time the physical laboratory at Heidelberg was very unpretentious, being located in a house, the "Riesengebäude," then 150 years old. The memorable researches were carried on in a small room. Illuminating gas had been introduced into the building in 1855.[2] In 1857 Bunsen and Roscoe first described the "Bunsen burner."[3] This new burner furnished Bunsen and Kirchhoff with a non-luminous gas-flame of fairly high temperature, in which chemical substances could be vaporized and a spectrum could be obtained, due purely and simply to the luminous vapor. In this way some of the errors of earlier experimenters were avoided.

In October, 1859, Kirchhoff and Bunsen published their first paper,[4] which contains their later researches *in nuce*. From experiments the conclusion is drawn by Kirchhoff "that a colored flame, the spectrum of which contains bright sharp lines, so weakens rays of the color of these lines, when they pass through it, that dark lines appear in place of the bright lines as soon as there is placed behind the flame a light of sufficient intensity, in which the lines are otherwise absent"; "that the dark lines of the solar spectrum, which are not caused by the terrestrial atmosphere, arise from the presence in the glowing solar atmosphere of those substances which in a flame produce bright lines in the same position." Kirchhoff

[1] For his contributions to chemistry, see *Nature*, Vol. 23, 1881, p. 597.
[2] Georg Quincke, *Gesch. d. Physik. Instituts. d. Univ. Heidelberg,* Heidelberg, 1885, p. 16.
[3] *Poggendorff's Annalen,* C, pp. 84–86; Rosenberger, III., p. 484.
[4] "Ueber die Fraunhoferschen Linien," in *Monatsberichte d. Akad. d. Wissensch. zu Berlin,* October, 1859, p. 662.

concluded that sodium, iron, magnesium, copper, zinc, barium, nickel, existed in the solar atmosphere.

The two investigators advanced, as scientifically established, the law that the bright lines in the spectrum may be taken as a sure sign of the presence of the respective metals. This conclusion was rendered doubly sure by the discovery in the mineral water at Dürkheim, through the spectrum, of two new metals. From the blue and the red lines, by which they were recognized, they were named "Cæsium" and "Rubidium." While spectrum analysis, as a terrestrial science, was due equally to Kirchhoff and Bunsen, its celestial applications belong to Kirchhoff alone. Kirchhoff's explanation of the Fraunhofer lines was epoch-making. Says Hemholtz:[1] "It had in fact most extraordinary consequences of the most palpable kind, and has become of the highest importance for all branches of natural science. It has excited the admiration and stimulated the fancy of men as hardly any other discovery has done, because it has permitted an insight into worlds that seemed forever veiled for us." In this connection Kirchhoff frequently related the following story:[2] "The question whether Fraunhofer's lines reveal the presence of gold in the sun was being investigated. Kirchhoff's banker remarked on this occasion: 'What do I care for gold in the sun if I cannot fetch it down here?' Shortly afterwards Kirchhoff received from England a medal for his discovery, and its value in gold. While handing it over to his banker, he observed, 'Look here, I have succeeded at last in fetching some gold from the sun.'"

It has been said that Kirchhoff's gift as an investigator was not to *initiate*, but to *complete*.[3] This is plainly seen in his work on spectrum analysis. The threads of his discovery had been seized upon by great men before him. So nearly had

[1] "A Memoir of Gustav Robert Kirchhoff," *Deutsche Rundschau,* February 1888, Vol. 14, pp. 232–245; translated in *Smithsonian Report,* 1889, pp. 527–540.

[2] *Smithsonian Report,* 1889, p. 537.

[3] W. Voigt, *Zum Gedächtniss von G. Kirchhoff,* Göttingen, 1888, p. 9.

English, French, and American scientists attained to Kirchhoff's results, that prolonged discussions have arisen on questions of priority. "All had seen something, made guesses, considered as possible or probable (without Kirchhoff having been aware of it at the time, however)." But it remains the great merit of Kirchhoff to have established a solid basis, to have arrived at sure knowledge.

One claim of priority was made in favor of William Hallowes Miller of Cambridge, who, it was argued, "anticipated by nearly sixteen years the remarkable discovery, ascribed to Kirchhoff, of the opacity of certain colored flames to light of their own color."[1] Another claim was made soon after Kirchhoff's paper of 1859 by William Thomson (later Lord Kelvin) in favor of **George Gabriel Stokes** (1819–1903) of Pembroke College, Cambridge, who, before Kirchhoff (perhaps about the year 1849), in course of a conversation, explained the formation of absorption lines as follows: "Vapor of sodium must possess by its molecular structure a tendency to vibrate in the periods corresponding to the degree of refrangibility of the double line D. Hence the presence of sodium in a source of light must tend to originate light of that quality. On the other hand, vapor of sodium in an atmosphere round a source must have a great tendency to retain itself, *i.e.*, to absorb and have its temperature raised by light from the source of the precise quality in question. In the atmosphere round the sun, therefore, there must be present vapor of sodium, which, according to the mechanical explanation thus suggested, being particularly opaque for light of that quality, prevents such of it as is emitted from the sun from penetrating to any considerable distance through the surrounding atmosphere."[2] Stokes did not ascertain experimentally whether or not the vapor of sodium has the special absorbing power anticipated, but he remembered a test, showing this power, made in France

[1] Crookes in *Chemical News*, May 18, 1862; *Philos. Magazine* (4), Vol. 25, 1863, p. 261.
[2] *Philos. Magazine* (4), Vol. 25, 1863, p. 261.

by Foucault.[1] He did not attach sufficient importance to his mechanical theory to have it appear in print. Sir William Thomson, however, adds this: "I have given it in my lectures regularly for many years, always pointing out along with it that solar and stellar chemistry were to be studied by investigating terrestrial substances giving bright lines in the spectra of artificial flames corresponding to the dark lines of the solar and stellar spectra." Stokes himself generously published the following disclaimer: "I have never attempted to claim for myself any part of Kirchhoff's admirable discovery, and cannot help thinking that some of my friends have been over zealous in my cause."[2]

LATER EXPERIMENTATION ON SPECTRA

Since the creation of the science of spectrum analysis by Kirchhoff and Bunsen, scientists have been busy perfecting the details of the theory, improving methods of experimentation, and enlarging our knowledge of celestial chemistry. It soon became evident that great caution must be exercised in deducing the chemical constitution and physical characteristics of bodies from the spectra which they give. Confusion is introduced by the occurrence of multiple spectra. As early as 1862, **Julius Plücker,** in Bonn, pointed out that the same substance may give different spectra at different temperatures. He and W. Hittorf found for hydrogen, nitrogen, and sulphur fumes two kinds of spectra, namely, a weak band spectrum and a bright line spectrum. **Adolph Wüllner** (1835–1908) of the Technicum in Aachen, in 1868, discussed the variation in the spectra of hydrogen, oxygen, nitrogen, when subjected in Plücker tubes to different degrees of pressure.[3] For oxygen he observed three spectra under different conditions of pressure. As in a denser gas the electric resistance to the discharge through the tube was greater, the temperature was probably higher. Hence Wüllner thought that in Plücker tubes varia-

---

[1] *L'Institut,* Feb. 7, 1849, p. 45.
[2] *Nature,* Vol. 13, 1875, p. 189.
[3] *Poggendorff's Annalen,* Vol. 135, p. 497.

tions in pressure of the gas were accompanied by changes in the temperature, and that the spectral changes resulted from alterations in both pressure and temperature. Ångström combated Wüllner's position, arguing that while a rise in temperature may bring out new lines and an increase in pressure may widen the lines, nevertheless a spectrum never changes into another of entirely new characteristics.[1] Some of Wüllner's results were attributed by Ångström to the presence of impurities in the gases. However, more extended research revealed that spectral changes depend not only upon variations in temperature and pressure, but also upon molecular constitution. The effect of molecular structure was investigated by Al. Mitscherlich, Clifton, H. E. Roscoe, and by **J. Norman Lockyer** (1836–1920).[2] Lockyer, in 1873 and 1874, advanced the view that each composite body has as definite a spectrum as a simple one; that line spectra are due to the free atoms, band spectra to molecules or groups of molecules. Lockyer's theory was regarded favorably by Ångström, but was opposed by Wüllner, who in 1879 [3] made experiments on nitrogen, showing that by gradual change of temperature the band spectra passed gradually into the line spectra. He argued that Lockyer's theory of the dissociation of molecules was not needed to explain the facts. Lockyer observed that line spectra (of calcium, for instance) change as the temperature rises. He then advanced the bold theory that just as the transition of band spectra into line spectra may be explained by the dissociation of molecules into atoms, so the changes in the line spectra, due to rise in temperature, may be explained by the breaking up of the atoms into still more elementary substances, thus indicating the compound nature of the chemical elements themselves.[4]

[1] *Recherches sur le Spectre Solaire,* Upsala, 1868. See Rosenberger, III., p. 701.

[2] Consult J. N. Lockyer, *Studies in Spectrum Analysis,* New York, 1893, Chap. VII.

[3] Rosenberger, III., p. 706. Consult report "On the Present State of Spectrum Analysis," *Report of Brit. Ass.,* Swansea meeting, 1880; abstracted in *Nature,* Vol. 22, p. 522.

[4] Lockyer, *op. cit.,* p. 189.

The Germans, **H. Kayser** and **C. Runge,** in a series of researches, beginning in 1890, have shown that the distribution of lines in the spectra of the elements is by no means so
irregular as it at first seems. They found that in the spectra
of the common elements there are line series. At one time
the presence in argon of more than one series was supposed
to indicate that it was a mixture of elements; but as the
same reasoning applied to oxygen, which has six series,
leads to conclusions presumably erroneous, this hypothesis
was abandoned.

It remained doubtful whether increased pressure augments
the breadth of lines. G. D. Liveing and J. Dewar combated
the theory that the continuous spectra are produced by the
broadening of the lines of the same gas at low pressure.[1]
An important observation was made in 1895 by W. J. Hum-
phreys and J. F. Mohler in the Johns Hopkins University
laboratory. Certain discrepancies noticed by L. E. Jewell led
them to undertake experiments which demonstrated that the
lines in the arc spectra of metals shift appreciably toward the
red when the pressure of the atmosphere surrounding the arc
is increased. This was distinguished from the Doppler effect
by the fact that the displacement is different for every metal
and for different spectral series of the same metal.[2] Another
interesting phenomenon, showing the influence of magnetization of light, was observed in 1896 by **P. Zeeman,** professor at
the University of Amsterdam. In 1862 Faraday had examined
the sodium lines when the flame was placed between the poles
of a magnet, but had failed to notice any effect; Zeeman, by
means of modern appliances, noticed a change. Light from an
electric arc was sent through a heated tube containing sodium
vapor and placed between the poles of an electro-magnet.
When acted upon by the magnet a slight broadening of the

[1] W. Huggins, Inaugural Address, *Nature*, Vol. 44, 1891, p. 373.
[2] *Astrophys. Jour.*, Vol. III., 1896, pp. 114–137; *Johns Hopkins Univ.
Circular,* No. 130; *Nature*, Vol. 56, 1897, pp. 415, 461.

lines was seen.[1] A. A. Michelson of the University of Chicago, using his new echelon spectroscope, showed that the phenomenon is much more complex. For instance, "all spectral lines are tripled when the radiations emanate in a magnetic field."

The spectroscope came to be used extensively in the chemical analysis of heavenly bodies,[2] but it received also an indirect application, which promised to become hardly less important. A telescope gives us no direct evidence of stellar motion in a direction toward us or from us, but now the spectroscope placed in our hands the means of detecting such motion. The principle involved was first worked out for sound by **Johann Christian Doppler** (1803–1853), a native of Salzburg, Austria. In 1835, having been unable to secure a suitable situation, he was about to emigrate to America, when he was made professor of mathematics at the Realschule in Prague.[3] He called attention, in a paper of 1842, to the fact that the color of a luminous body, just like the pitch of a sounding body must be changed by motion of the body to or from the observer. In the year 1845, **Christoph Heinrich Dietrich Buys-Ballot** (1817–1890), director of the royal meteorological institute at Utrecht, experimented on railroad trains, and verified the theory as applied to sound. A person on a train rushing through a station finds the pitch of a sounding bell at the station higher on approach and lower on recession than it actually is. Doppler argued that most probably all stars emitted white light, and that the color of some of them was due to their motion toward us or away from us. As Buys-Ballot pointed out, this conclusion is erroneous. The approach of a star would simply produce a slight shift of the entire spectrum in the direction of the ultra-violet region, some infra-red rays becoming visible

---

[1] *P. Zeeman in Phil. Mag.*, Vol. 43, pp. 226–239; *Nature*, Vol. 55, pp. 192, 347; consult O. Lodge in *Electrician* (London), Vol. 38, pp. 568, 643.

[2] For the history of astrophysics consult A. M. Clerke, *History of Astronomy during the Nineteenth Century.* For "Literature of the Spectroscope," see *Smithsonian Miscellaneous Collections*, Vol. 32, 1888.

[3] Before his death he was professor of experimental physics at the University of Vienna. See F. Poske, *Zeitsch. f. d. Physik. u. Chem. Unterricht*, Vol. 9, 1896, p. 248.

and some violet rays becoming invisible. No change in color
could take place. But in 1848 Fizeau pointed out that this
shifting must become noticeable through the examination of
the lines of the spectrum. For instance, if the hydrogen lines
of an approaching star are compared with those of a hydrogen
tube in the laboratory, the former are moved toward the violet,
while the latter are fixed. The displacement is so slight that
many years elapsed before instruments were devised by which
accurate measurements could be taken. The initiative in this
delicate work was taken in 1868 by the English astronomer,
Sir William Huggins (1824–1910), and, in 1871, Hermann
Carl Vogel (1841–1907) of Potsdam detected the shifting
effects due to the sun's rotation. Later Doppler's principle
has been applied with great success to the motions of stars and
to the discovery of double stars by Vogel, Edward C. Pickering
(1846–1919) of Harvard, **James E. Keeler** (1857–1900) of
the Lick Observatory, and others. Some double stars discovered by this method are so close to each other that they
appear like a single star even when examined by our most
powerful telescopes. In 1895 Keeler gave observational proof
that Saturn's ring-system was not a solid whole, for the inner
edge of the inner bright ring moved $12\frac{1}{2}$ miles per second,
while the outer edge of the outer ring moved only 10 miles per
second. W. W. Campbell, at the Lick Observatory, applied
Doppler's principle, by aid of the spectrograph, to the motions of stars in the line of sight, and found that the stars
of different spectral classes are moving through space with
different velocities. This conclusion was confirmed by Lewis
Boss (1846–1912) of the Dudley Observatory at Albany, and
by Jacobus C. Kapteyn (1851–1922) of the observatory at
Leyden.

Use of Gratings in Observing the Solar Spectrum

There are two methods of obtaining spectra: one is by the
aid of a prism or a train of prisms, the other by the use of a
grating. The former means was employed by Kirchhoff and

Bunsen; the latter was used to some extent by Fraunhofer and J. W. Draper. The theory of the grating ("striated surfaces") had been outlined by Thomas Young. After Fraunhofer the first improvement in the art of manufacturing gratings was made by the optician, Friedrich Adolph Nobert (1806–1881) of Greifswald in Pomerania. He made glass micrometers, which were used to determine the magnifying power of microscopes, and he furnished gratings to Ångström and E. Mascart (1837–1908). **Anders Jonas Ångström** (1814–1874), professor of physics at Upsala, published in 1868, in his *Recherches sur le Spectre Solaire,* a table of wavelengths which for a long time served as a standard. All the measurements are in error by about one part in seven or eight thousand, owing mainly to the fact that the metre which he used as the standard of length was a trifle too short.[1] Ångström became aware of this as early as 1872, but he did not live to make the needed alterations. The corrections were made by his pupil, R. Thalén, in a publication of 1885. The unit in which Ångström expressed his wave-lengths, namely 10^{-8} cm., has been named the "Ångström unit" and is now generally adopted. In 1907 this unit was redefined, at a meeting of the International Solar Union held in Paris, as the 1/6438.4696th part of the wave-length of the red Cadmium line at 15° C. and 760 mm. atmospheric pressure. It is thus seen that the length of this line is the natural standard for unit wave-length as well as for the meter. Originally based upon a macrocosmic natural unit (one ten-millionth part of the earth's quadrant), the meter is now defined by a microcosmic natural unit. In this instance the microcosmos proves more stable than the macrocosmos.

Nobert's method of ruling diffraction gratings was jealously guarded by him as a trade secret. Since his time the best gratings have been made in the United States. About 1863 Lewis Morris Rutherfurd (1816–1892), a graduate of Williams College, and a lawyer, who studied astronomy in his own

[1] L. Bell, "The Absolute Wave-Length of Light," *Phil. Mag.* (5), Vol. 25, 1888, p. 245.

private observatory near New York, became interested in the preparation of gratings. Rutherfurd, after numerous preliminary experiments, constructed a machine of his own device, and ran it by means of a small water motor. "A diamond point traced parallel lines upon a glass plate pushed regularly forward by a system of levers acting on an acute glass wedge, this in its turn pushing the plate sideways."[1] Except for occasional slight changes in the intervals between the lines the gratings were admirable. Following the advice of Ogden N. Rood of Columbia College, he constructed, in 1867, a machine in which the plate was moved by a screw in place of levers. After several years' effort he produced gratings far superior to Nobert's. In 1875, or earlier, Rutherfurd silvered the gratings with the view to their more convenient spectroscopic use, but later he made gratings upon speculum metal in order to avoid the great wear upon the diamond.[2] In 1877, the ruling machine was enlarged. Armed with Rutherfurd's superior gratings, Charles Saunders Peirce, then of the United States Coast Survey, again attacked the problem of wave-lengths where Ångström had left it ten years previously.[3]

The next improvement in the manufacture of gratings was made by **Henry A. Rowland** of the Johns Hopkins University. His attention was first called to the construction of dividing engines by the inspection of an engine made by **William Augustus Rogers** (1832–1898), at Waltham, Mass.[4] Rogers's aim was to produce lines of extreme fineness for recticules in optical instruments, and for delicate tests of microscope objectives. He was able to rule as many as 4800 lines to the millimetre. Rowland devoted about one year to the construction of a dividing engine. The making of an accurate screw was the most delicate part of the task. The process consisted

[1] B. A. Gould in *Nat. Acad. of Sciences, Biographical Memoirs,* Vol. 3, p. 428.

[2] For details, consult article, "Ruling Machines," in *Johnson's Universal Cyclopædia.*

[3] *Am. Jour. Sci.* (3), Vol. 18, 1879, p. 51.

[4] *Proc. Am. Acad. of Arts and Sci.,* New Series, Vol. II., 1883–1884, p. 482.

in grinding the screw in a long nut in which it was constantly reversed. When it was finished, there was not an error of half a wave-length, although it was nine inches long.[1] Rowland invented concave gratings, and ruled them on his engine. The collimator could thereby be dispensed with. A second and a third engine were later prepared under Rowland's direction, and for many years Rowland's gratings had no rival.[2] He made a large *Photographic Map of the Solar Spectrum,* being altogether over 35 feet long. It was completed in 1888. He prepared a table of solar spectrum wave-lengths which was published in the *Astrophysical Journal,* Vols. 1–6, 1895–1897. The relative values of these wave-lengths have been found quite satisfactory, but more recently the wave-length of D_1, carefully determined by Louis Bell and others, has been found by Michelson's interferometer method to need a slight correction, so that the absolute values of wave-lengths in Rowland's table must be altered correspondingly. Rowland gave for D_1 5896.156 Å; J. Hartmann in 1909 gave 5895.932 Å. In place of D_1 Michelson selected the red Cadmium line as the standard line of reference.

EXPLORATIONS ABOVE AND BELOW THE VISIBLE SOLAR SPECTRUM

That the solar spectrum is not confined to the visible part, extending from the red to the violet, was first shown by Sir William Herschel (1738–1822), who in 1800 discovered that there are infra-red solar rays. Placing the thermometer in successive colors, he discovered the unequal distribution of heat in the solar spectrum, the heating being greatest below the red. Before him no one had suspected such an inequality. "It is sometimes of great use in natural philosophy," says the veteran astronomer,[3] "to doubt of things that are commonly

---

[1] Consult Rowland's article, "Screw," in *Encyclopædia Britannica,* 9th ed.

[2] For a biographical sketch of Rowland, and a picture of his second dividing engine, see Appleton's *Pop. Sci. Month.,* Vol. 49, 1896, pp. 110–120.

[3] *Phil. Trans.,* 1800, p. 255.

taken for granted; especially as the means of resolving any
doubt, when once it is entertained, are often within our reach.''
He speaks of solar heat as occasioned by "rays," subject to
the laws of reflection and refraction. Thomas Young, in his
Lectures of 1807, says, ''This discovery must be allowed to be
one of the greatest that has been made since the days of
Newton.'' Nevertheless, the mass of physicists and text-book
writers, for over half a century, failed to see the truth foreshadowed by W. Herschel, and afterwards established more
clearly by Melloni. Herschel's views were attacked by **John
Leslie** (1766–1832) of Edinburgh, the inventor of the differential thermometer. This able and earnest investigator, like all
seekers after the truth, fell into error. He saw no affinity
between radiant heat and light. He says: "What, then, is
this calorific and frigorific fluid after which we are inquiring?
It is no light, it has no relation to ether, it bears no analogy
to the fluids, real or imaginary, of magnetism and electricity.
But why have recourse to invisible agents? *Quod petis, hic
est*. It is merely the ambient air.'' Thus Herschel's heating effects in the infra-red were attributed to currents of air
from the visible part of the spectrum. However, Leslie found
no followers, after Sir Humphry Davy had shown that in a
partial vacuum the radiation was three times greater than
in air at ordinary pressure, and after Johann Wilhelm Ritter
(1776–1810) and Wollaston had discovered dark chemical rays
in the ultra-violet.[1] In 1811 a young Frenchman, De la Roche,
showed that, of two successive screens of the same kind, the
second absorbs heat in a less ratio than the first, and he concluded that radiant heat is of different kinds.[2] W. Herschel
had previously shown that "radiant heat is of different refrangibility.''

But no marked progress was made in the knowledge of
radiant heat until **Macedonio Melloni** (1798–1854) [3] began his

[1] Rosenberger, III., p. 67.
[2] S. P. Langley, *Address* before A.A.A.S., 1888, p. 14.
[3] We have taken these dates from Rosenberger. Marie and Larousse
give 1801–1853.

researches. From early boyhood he displayed great love for science. He "was born a physicist," and began to teach physics as soon as he left the school-bench. For seven years he taught at the University of Parma. Political troubles banished him from Italy. In France he found in Arago a good friend. Melloni accepted a professorship in the Department of the Jura, but in 1837 he was permitted to return to his native country, where, in 1839, he was appointed Director of the Cabinet of Arts and Trades in Naples.[1] In 1850 Melloni published a great work, *La Thermochrôse, ou la coloration calorifique,* in which he embodied his researches on radiant energy. In the preface he gives the story of his early passion for nature. The passage is, in part, as follows:

"I was born at Parma, and when I got a holiday used to go into the country the night before, and go to bed early, so as to get up before the dawn. Then I used to steal silently out of the house, and run, with bounding heart, till I got to the top of a little hill, where I used to set myself so as to look toward the east." There, he tells us, he used to wait the rising sun and enjoy the glorious spectacle. "But nothing," he continues, "so rapt my imagination as the bond, so intimate, which unites the phenomena of life to the brilliant star of day," whose beams are accompanied by mysterious heat.[2]

To insure progress in the study of radiant heat it was necessary that the thermometer used by Herschel be superseded by a more delicate instrument. Such a one was the thermo-multiplier,[3] or thermopile, invented by **Leopoldo Nobili** (1784–1835), professor in Florence, and perfected by him and Melloni. One of the results, recognized more or less clearly by W. Herschel, De la Roche, and others, was emphasized by Melloni; viz. that radiant heat is of different kinds, that there is variety among heat rays just as there is variety among the visible rays. The color of heat, as the phenomenon is meta-

[1] J. Lovering's biographic sketch in *Proc. of the Am. Acad. of Arts and Sci.,* Vol. III., 1857, p. 164.

[2] Langley, *op. cit.,* p. 16.

[3] *Poggendorff's Annalen,* Vol. 20, 1830, p. 245; Vol. 24, 1831, p. 640.

phorically called by Melloni, is not perceived by the eye, but can be detected, as can colors of light, by prismatic dispersion or by experiments in which some color varieties are absorbed more than others. Melloni invented the word *thermochrôse*, signifying "heat-color." He arrived at a close realization of the identity of radiant heat and light. In 1843 he said, "Light is merely a series of calorific indications sensible to the organs of sight, or *vice versa*, the radiations of obscure heat are veritable invisible radiations of light." [1] But if it is true that where light is there must be radiant heat, then lunar rays must exhibit heat-effects. He tried the experiment, failed at first, but succeeded afterwards. On Mount Vesuvius, in 1846, by the employment of a polyzonal lens, one metre in diameter, together with a thermopile and galvanometer, he succeeded in getting feeble indications of heat from lunar rays. Melloni made numerous experiments on the absorption of radiant heat by solids and liquids. He coined the word *diathermancy*, which has the same significance for radiant heat that the word *transparency* has for visible light. In his experiments, the radiation from a lamp, or other source, was allowed to pass through the air to the thermopile; the deflection of the galvanometer was then noted. Next, the substance whose diathermancy was to be tested (water, rock-salt, glass, or ice) was placed in the path of the rays directed upon the pile, and the consequent deflection noted. Melloni's tests seemed to show that rock-salt was perfectly transparent to all kinds of calorific rays—a conclusion now known to require some qualification. Ice and glass absorb most of these rays. Melloni demonstrated clearly that different solids and liquids possess different transmissive powers and that (except in rock-salt) the diathermancy varies with the source of the heat. Glass transmits 39% of the radiation from a Locatelli lamp, but only 6% of that from copper at 400° C.

While Melloni measured the diathermancy of different thicknesses of solids and liquids, **John Tyndall** (1820–1893)

[1] Translated by Langley, *op. cit.*, p. 18.

effected the same for gases and vapors. Tyndall was born near Carlow in Ireland. When about twenty-one years old he went to England and attached himself to a Manchester firm of railway engineers. In 1847 he accepted a position as teacher of mathematics and surveying in the newly established Greenwood College, where science was to be taught experimentally. About one year later he went to the University of Marburg to study mathematics, physics, and chemistry. The last study was taken under Bunsen. A strong influence toward physics was exerted upon him by Karl Hermann Knoblauch (1820–1895), who had verified and extended Melloni's work on radiant energy. After graduating in 1850, Tyndall went to Berlin and worked one year in Magnus's laboratory on diamagnetism and magne-crystallic action. After his return to England he delivered, in 1853, a lecture at the Royal Institution which "took his audience by storm." [1] He was elected professor of natural philosophy in the Royal Institution, which had become famous through the labors of Thomas Young, Sir Humphry Davy, and Faraday. It was in the laboratory of that place that Tyndall's subsequent researches were made, except his observations of natural phenomena in the Swiss Alps during his vacations. His most important original work was in the domain of heat. He possessed extraordinary powers of popularizing difficult subjects. Perhaps his greatest services to science are through his books, *Heat a Mode of Motion, Six Lectures on Light* (delivered in America in 1872–1873), *Forms of Water,* etc., which are models of popular exposition.

Melloni had concluded from experiments with his thermo-electric apparatus that, for a distance of 18 or 20 feet, the absorption of radiant heat by atmospheric air is perfectly insensible. Tyndall, with more delicate appliances, verified this

[1] E. Frankland, "John Tyndall," in *Proc. Royal Soc. of London,* Vol. 55, 1894, p. xviii. For Tyndall's celebrated "Prayer-test" see *Contemporary Review,* Vol. 20, 1872, pp. 205–210. The same volume contains replies by *James M'Cosh* and others. Tyndall's "Belfast Address," which, at the time, brought upon him the charge of "infidelity," is given in *Report of British Association,* 1874.

conclusion: dry air is a practical vacuum, as regards the rays of heat. In general, the elementary gases absorb scarcely perceptible amounts of radiant heat. But Tyndall found it different with compound gases; they absorb portions varying directly with the complexity of their molecules. Thus the vapor of ether, having fifteen atoms in one molecule, absorbed for equal volumes at maximum density, 100 times the quantity of radiant heat intercepted by the vapor of carbon disulphide, containing only three atoms. Tyndall found that the radiating powers follow precisely the same order as the powers of absorption. Thus, oxygen, hydrogen, and nitrogen do not radiate heat, while ammonia will show decided effects. The same subject was investigated by H. G. Magnus of Berlin, and the agreement between the two investigators was very close, except in case of aqueous vapor. Magnus found that it had little or no action; Tyndall found it to be considerable for heat rays of low refrangibility. The question is an important one in meteorology. The controversy lasted many years.[1] But in 1881 Tyndall published a paper [2] which finally proved that he was right. At that time Alexander Graham Bell had obtained musical sounds through the action of an intermittent beam of light falling upon solid bodies enclosed in a glass flask. The ear was placed in communication with the interior of the flask by means of a hearing tube. When a beam of light fell upon the substance in the tube, it expanded and a pulse of air was expelled. When the light was cut off, the opposite effect took place. Thus, sound was produced. Bell showed some of these experiments to Tyndall in the laboratory of the Royal Institution, whereupon Tyndall made experiments on flasks filled with different gases.[3] He says that when a flask containing moist air was placed in the intermittent

---

[1] For historic remarks on this point, consult Tyndall, *Contributions to Molecular Physics in the Domain of Radiant Heat,* London, 1872, pp. 59–64.

[2] "Action of an Intermittent Beam of Radiant Heat upon Gaseous Matter," *Proc. Roy. Soc.,* Vol. 31, 1881, p. 307; Nature, Vol. 25, 1882, pp. 232–234.

[3] A. G. Bell, *Upon the Production of Sound by Radiant Energy,* Washington, 1881, p. 19.

beam, "I heard a powerful musical sound produced by the aqueous vapor. I placed the flask in cold water until its temperature was reduced from about 90° to 10° C., fully expecting the same sound would vanish at this temperature; but . . . the sound was distinct and loud. Three empty flasks filled with ordinary air were placed in a freezing mixture. On being rapidly transferred to the intermittent beam, sounds much louder than those obtained from dry air were produced." Thus the aqueous vapor showed absorption, and the controversy was finally ended.

Leslie, Melloni, and Tyndall pointed out an error of wide prevalence regarding the influence of color on absorption. Benjamin Franklin had placed cloths of various colors upon snow and allowed the sun to shine upon them. They absorbed solar rays to different degrees and sank to different depths in the snow. From this Franklin concluded that dark colors were the best absorbers, and light colors the worst. But this generalization requires qualification. Did the radiation from the sun or other luminous body consist exclusively of visible rays, then the problem would be simpler, but the invisible rays often produce effects exactly opposite to what Franklin's theory would lead us to expect. Tyndall coated the bulb of a delicate mercury thermometer with alum (a white powder), and the bulb of a second thermometer with iodine (a dark powder). On exposing the bulbs at the same distance to the radiation from a gas flame, the alum-covered thermometer rose nearly twice as high as the other; alum was a better absorber than iodine. Tyndall says that "radiation from the clothes which cover the human body is not at all, to the extent sometimes supposed, dependent on their color. The color of animal's fur is equally incompetent to influence radiation. These are the conclusions arrived at by Leslie and Melloni *for obscure heat.*" [1]

[1] Tyndall, *Heat a Mode of Motion,* New York, 1897, p. 299,

RADIATION

It is a matter of common knowledge that at moderate temperatures a body gives out radiation which is invisible, the frequency of the undulations being too low to affect the eye. But when the temperature of a solid rises above 525° C. (according to Draper) one sees, as a rule, a dull red. As the temperature rises still higher one might expect to observe at one stage only violet light, that being the light of greatest frequency which is capable of affecting the eye. As a matter of fact, the light we observe is not violet, but white. That is, as the temperature rises, the resulting radiation of greater frequency is accompanied by radiation of lower frequency, the white light being the composite effect of rays from the red to the violet end of the visible spectrum. The question arises, how does the intensity of rays of different frequency change with the rising temperature and which frequency is dominant for a given temperature? In other words, what is the spectral distribution of radiation for different temperatures?

Fundamental questions of radiation were considered early by Pierre Prevost (1751–1839) of Geneva in Switzerland. He held that each body gives off heat radiation and receives such radiation from neighboring bodies. According to this "theory of exchanges," if the temperatures of all bodies are the same, heat is still exchanged between the bodies; each receives as much as it emits. An extension of Prevost's theory of exchanges was made by **Balfour Stewart** (1828–1887) of Edinburgh, who advanced the theorem on the relation of absorption to emission at any constant temperature: "The absorption of a plate equals its radiation, and that for every description of heat." [1] Later Stewart examined the problem of an absorbing and radiating body moving inside of an enclosure, the body and enclosure being initially at the same temperatures throughout. [2] By Doppler's principle the radia-

[1] B. Stewart, *Trans. Roy. Soc. of Edinburgh*, Vol. 22, 1861, p. 13. Stewart's article is dated March 9, 1858.

[2] *Report of British Ass'n for 1871*, London, 1872, Abstracts, p. 45.

tion of the moving body in its front will vibrate more rapidly than the radiation in its rear. The moving body ''is not therefore giving the enclosure those precise rays which it would have given it had it been at the same temperature and at rest. . . . The enclosure is therefore receiving one set of rays and giving out another,'' hence parts of the enclosure will not all remain at the same temperature. We can use these particles of different temperature for transmitting heat into the energy of mechanical motion, just as in a steam-engine. The result is an increase in the amount of mechanical energy within the enclosure, which is impossible,—unless we acknowledge the possibility of perpetual motion. ''It is not, therefore, allowable to suppose that in such an enclosure the moving body continues to retain all its energy of motion, and consequently such a body will have its energy of motion gradually stopped.'' Stewart concluded that we should expect some loss of mechanical energy in the case of celestial bodies approaching or receding from each other. Since the advance of Maxwell's electromagnetic theory, the solution of Stewart's paradox would be approached by the consideration also of the pressure exerted by radiation. With the aid of very light mirrors in a vacuum it was proved in 1901 by the Russian physicist **Peter N. Lebedev** (1866–1911)[1] and by the American physicists **Ernest Fox Nichols** (1870–1924)[2] and G. F. Hull, that a light wave exerts pressure, as was predicted from the electromagnetic theory of light. Lebedev and others applied this result to the explanation of the bending away from the sun of comet tails, when the comet is near the sun. In that case the light pressure exceeds gravitational attraction.

Stewart's papers received no attention on the European continent. There the researches of Kirchhoff played a leading rôle. About the same time as Stewart, he reached the conclusion ''that for radiation of the same wave-length at the

[1] P. Lebedev, *Annal d. Phys.*, 4. S., Vol. 6, 1901, p. 433; Vol. 32, 1910, p. 411.
[2] E. T. Nichols and G. F. Hull, *Phys. Rev.*, Vol. 13, 1901, p. 307; *Astrophys. Jour.*, Vol. 15, 1902, p. 62.

same temperature, the ratio of the emission and the absorption powers is the same for all bodies."[1]   He published important results during 1860–1862.   In general, when radiation falls upon bodies, it is partly reflected, partly transmitted, and partly absorbed.   The case of complete absorption proved to be of special theoretical interest.   Kirchhoff defined a perfectly "black body" as one which at all temperatures completely absorbed all heat radiation falling upon it.   Lamp black does not quite satisfy the requirements of this hypothetical body.   Kirchhoff recognized that the powers of emission and absorption of any one body are functions only of the absolute temperature T and the wave-length λ.   If we designate the emission by $e\ (\lambda\ T)$ and the absorption by $a\ (\lambda\ T)$, then for any two bodies we have the ratio $e\ (\lambda\ T)/a\ (\lambda\ T) = e_1\ (\lambda\ T)/a_1\ (\lambda\ T)$, where e_1 and a_1 refer to the second body. For "black bodies," $a\ (\lambda\ T) = a_1\ (\lambda\ T) = 1$, hence $e\ (\lambda\ T) = e_1\ (\lambda\ T)$.   That is, for all "black bodies" the power of heat emission is one and the same function of λ and T, and is independent of the material of the black body.   Since the ratio of emission to absorption is the same for any two bodies, we may take one of them to be a "black body," for which the absorption is by definition complete or unity.   We see therefore that the ratio of the emission to the absorption of *any body* is the same function of λ and T as is the emission of a "black body." Therefore, if it is experimentally possible to realize the conditions of a "black body," Kirchhoff's theoretical result suggests the possibility of experimentation by which some light may be expected as to the nature of this function of λ and T — this "world function" as it has been called.

As to the experimental realization of a "black body," Kirchhoff entertained an idea akin to that of Stewart.   Kirchhoff suggested a closed box with black walls inside, kept at a constant temperature, T, and having a very small opening through which radiation may pass from the inside to the outside.   This radiation is shown on theoretical grounds to be

[1] *Monatsber. d. Acad. der Wissensch. zu Berlin,* Dec. 1859, p. 783.

the same as that of a hypothetical "black body." In the spectrum of this radiation the nature of the relation between λ and T can be studied experimentally. But many years passed before the laboratory technique was sufficiently developed.

Important experimental contributions to our knowledge of radiant energy were made by **Samuel Pierpont Langley** (1834–1906). He was born at Roxbury, Boston, studied architecture and civil engineering, and after two years spent abroad, in 1865 became assistant in the Harvard Observatory; later he became assistant professor of Mathematics in the Naval Observatory, and in 1867 director of the Allegheny Observatory. From 1887 until his death he served as secretary of the Smithsonian Institution in Washington. He was a very reserved and a lonely man, without family ties. His work on the sun grew out of a childish interest in the great center of our system, upon which life on this planet depends.

To make marked progress in the study of radiation it seemed necessary to invent a more delicate instrument than the thermopile of Melloni and Tyndall. Langley's new device was the bolometer, first described in 1881.[1] It may be described as a delicate Wheatstone's bridge for measuring differences in temperature. A very fine strip of platinum (at first iron was used) serves as a conducting wire in a circuit. If radiation falls upon it, its temperature is raised and its electric resistance increased. A delicate galvanometer records the resulting disturbance in the electric current. The bolometer has been made to indicate a change of temperature of .0000001 of a degree centigrade. Some of its first results were to show that the maximum heat in the solar spectrum was in the orange, not in the infra-red, as claimed by W. Herschel and others. The earlier observers had used the prismatic spectrum, which is subject to two important errors: (1) the prism absorbs part of the radiation, exercising so-called "selective absorption"; (2) the prism concentrates the rays in the lower part of the spectrum as compared with the upper,

[1] *Am. Jour. Sci.* (3) Vol. 21, pp. 187–198. A later form of it is described in the same journal, (4) Vol. 5, 1898, pp. 241–245.

thus falsifying the true distribution of heat. These errors are avoided by the use of a grating, which yields a "normal spectrum." For many years the belief (unsupported by experiment) was prevalent that our atmosphere acted exactly the part of glass in a hot-bed, and that it kept the planet warm by absorbing the *infra-red* rays radiated by the earth. Langley proved experimentally that this was not true. The infrared rays pass through with comparative ease. His experiments at Allegheny City, continued in 1881 on the crest of Mount Whitney in the Sierra Nevadas,[1] showed that the atmosphere acts "with selective absorption to an unanticipated degree, keeping back an immense proportion of the blue and green." The atmosphere not only keeps back a part of the solar radiation, but totally changes its composition in doing so. By taking out more of the blue and green, the residue coming down to us produces the sensation of what is familiarly known as "white" light, so that "white" is *not* the sum of all the radiation from the sun. Could we rise above the earth's atmosphere, then the sun would appear to us greenish blue. The pure original sunlight is no more like the radiation falling upon the earth's surface than the electric light is like that which reaches the eye through reddish glasses.

Assisted by Frank Washington Very (1852–1927), Langley experimented on the temperature of the moon.[2] The bolometer "gave indications of two maxima in the heat-curve, the first corresponding to the heat from the solar reflected rays, the second (indefinitely lower down in the spectrum) corresponding to a greater amount of radiant heat emitted from a source at a far lower temperature," viz. from the surface of the moon itself. The mean temperature of the sunlit lunar soil "is most probably not greatly above zero centigrade." The determination is founded on the fact, experimentally established by Langley, "that the position of the maximum in

[1] *Am. Jour. Sci.* (3), Vol. 25, 1883, pp. 169–196.
[2] *Am. Jour. Sci.*, Vol. 38, 1889, pp. 421–440. This is only in abstract. The full memoir appeared in *Memoirs of the National Acad. of Sciences,* Vol. IV.

a curve, representing invisible radiant heat, furnishes a reliable criterion as to the temperature of the radiating (solid) body.''

By the study of the radiation of the fire-fly, Langley and Very showed [1] ''that it is possible to produce light without heat, other than that in the light itself; that this is actually effected now by nature's processes''; ''that nature produces this cheapest light at about one four-hundredth part of the cost of the energy which is expended in the candle-flame, and at but an insignificant fraction of the cost of the electric light.''

Langley demonstrated that the visual effect produced by any given constant amount of energy varies enormously according to the color of the light in question. For the same color, it varies with eyes of different individuals. The sensation of crimson light ordinarily requires that the energy of the waves arrested by the retina, during the act of perception, be about .001 of an erg, while the sensation of green can be produced by .000,000,01 of an erg. In other words, about 100,000 times the energy is demanded to make us see red that is needed to make us see green. [2]

Langley explored widely the infra-red region of the solar spectrum. J. W. Draper had, in his photograph of 1842, observed three wide bands in this region. The same were noticed by Foucault and Fizeau in 1846. Captain W. de W. Abney (1844–1920) in 1880 mapped by photography the infra-red prismatic spectrum as far as 1.075μ. Langley got heating effects of more than twice that wave-length; his delicate filament of platinum groping its way down to nearly 3μ, that is, nearly to rays of .003 mm. wave-length. At this place solar heat seemed to be abruptly cut off. The visible part of the solar spectrum extends from about the line $H = .39\mu$ to $A = 76\mu$; the invisible spectrum, as explored by Langley, reaches from $.76\mu$ to nearly 3μ. Langley studied also invisible infra-red radiations from terrestrial sources, and learned with certainty

[1] *Am. Jour. Sci.* (3), Vol. 40, 1890, pp. 97–113.
[2] Langley, *Phil. Mag.*, Vol. 27, 1889, p. 23.

of wave-lengths greater than .005 mm., and had grounds for estimating that he had recognized radiations whose wave-length exceeds .03 mm., so that, while he directly measured nearly eight times the wave-length known to Newton, he had probable indications of wave-lengths much greater.[1] In place of the bolometer, H. Rubens (1865–1922) and E. F. Nichols used a modified form of Crookes's radiometer. They isolated and identified rays from hot zirconia of .05 mm. wave-length.[2] These are about 1/100 the length to the shortest Hertzian waves. Thus, homogeneous radiation of nearly every wave-length from Hertzian waves, several kilometers long, down to ultra-violet rays, less than .0002 mm., was definitely known.

The ultra-violet rays in the solar spectrum, the existence of which was discovered by Ritter and Wollaston, were studied by Biot, who found that the absorptive power of glass, rock-salt, and quartz for these rays is independent of their absorptive power for visible rays. A. C. Becquerel showed that quartz is especially transparent to these rays; even a dark piece will let more through than a clear pane of glass. The ultra-violet region has been studied both for solar and artificial radiation. Franz Exner and E. Haschek, using a Rowland grating, in 1896 studied the spark spectra of eleven metals by photography, and took measurements on more than 19,000 ultra-violet lines.[3]

Curious observations have been made on "anomalous dispersion." The existence of this phenomenon was first discovered by Fox Talbot about 1840. The term was invented in 1862 by Le Roux,[4] who noticed that the vapor of iodine absorbs the middle part of the visible spectrum; and that, as compared with other bodies, it refracts the blue to a less degree than the red. In 1870 C. Christiansen (1843–1917) saw that a hollow glass prism filled with a solution of fuchsine

[1] *Am. Jour. Sci.* (3), Vol. 32, 1886, p. 24.
[2] *Physical Review*, Vol. IV., 1897, pp. 314–323.
[3] *Sitzungsberichte d. K. Akad. d. W. Wien*, Vol. 105, pp. 389–436, 503–574, 707–740; *Astrophys. Jour.*, Vol. 5, 1897, p. 290.
[4] *Compt. Rend.*, Vol. 55, p. 126.

gave the order of the colors, violet, red, yellow, instead of red, yellow, violet. **August Kundt** (1839–1894), professor at Würzburg, after 1888 professor in Berlin, described a similar behavior in cyan, mauve anilin, anilin blue and other substances [1] whose color by reflection is different from their color by transmission. His observations were not confined to substances in the liquid state. In 1880 he accidentally discovered anomalous dispersion in the vapor of sodium. In the dispersion, caused by very thin films of certain metals, Kundt noticed a strange fact. In gold, silver, and copper the ray was bent away from the normal, on passing from air into the film; that is, the index of refraction turned out to be less than unity. For gold and copper the red ray was bent further from the normal than the blue ray. For platinum, iron, nickel, bismuth, the index was greater than unity, and in each case greater for the red light than the blue, showing that the red was deviated further toward the perpendicular than the blue. The preparation of the metallic prisms of very small angle and of sufficient transparency for these experiments was effected by electrolytic deposition upon platinized glass. This work occupied two years, and the small number of usable prisms was chosen out of more than 2000 made. The velocity of light in these metals stands in close relationship to their power of conducting electricity and heat; the greatest velocity being through the best conductors.[2] The phenomena of anomalous dispersion play an important rôle in modern theories of dispersion, advanced by Ketteler (1836–1900), Helmholtz, and others.

The nomenclature of the subject of radiant energy is in need of revision. The expression "radiant heat" is still much used; but the term is self-contradictory, if by heat we mean a form of energy due to molecular motion in ponderable matter. Where there are no molecules there can be no heat. The phenomena of "radiant heat" do not belong to the

[1] *Poggendorff's Annalen,* Vol. 142, p. 163; Vol. 143, pp. 149, 259; Vol. 144, p. 128; Vol. 145, pp. 67, 164.
[2] Kundt, *Phil. Mag.* (5), Vol. 26, 1888, p. 2.

science of heat at all, unless we resort to the objectionable course of attaching a double meaning to the word "heat" by allowing it to designate a form of energy due to ethereal waves as well as that due to molecular agitation. The terms "diathermanous" and "athermanous" are ill chosen, because they etymologically refer to thermic or heat phenomena, when really we are dealing with ether-waves.[1]

PHOTOGRAPHY IN COLORS

The problem of photography in natural colors is as old as photography itself. The first efforts at solution were by the chemical method. The trials which are best known are those made by Edmond Becquerel, who succeeded in obtaining upon a silver plate covered with a film of violet subchloride of silver the impression of all the colors of the solar spectrum. But they vanished as soon as they were exposed to the light.[2]

In the second method of color photography three separate colorless negatives are taken of an object by light passing through three differently colored screens. From these, three colorless positives are made. Then each positive is dyed with the color corresponding to the light used in obtaining its negative. On superimposing the colored positives and viewing them by transmitted light, the object photographed is seen in its natural colors. This process was suggested by Clerk Maxwell as a natural deduction of Young's theory of vision which made red, green and violet the fundamental colors perceived by the retina. It was employed in France by Charles Cros and at the same time (1869) by Ducos du Hauron. The Germans claim the priority of the idea for Baron Bonstetten. The process has been improved by J. Joly.[3]

The third method, due to interference of light, was published by **G. Lippmann** (1846–1921) of Paris.[4] A transparent

[1] The Nomenclature of radiant energy is discussed in *Nature,* Vol. 49, 1893, pp. 100, 149, 389.

[2] L. Weiller in *Pop. Sci. Monthly,* Vol. 45, 1894, p. 539.

[3] *Nature,* Vol. 53, 1896, p. 617; consult E. J. Wall, *The History of Three-Color Photography,* Boston, 1925.

[4] *Nature,* Vol. 53, pp. 617, 618.

photographic film is placed in contact with a layer of mercury. The light reflected from the mercury interferes with the incident light so as to form standing waves in the film. In this way the film is divided into a number of thin, equidistant strata, parallel to the surface of the glass. The distance between these layers is half the wave-length of the incident light. They act as reflecting surfaces, and appear colored when viewed at the proper angle. Thus, if the strata at any point are formed by violet light, they will reflect only violet light. It is interesting to notice that Lippmann was led to these experiments through an effort to transport into the domain of light the acoustic property of an organ-pipe, according to which the fundamental pitch which it gives forth depends only upon its length.

A WAVE-LENGTH AS A STANDARD OF LENGTH

The unique idea of adopting the wave-length of some particular ray of light as a "standard of length" was first advanced in 1829 by the Frenchman Jacques Babinet (1794–1872).[1] The wave-lengths of light were assumed to be of constant value. The first attempt to carry out this plan was made by C. S. Peirce, in conjunction with Rutherfurd.[2] The scheme approached more nearly to a practical realization in the hands of A. A. Michelson and Edward W. Morley, who in 1887 suggested the wave-length of sodium light as the standard and explained their inferential comparator for determining the length of the metre in terms of the wave-length.[3] Later a green mercury ray was tried in place of the sodium light.[4] In 1892 Michelson, by invitation, took his apparatus from Clark University to Paris, for the purpose of instituting a comparison of the length of the new international metre, with the wave-lengths of the red cadmium line which was found to be preferable to others on account of its great homo-

[1] Rosenberger, III., p. 193.
[2] *Nature*, Vol. 20, 1879, p. 99.
[3] *Am. Jour. Sci.*, Vol. 34, 1887, pp. 427–430.
[4] *Am. Jour. Sci.*, Vol. 38, 1889, p. 181.

geneity. This delicate undertaking was carried out in the Pavillon de Breteuil.[1] Thus the fundamental unit of the metric system was compared "with a natural unit with the same degree of approximation as that which obtains in the comparison of two standard metres. This natural unit depends only on the properties of the vibrating atoms and of the universal ether; it is thus, in all probability, one of the most constant dimensions in all nature." Michelson found the red cadmium line to be 6438.4722 Å at 15° C. and 760 mm. atmospheric pressure; in 1907 the French physicists R. Benoit, Ch. Fabry, A. Perot found it to be 6438.4696 Å.

The Human Eye

Once there was a wide-spread conviction that the human eye was an optical instrument of such great perfection that none formed by human hands could rival it. Actual examination of the action of the eye, carried on mainly by Helmholtz, brought about a change in these views. Says he, "Now it is not too much to say that if an optician wanted to sell me an instrument which had all these defects, I should think myself quite justified in blaming his carelessness in the strongest terms, and giving him back his instrument."[2] This statement is supported by passages like the following:[3] "A refracting surface which is imperfectly elliptical, an ill-centred telescope, does not give a single illuminated point as the image of a star, but according to the surface and arrangement of the refracting media, elliptic, circular, or linear images. Now the images of an illuminated point, as the human eye brings them to focus, are even more inaccurate: they are irregularly radiated. The reason of this lies in the construction of the crystalline lens, the fibres of which are arranged around six diverging axes, so that the rays which we see around stars and

[1] *Compt. Rend.*, Vol. 116, 1893, pp. 790–794; *Astronomy and Astro-Physics*, Vol. XII., 1893, pp. 556–560.
[2] H. Helmholtz, *Popular Lectures*, trans. by E. Atkinson, London, 1873, p. 219.
[3] *Ibidem*, p. 218.

other distant lights are images of the radiated structure of our lens; and the universality of this optical defect is proved by any figure with diverging rays, being called 'star-shaped.' It is from the same cause that the moon, while her crescent is still narrow, appears to many persons double or threefold.'' The mechanism by which the eye accommodates itself to viewing objects at various distances was a great riddle until the French surgeon, Louis Joseph Sanson, first observed very faint reflection of light through the pupil from the two surfaces of the crystalline lens. Max Lagenbeck found that this reflection altered during the act of accommodation. Helmholtz and others, by these alterations, studied the changes of the lens, and arrived at the conclusion that the eye adjusts itself by the contraction of the ciliary muscle, causing the tension of the lens to be diminished and its surfaces (chiefly the front one) to become more convex than when the eye is at rest, the images of near objects being thus brought to a focus on the retina.[1]

Helmholtz irreverently disclosed the fact that in blue eyes there is no real blue coloring matter whatever; the deepest blue is nothing but a turbid medium. The optic action is the same as in case of smoke which appears blue on a dark background, though the particles themselves are not blue; or in case of the sky, which, according to Newton, Stokes and Rayleigh,[2] looks blue through the agency of extremely fine dust suspended in the air.[3] This dust, when illuminated by sunlight, reflects a greater proportion of the shorter waves of bluish light and transmits a greater proportion of longer waves of reddish light.

Helmholtz and Maxwell experimented on the effects produced by mixing colors. That a mixture of yellow and blue

[1] H. Helmholtz, *Popular Lectures,* trans. by E. Atkinson, London, 1873, p. 205.

[2] *Phil. Mag.,* Vol. 41, pp. 107, 275.

[3] James Dewar attributes the blueness of the sky to the oxygen in the air; liquefied oxygen is blue.

light produces gray and not green was probably first pointed out by James D. Forbes.[1]

THEORIES AND EXPERIMENTS RELATING TO THE LUMINIFEROUS ETHER

The great majority of nineteenth century physicists since the time of Fresnel were more confident of the existence of the luminiferous ether than of matter. And yet difficulties were encountered in postulating properties which were consistent. To explain polarization of light, Fresnel and Young were driven to the assumption that light waves have vibrations transverse to the direction of propagation, and this in turn necessitated an ether that was an elastic solid, for an elastic fluid like air would admit of only longitudinal vibrations. But if this ether is an elastic solid, how can the planets move through it without hindrance? Do the planets slacken in their revolutions? Many centuries of astronomical observation show no sign of such retardation. Stokes and Kelvin offered the explanation that ether was like shoemaker's wax, which would vibrate under a sharp blow, yet would be plastic and permit slow motions of a heavy solid through it. At one time, visitors to Kelvin's lecture room at Glasgow were shown the shoemaker's wax experiment, in which the lead bullets from above and the wooden cubes from below were working their way through as he conceived that the earth ploughs through

[1] Campbell and Garnett, *The Life of James Clerk Maxwell*, London, 1882, p. 214. Maxwell "was fond of insisting, to his female cousins, aunts, etc., on the truth that blue and yellow do not make green. I remember his explaining to me [L. Campbell] the difference between pigments and colors" (p. 198). While Maxwell sometimes mixed colors by rotation, he usually used a "color-box" which he perfected in 1862. "A beam of sunlight is to be divided into colors by a prism, certain colors selected by a screen with slits. These gathered by a lens, and restored to the form of a beam by another prism, and then viewed by the eye directly" (p. 334). While he was professor at King's College, he resided at 8, Palace Gardens Terrace, Kensington, "where he carried on many of his experiments in a large garret which ran the whole length of the house. When experimenting at the window with the color-box (which was painted black, and nearly eight feet long), he excited the wonder of his neighbors, who thought him mad to spend so many hours in staring into a coffin" (p. 318).

the ether.[1] To explain Bradley's aberration of light, Fresnel assumed that the telescope moves with the earth through space without disturbing the ether and the wave motion in it. Likewise in explaining the diminution of light velocity in a dense medium, Fresnel assumed that the ether is at rest in free space and in opaque bodies, while in the interior of moving transparent bodies it moves with a velocity of the body in the ratio $(n^2 - 1)/n^2$, where n is the index of refraction. But if the ether is not moved in the least by dark bodies passing through it, how can a light wave cause molecular motion called heat, and how can molecular motion set up vibrations in the ether? In 1845 George Gabriel Stokes (1819–1903) of Cambridge, England, modified the hypothesis by assuming that the ether close to the surface of the earth is completely dragged along by the earth, while higher up it is only partially dragged, and "at no great distance, it is at rest in space."[2] Stokes' theory produced a turbulent ether which was not very successful in explaining Bradley's aberration of light and the rectilinear path of vertical rays. H A. Lorentz expressed to Lord Rayleigh his dissent, "The conditions which Mr. Stokes has imposed on the movement of the ether being irreconcilable to each other."[3] All in all, physicists preferred a free ether which was not dragged along by moving bodies. However, in 1881 A. A. Michelson undertook to test by direct experiment, whether the ether was stationary or not. At the time he was in Germany, and the trial was made at the Physical Institute in Berlin, then for greater quiet in a cellar at the Astrophysikalische Observatorium in Potsdam. No ether drift was noticed. But the experiment was inconclusive and its mathematical treatment needed correction. Lord Rayleigh was among the few interested, and wrote to Michelson, urging further experimentation. On March 6, 1887, Michelson replied from Cleveland,

[1] *Science*, Vol. 60, 1924, p. 150.
[2] G. G. Stokes, *Phil. Mag.*, 3. S., Vol. 27, 1845, p. 9–15.
[3] *J. W. Strutt, Third Baron Rayleigh*, by his son, R. J. Strutt, Fourth Baron Rayleigh, London, 1924, p. 346.

Ohio: "I have never been fully satisfied with my Potsdam experiment, even taking into account the correction which H. A. Lorentz points out. . . . I have repeatedly tried to interest my scientific friends in this experiment without avail, and the reason for my never publishing the correction was (I am ashamed to confess it) that I was discouraged at the slight attention the work received, and did not think it worth while. Your letter has however once more fired my enthusiasm and has decided me to begin the work at once." [1]

In 1887, Michelson, and Edward Williams Morley (1838–1923) professor of chemistry at Western Reserve University, performed at the Case School of Applied Science at Cleveland, Ohio, the now famous experiment [2] which, according to the interpretation given at that time, indicated that the earth drags the ether with it completely or almost completely, that "considering the motion of the earth in its orbit only," the relative motion of the earth and the ether is probably less than one-sixth of the earth's orbital velocity and certainly less than one-fourth." The experiment caused consternation among the physicists. Glazebrook in 1896 exclaimed, "We are still waiting for a second Newton to give us a theory of the ether which shall include the facts of electricity and magnetism, luminous radiation, and it may be gravitation." [3] Kelvin [4] in 1900 spoke of "two clouds" obscuring "the beauty and clearness of the dynamical theory which asserts light and heat to be modes of motion." One of the clouds was the unexplained Michelson and Morley experiment.

HEAT

CALORIC THEORY

The first prominent physicist who endeavored to overthrow the caloric theory of heat was **Benjamin Thompson, Count**

[1] *Loc. cit.,* p. 343.
[2] A. A. Michelson and E. W. Morley, *Silliman's Jour.* 3. S., Vol. 34, 1887, p. 333.
[3] R. T. Glazebrook, *James Clerk Maxwell,* New York, 1896, p. 221.
[4] Kelvin, *Phil. Mag.,* 6. S., Vol. 2, 1901, p. 1, 2.

Rumford (1753–1814).[1] He was born at North Woburn in a humble New England home, within two miles of the native place of another great Benjamin,—Franklin. These men never met, but both achieved great things in physical investigation. In Benjamin Thompson a taste for research displayed itself early. An old note-book of his contains the entry: "An account of what work I have done towards getting an Electrical Machine. Two or three days' work making wheels. One half day's work making pattern for small Conductor. Making pattern for Electrometer." At one time he walked eight miles from Woburn to Cambridge to attend the lectures on natural philosophy of Professor John Winthrop at Harvard College.[2] At the age of nineteen he taught school in the district at Wilmington. At the outbreak of the War of the Revolution Thompson seemed to favor the Tory party; he was viewed with suspicion as being an enemy to his country; was arrested and confined in Woburn. Yet no positive and direct evidence has ever been found of any unfriendly act done by Thompson, or even of any speech of such a character attributed to him.[3] At the age of twenty-two, Thompson fled to England, leaving behind him a wife and daughter. As far as known he never even wrote to his wife. In this prominent scientist, "the life of the intellect appeared to have interfered with the life of the affections." For a time he participated in the war on the side of the British.

In 1777 he began his career as an experimental scientist by a research on the cohesive strength of different substances. The following year he was admitted as a fellow of the Royal Society. Having a strong predilection for a military life, he left England in 1783 to serve with the Austrians in a war then meditated against the Turks. As war did not break out, he

[1] G. E. Ellis, *Memoir of Sir Benjamin Thompson, Count Rumford*, with notices of his daughter, published in connection with an edition of Rumford's complete works, by the American Academy of Arts and Sciences, Boston.

[2] It was as a grateful return for the favors he had thus enjoyed at the college that Count Rumford later gave to it the endowment which founded the professorship that bears his name. *Ibidem*, p. 36.

[3] *Memoir of Sir Benjamin Thompson, Count Rumford*, p. 58.

entered into the service of the Elector of Bavaria, who, in 1790 made him a count. He established houses of industry, schools of industry, founded a military academy at Munich, and at the same time continued his physical researches.[1] On the death of the elector, in 1799, Rumford went to London, where he founded the *Royal Institution* for the diffusion of a knowledge of applied science. It is pleasant to contemplate that, while the Royal Institution was founded by an American, the *Smithsonian Institution,* in Washington, owes its origin to an Englishman. In 1803 Rumford went to France, and married the widow of the chemist Lavoisier. A divorce soon followed. He died at Auteuil, near Paris.

Of his various experiments, the ones on the source of heat excited by friction, published in 1798, are of the greatest interest. While engaged at Munich in the boring of cannon, he was surprised at the heat generated. Whence comes this heat? What is its nature? He arranged apparatus so that the heat generated by the friction of a blunt steel borer raised the temperature of a quantity of water. In his third experiment,[2] water rose in one hour to 107° F.; in one hour and a half to 142°; "at the end of two hours and thirty minutes the water *actually boiled!*" "It is difficult to describe the surprise and astonishment, says Rumford, "expressed in the countenances of the bystanders, on seeing so large a quantity of cold water (18¾ pounds) heated, and actually made to boil, without any fire . . . yet I acknowledge fairly that it afforded me a degree of childish pleasure, which, were I ambitious of the reputation of a *grave philosopher,* I ought most certainly rather to hide than to discover." The source of heat generated by friction "appeared evidently to be *inexhaustible.*" The reasoning by which he concluded that heat was not matter,

---

[1] "His labors in the production of cheap and nutritious food necessarily directed Rumford's attention to fireplaces and chimney flues. When he published his *Essays* [1795–1800, 4 volumes], in London, he reported that he had not less than 500 smoky chimneys on his hands."— John Tyndall, *New Fragments,* New York, 1892, p. 123.

[2] *The Complete Works of Count Rumford,* published by the American Academy of Arts and Sciences, Boston, Vol. I., pp. 481–488.

but was due to motion, is not regarded as absolutely conclusive. It was not based sufficiently on exact measurement. He says, "It is hardly necessary to add, that anything which any *insulated* body, or system of bodies, can continue to furnish *without limitation,* cannot possibly be *a material substance;* and it appears to me to be extremely difficult, if not quite impossible, to form any distinct idea of anything capable of being excited and communicated in the manner in which heat was excited and communicated in these experiments, except it be *motion.*"

In 1804 Rumford wrote in a letter to Marc Auguste Pictet, of Geneva, "I am persuaded that I shall live a sufficient long time to have the satisfaction of seeing caloric interred with phlogiston in the same tomb." This hope was hardly realized. For nearly half a century later the large majority of physicists and chemists continued in the belief that heat was a substance.

Rumford himself felt that, in his experiments on heat from friction, he was less thorough in his quantitative than in his qualitative work. He says that no estimate was made of the heat accumulated in the wooden box holding the water, nor of that dispersed during the experiment. From Rumford's data we may make a rough estimate of the dynamical equivalent of heat. He estimated the thermal capacity of the water and metal as the equivalent to that of 26.58 pounds of water. Enough heat could be generated in $2\frac{1}{2}$ hours, by the use of one horse, to raise the temperature from 33° to 212° F. Hence, the rate of increase in temperature was 1.2° per minute; the number of calories of heat generated per minute was 1.2×26.58, or 31.92, which must be equivalent to one horsepower, or 33,000 foot-pounds per minute. Hence one calorie, using Fahrenheit degrees, is equivalent to 1034 foot-pounds. Joule's estimate was 772 foot-pounds.

Rumford's conclusion regarding the nature of heat was vigorously attacked by the calorists, but it was thoroughly confirmed in 1799 by Sir Humphry Davy.[1] By means of

[1] Davy's *Complete Works,* Vol. II., p. 11.

clockwork he produced friction between two metals (between wheel and plate) in the vacuum of an air pump. Wax on the plate melted, although the temperature of the receiver was kept below the freezing-point. He also melted ice by friction in the open, when the surrounding temperature was below freezing. From this he concluded that friction causes vibration of the corpuscles of bodies, and this vibration is heat. However, he was not so confident of the correctness of this view as Rumford, and it was not till 1812 that he felt sure in asserting that "the immediate cause of the phenomenon of heat is motion, and the laws of its communication are precisely the same as the laws of the communication of motion."[1] Arguing from Rumford's experiments, a refutation of the caloric theory was given in 1807 by Thomas Young in his *Natural Philosophy*. But Rumford, Davy, and Young made, at the time, but few converts.[2]

EXACT THERMOMETRY

An important observation bearing on exact thermometry was announced in 1822 by Flaugergues,[3] who observed the gradual change of the zero point of mercury in glass thermometers. Glass does not immediately return to its original volume on cooling from a high temperature. In course of time the capacity of the bulb diminishes a little, rather rapidly at first, and then very slowly for years afterwards. This property has been the source of an untold amount of annoyance to persons aiming to secure very accurate determinations of temperature. Joule examined the "zero reading" of a delicate thermometer at intervals over a period of thirty-eight years, with the following results: April, 1844, 0° F.; February, 1846, .42°; January, 1848, .51°; April, 1848, .53°; February, 1853, .68°; April, 1856, .73°; December, 1860, .86°; March, 1867, .90°; February, 1870, .93°; Febru-

---

[1] Davy, *Elements of Chemical Philosophy*, p. 94.
[2] For details consult G. Berthold, *Rumford und d. Mechanische Wärmetheorie*, Heidelberg, 1875.
[3] *Ann. de Chimie et de Physique*, Vol. 21, p. 333.

ary, 1873, .94° ; January, 1877, .978° ; November, 1879, .994° ; December, 1882, 1.020°.[1] Researches on glass, carried out in Europe, resulted in the discovery of a material free from many of the objections to ordinary glass, and the accuracy of mercury thermometers was increased fivefold.[2] Wiebe and Schott of Jena have shown that glass containing either sodium or potassium, but not both, gives the least displacement of the zero.[3]

Platinum thermometers came to be recommended for accurate research.[4] They were made by welding a coil of fine platinum wire to leads of relatively low electric resistance. The coil and leads must be suitably insulated and supported. It is an improved form of William Siemens's electrical pyrometer. The platinum thermometer shows comparative freedom from change of zero. It indicates temperature by its change of electrical resistance, which is always very nearly the same at the same temperature.[5]

The first careful comparison of the mercury thermometer with the air thermometer was made in 1815 by Dulong and Petit.[6] They assumed that mercury thermometers agreed among themselves, so that a table of corrections carefully prepared for one mercury thermometer was applicable to all. That this is not the case was shown by Regnault.[7] Not only have different kinds of glass different coefficients of expansion, but they have different laws of expansion. More than this, I. Pierre [8] showed that two mercury thermometers, made

[1] Joule, *Scientific Papers*, p. 558.

[2] *Nature*, Vol. 55, 1897, p. 368.

[3] *Nature*, Vol. 52, 1895, p. 87.

[4] H. L. Callendar, *Phil. Mag.* (5), Vol. 32, 1891; E. H. Griffiths, *Science Progress*, Vol. II., 1894–1895, article, "The Measurement of Temperature."

[5] For detailed information, consult "Metals at High Temperatures," *Nature*, Vol. 45, 1892, pp. 534–540; "Long-range Temperature and Pressure Variables in Physics," *Science*, N. S., Vol. VI., 1897, pp. 338–356.

[6] *Ann. de Chimie et de Physique*, Vol. 2, 1815, pp. 240–254; reprinted in Ostwald's Klass., No. 44, pp. 31–40.

[7] *Ann. de Chimie et de Physique* (3), Vol. 5, p. 83; *Ostwald's Klass.* No. 44, pp. 164–181.

[8] *Ann. de Chimie et de Physique* (3), Vol. 5, 1842, p. 427.

of the same piece of glass with equal care, did not agree exactly with each other. Regnault showed that, between 0° and 100° C., the air thermometer and the mercury thermometer of ordinary soft glass agree very closely, though at about the middle of the scale the air thermometer lags behind the other by about .2°. Above 250° C. the mercury thermometer reads considerably higher; at 300° the difference is 1°; at 350° it is 3°. Olszewski showed that in low temperatures hydrogen thermometers are still quite reliable; at — 220° C. their error is not more than 1°. Among the most careful measurements on exact thermometry were those carried on in connection with determinations of the mechanical equivalent of heat, by Rowland and others.

Considerable confusion existed at one time in the minds of leading physicists, and still exists in some of our text-books, on the subject of temperature. It was stated as a merit of the mercurial thermometer that mercury "expands uniformly," or of the air thermometer that air "expands uniformly" or "expands nearly uniformly," and yet no standard of reference was given by which this uniformity was supposed to have been established. As a matter of fact, we may take any substance as a standard and then define equal increments of temperature as those which give equal increments of that substance. But, if mercury be so taken, then the assertion that mercury expands "uniformly" is destitute of good sense. Mercury gives us an arbitrary scale of temperature differing, probably, from every other similar scale. Air does not expand quite uniformly, if mercury is the arbitrary standard, and vice versa. One of the first to possess clear notions on this subject was Lord Kelvin, who, in 1848, established the "absolute thermodynamic scale" of temperature,[1] which is independent of the particular properties of any particular substance and, therefore, constitutes a much more satisfactory foundation for

[1] William Thomson, *Proc. Cambridge Phil. Soc.*, 1848. Consult also his article "Heat" in *Encycl. Brit.*, 9th ed. For a "Kritik des Temperaturbegriffes," see Mach, *Principien d. Wärmelehre*, Leipzig, 1896, pp. 39–57.

thermometry than any arbitrary scale. It is now our ultimate scale of reference. The air thermometer gives indications agreeing very closely with the absolute thermodynamic scale.

Mathematical Theory of the Flow of Heat

The propagation of heat in solid bodies was investigated mathematically by **Joseph Fourier** (1768–1830), who published, in 1822, a work entitled *La Théorie Analytique de la Chaleur*, which not only marked an epoch in the history of mathematical physics, but stimulated experimental inquiry. Fourier assumed the conductivity of a substance for heat to be constant for all temperatures. But **James David Forbes** (1809–1868), professor at Edinburgh, showed that this is not true, that from 0° to 100° the conductivity of iron diminishes 15.9%; of copper, 24.5%. He noticed at the same time that there was an accompanying decrease in electric conductivity.

Laws of Gases. Balloon Ascensions

At the beginning of the nineteenth century, the laws of gases were diligently studied. Amontons had arrived at an approximate value for the coefficient of expansion of air under constant pressure, but the measurements made by about twenty physicists of the eighteenth century differed very widely from each other. The first to deduce the law as we now know it was **Jacques Alexandre César Charles** (1746–1823), who was professor of physics at the Conservatoire des Arts et Métiers in Paris. He discovered what is known as the "law of Charles" or "law of Gay-Lussac." Charles failed to publish his results and it was only by accident that they became known to Gay-Lussac. Gay-Lussac's researches were published in 1802.[1] He attributed the want of agreement in earlier experiments to the presence of moisture. Gay-Lussac's own elaborate investigation led him to the conclusion "that in

[1] *Annales de Chimie*, Vol. 43, pp. 137–175; *Ostwald's Klass.*, No. 44, pp. 3–25.

general all gases by equal degrees of heat, under the same conditions, expand proportionately just alike."

The practical side of Charles' study of gases related to the design of balloons. He was best known for his improvements in this field and as a bold navigator of the air. At his suggestion, hydrogen, then a new gas (discovered by Henry Cavendish in 1766), was used in filling balloons. In 1773 the two brothers Montgolfier had raised the first balloons at Annonay in southern France, and had caused a great sensation. They used hot air. Charles, assisted by the mechanic Robert, in 1783, raised the first hydrogen balloon from the *Champ de Mars* in Paris. Later he and Robert made balloon ascensions together. Balloon ascensions engaged the attention also of Gay-Lussac.

Joseph Louis Gay-Lussac (1778–1850) was educated at the Polytechnic School, became assistant to the chemist Berthollet, and later professor of chemistry at the Polytechnic School of Physics, at the Sorbonne. His physical researches are principally on the expansion of gases. To ascertain the chemical and electric condition of the air in the upper strata, and also to measure the force of terrestrial magnetism at great elevations, he and Biot ascended in a balloon which had survived Napoleon's campaign in Egypt. "Supplied with a full complement of barometers, thermometers, hygrometers, electrometers, and instruments for measuring magnetic force and dip, as well as frogs, insects, and birds for galvanic experiments, the scientific voyagers embarked on August 23, 1804. They began their experiments at an altitude of 6500 feet and continued them to the altitude of 13,000 feet, and with a success commensurate with their wishes. The last part of the excursion, and especially the landing which they made, was so difficult . . . that . . . Biot, though a man of activity and not deficient in personal courage, was so much overpowered by the alarms of their descent, as to lose for a time the entire possession of himself." [1] Gay-Lussac made another balloon

[1] *Proc. of the Am. Acad. of Arts and Sci.*, Vol. VI., p. 20.

excursion the same year. Air bottled at a height of 6300 metres was found to have the same composition as air near the surface.

The expansion of gases was investigated also by **John Dalton** (1766–1844) of Manchester, the great founder of the chemical atomic theory.[1] His conclusions did not quite agree with Gay-Lussac's. The latter had shown that, using a mercury thermometer, the expansion per degree is a constant fraction of the volume at some arbitrary fixed temperature. Dalton, on the other hand, claimed that the increment of volume for each equal rise of temperature is a constant fraction of the volume at the temperature immediately preceding. The question was decided by Dulong and Petit in favor of Gay-Lussac.[2] The value of the coefficient of expansion for the interval from 0° to 100°, as determined by Gay-Lussac and Dalton, was .375; as determined in 1837 by Fredrik Rudberg (1800–1839), professor at Upsala, it was .365; as determined by Magnus and Regnault, it was between .366 and .367. The whole subject of the expansion of gases was independently re-investigated with the aid of more refined methods by the two experimentalists last named.

We pause a moment to catch a glimpse of some of the men just mentioned. **Alexis Thérèse Petit** (1791–1820) was professor of physics at the Polytechnic School in Paris. **Pierre Louis Dulong** (1785–1838) held the same position for some years after 1820. At first Dulong practised medicine, but as he not only treated the poor free of charge, but also bought medicine for them, he found his vocation too expensive. As a physicist, his wealth was absorbed by the cost of his expensive apparatus.[3] Most of his researches were carried on in conjunction with other men. Some were carried on with Petit; others with Arago, Berzelius, Despretz. **Henri Victor Regnault** (1810–1878) was professor in Lyons, then in Paris

---

[1] Consult H. E. Roscoe, *John Dalton and the Rise of Modern Chemistry*, 1895.

[2] *Ostwald's Klass.*, No. 44, pp. 28, 40.

[3] Rosenberger, III., p. 221.

at the Polytechnic School, and at the *Collège de France*. After 1854 he was director of a porcelain manufactory at Sèvres. He displayed wonderful patience and skill in the execution of careful measurements. His numerical tables on the dilatation of elastic fluids, on the elastic force of steam, on the heat of vaporization of water, on the specific heat of water at different temperatures, etc., ranked among the best. But he lacked that creative genius which enables its possessor not only to experiment but to grapple with great questions of theoretical science. Regnault proved that all gases do not possess quite the same coefficient of expansion; that, except for hydrogen, it increases with the initial pressure; that no gas obeys Boyle's law exactly.[1]

Regnault's experiments showed that, as the pressure increased, the product of the pressure and volume, pv, diminished in all gases, except hydrogen. If Boyle's law were followed, this product would be constant. Regnault's observations extended over a comparatively small range of pressures. That pv, as p increases, does not diminish for all pressures beyond this range, but reaches a minimum, and then increases, as in case of hydrogen, was first shown by the Vienna physician, Johann August Natterer, in the years 1850–1854 [2] while he was endeavoring to liquefy oxygen, hydrogen, and air. For twenty years this interesting observation was not extended. In 1870 the subject was taken up by Cailletet (1832–1905) and later by **E. H. Amagat** (1841–1915). The experiments of the latter were particularly instructive.[3] For an

[1] Three papers by Regnault and two by Magnus, on the expansion of gases, are reprinted in *Ostwald's Klass.*, No. 44. Regnault's most valuable experimental results are collected in Vols. 21 and 26 of the *Mémoires* of the French Academy. At the close of the Franco-Prussian War Regnault found, on returning to his laboratory at Sèvres, that the results of his last great research on the phenomena of heat accompanying the expansion of gases, derived from over 600 observations, had been destroyed. The announcement of this loss was his last communication to the scientific world. One of his sons, a promising artist, died on the battle-field. See *Nature*, Vol. 17, 1878, pp. 263, 264.

[2] *Pogg. Ann.*, Vol. 62, p. 139; Vol. 94, p. 436.

[3] Amagat, *Ann. de Chimie et de Physique* (5), Vol. 19, 1880, p. 435, and other articles in the same journal. Summaries of his work are

increase of pressure from 30 to 320 atmospheres pv increases continually in hydrogen; it first diminishes a trifle and then increases in nitrogen at (17.7° C.); it diminishes greatly and then increases rapidly in ethylene and carbon dioxide. The variations of pv are very rapid near the critical point; they are more pronounced for low temperatures.

LIQUEFACTION OF GASES

The first important work on the liquefaction of gases was performed by Faraday.[1] His experiments, begun in 1823, showed that the capability of being liquefied was a property common in most gases. A bent glass tube was taken; into its longer leg, which was closed, there was introduced a substance which would evolve, when heated, the particular gas to be tested. The shorter leg of the tube was then sealed up, and cooled by being placed in a freezing mixture. When the longer leg was heated, and gas was generated, the pressure in the tube increased, and in many cases the gas condensed in the shorter leg. Thus, by heating sodium bicarbonate, carbonic acid gas was obtained, which was liquefied in the short leg. By this method Faraday liquefied H_2S, HCl, SO_2, C_2N_2, NH_3, Cl_2. Thilorier in 1835 produced in larger quantities liquid and solid CO_2. By mixing solid CO_2 with ether, he obtained low degrees of temperature previously undreamed of. Notwithstanding the researches of Thilorier, of Natterer, and of Faraday in 1845, several gases still resisted liquefaction. They were classed under the name of "permanent gases," a title which they bore over a quarter of a century, until 1877.

Meanwhile new things were being ascertained regarding the continuity of the gaseous and liquid states of matter. As early as 1822 **Charles Cagniard-Latour** (1777–1859), an engineer, later attaché to the Ministry of the Interior in Paris,

found in Preston, *Theory of Heat*, London, 1894, pp. 403–410; Ostwald, *Lehrb. d. Allgem. Chemie*, Vol. I., 1891, pp. 146–159.

[1] Before Faraday, several gases had been liquefied by cooling: *Marum*, liquefied ammonia; *Monge* and *Clouet*, sulphurous acid; *Northmore*, chlorine (in 1805); *Stromeyer*, arsenic trihydride. See Ostwald, *op. cit.*, Vol. I., p. 294; *Nature*, Vol. 17, 1878, p. 177.

observed that ether, alcohol, and water, when heated in hermetically sealed tubes, were apparently totally changed into vapor occupying only from two to four times the original volume of the liquid. But the discovery of the continuity of the liquid and gaseous states belongs to **Thomas Andrews** (1813–1885), the vice-president and professor of chemistry in the college at Belfast. In his experiments pressure was produced by screwing up mercury into a capillary tube, in which the gas was kept at the desired temperature. In 1863 he wrote: "On partially liquefying carbonic acid by pressure alone, and gradually raising at the same time the temperature to 88° F. [30.92° C.], the surface of demarcation between the liquid and gas became fainter, lost its curvature, and at last disappeared. The space was then occupied by a homogeneous fluid, which exhibited, when the pressure was suddenly diminished or the temperature slightly lowered, a peculiar appearance of moving or flickering striæ throughout its entire mass. At temperatures above 88° F. no apparent liquefaction of carbonic acid, or separation into two distinct forms of matter, could be effected, even when a pressure of 300 or 400 atmospheres was applied."[1] This temperature of 30.92° C., at which the liquid and the gaseous states of CO_2 merge into one another, has been called by Andrews the "critical point." Every gas has its own critical temperature. Below this the substance may exist partly as a vapor, partly as a liquid. Above it this is not true; the substance may be made to pass from a gas to a liquid without a break of continuity, so that it is impossible to state when it ceases to be a gas and begins to be a liquid. J. D. van der Waals treated the subject from the standpoint of the mathematical theory of gases. **William Ramsay,** in 1880, concluded that "the critical point is that point at which the liquid owing to expansion, and the gas owing to compression, acquire the same specific gravity, and consequently mix with each other."[2] Three

[1] Miller's *Chemical Physics*, 3d ed., p. 328.
[2] *Nature*, Vol. 22, 1880, p. 46.

years later the same result was obtained by Jules Celestin Jamin (1818–1886).[1]

Andrews had, in 1869, expressed the opinion that the failure to liquefy the "permanent gases" was due to the fact that their critical temperatures were much lower than the lowest temperature hitherto obtained. Taking this hint, two young investigators—Pictet and Cailletet—made the year 1877 memorable in the history of science by their brilliant demonstration that the "permanent gases" may be liquefied, and that molecular cohesion is a property of all bodies without exception. The means at the command of both experimenters arose from their industrial equipments, one for making iron, the other for making ice. **L. Cailletet,** in his day one of the greatest ironmasters of France, employed the enormous resources at his disposal at the Châtillon-sur-Seine in Paris.[2] **Raoul Pictet** (1846–1904) of Geneva was interested in the artificial production of ice, and later had a laboratory in Berlin for experimentation on low temperatures. Low temperatures found industrial application; for instance, in the purification of chloroform. On December 24, 1877, at the same meeting of the French Academy, it was announced that, working independently and by different methods, Cailletet and Pictet had liquefied oxygen. A week later Cailletet performed a series of experiments in the laboratory of the *École Normale* at Paris in the presence of leading French scientists. He then and there liquefied hydrogen, nitrogen, and air. The same result was achieved by Pictet. Cailletet's process consists in compressing the gas into a small tube, cooling it, and then suddenly allowing it to expand by removal of the pressure. This instantaneous expansion of the gas causes such a low degree of cold that a large portion of the gas is condensed into a cloud of vapor. In case of oxygen the temperature of the tube was reduced to — 29° C. by the application of sulphurous acid. The pressure was 300 atmospheres. The sudden expansion

[1] *Compt. Rend.*, Vol. 96, 1883, p. 1448.
[2] *Nature*, Vol. 17, 1878, pp. 177, 178.

probably lowered the temperature as much as 200°.[1] Pictet
used more elaborate apparatus (costing about 50,000 francs),
and obtained the condensed gases on a larger scale. The low
temperatures were obtained on the principle of evaporation.
A vacuum pump withdrew from a tube the vapor above liquid
sulphurous acid; the vapor was then liquefied, cooled, and returned to the tube. Thus a complete circulation was maintained. In this way the temperature of the liquid fell to
about — 70° C. Within this tube was another thinner tube
containing liquid carbonic acid. The object of the former
liquid was to keep the latter cool. The carbonic acid was let
into another tube, where its temperature was reduced by
evaporation, brought about as before by a vacuum pump, to
— 140° C. The vapor of CO_2 was condensed by the sulphurous acid. Thus by compression, liquefaction, and exhaustion,
there was a circulation of CO_2 like that of sulphurous acid.
A tube containing oxygen passed inside the tube of solidified
CO_2 at — 140°. The oxygen was generated by heating chlor-
ate of potash in a strong shell at one end of the last-mentioned
tube. The other end of that tube was furnished with a stop-
cock. The oxygen was condensed in the tube by the combined
action of its own pressure of several hundred atmospheres and
the intense cold. On opening the stop-cock a small stream of
oxygen escaped. In its central portion it was white, indicating
the liquid or solid condition. In case of hydrogen, the escaping stream was steel-blue.

In larger quantities the three gases, oxygen, nitrogen, and
hydrogen, were liquefied by **Sigmund v. Wroblewski** (1848–
1888) and Karl Olszewski of the University of Cracow in
Austria-Hungary, and by **James Dewar** of the Royal Institution in London. Their apparatus is based on the general
principle of that designed by Pictet, only it has been found
better to use other liquids, like ethylene or oxygen. Olszewski
determined critical points, boiling-points, freezing-points,
and densities. He found boiling-points as follows: oxygen,

[1] A large figure of Cailletet's apparatus will be found in *Nature,*
Vol. 17, p. 267.

— 182.7° C.; argon, — 187°; nitrogen, — 194.4°; hydrogen, — 243.5°. Freezing-points: argon, — 189.6°; nitrogen, — 214°.[1] James Dewar succeeded in 1898 in obtaining liquid hydrogen in larger quantities (half a wine glass), and in liquefying helium. In 1891 he announced that liquid oxygen and liquid ozone are attracted by the poles of a magnet. J. Dewar and J. A. Fleming have examined the electric resistance of metals at low temperatures. The resistance of some pure metals (platinum, for instance) diminishes at low temperatures at such a rate that, if the rate is kept up in the lower temperatures not yet reached, it will vanish at the absolute zero.

FORMATION OF DEW

The study of phenomena of heat led to a better comprehension of meteorological phenomena. At one time it was believed that dew fell from the stars, or, at any rate, from great heights. The first scientific study of the formation of dew was made by the London physician, **William Charles Wells** (1757–1817), and the results published in his *Essay on Dew*, 1814. In a clear, quiet night, the grass radiates heat into free space, whence no heat returns. Being a poor conductor, the lower parts of the grass receive little heat from the earth. The grass cools and vapor condenses upon it. Good conductors, like metals, receive heat from surrounding bodies, and, therefore, are not covered with dew. A cloudy sky hinders the formation of dew by returning the radiated heat. Winds are unfavorable, because they carry heat to the cooling objects. Wells supposed that only a very small part of the dew deposited comes from vapor rising from the earth or the evaporation from plants. Later investigations by Badgeley [2] and R. Russell [3] have shown that Wells underestimated the rôle played by both the earth and the plant. The vapor was shown by experiment to come largely from the

[1] See table in *Nature,* Vol. 51, 1895, pp. 355, 356.
[2] *Proc. of the Royal Meteor. Soc.,* April, 1891.
[3] *Nature,* Vol. 47, 1892, pp. 210–213.

earth beneath, and not from the air above. This was contrary to the commonly received view.

New informaion was obtained on the formation of rain and fog. It was concluded by Coulier, E. Mascart,[1] and especially by John Aitken,[2] that in the development of fogs and clouds, the presence of dust is essential. That is, "whenever water vapor condenses in the atmosphere, it always does so on some solid nucleus;" "dust particles in air are nuclei on which vapor condenses;" except for dust we should have no fogs, no clouds, no mists, and probably no rain. City fogs are due to dust. It is not true that dust is always absolutely essential for cloudy condensation; it may be brought about by the presence of hydrochloric, sulphuric, or nitric acids, or by very high degrees of supersaturation. Yet the conditions in the atmosphere are such that, except for dust, we could hardly have rain. Aitken invented a dust counter; he made extensive observations in England and in Switzerland. By observations on the Rigi he concluded "that whenever a cloud is formed, it at once begins to rain, and the small drops fall into the drier air underneath, where they are evaporated, the distance to which they will fall depending on their size and the dryness of the air."

BEGINNINGS OF THERMODYNAMICS

One of the earliest recorded experiments on the heating and cooling of a gas, by condensation and rarefaction, respectively, was made by a workman in a French gun factory, who ignited tinder by compression of air. An account of this experiment was sent to Paris by Mollet, professor at Lyons. The subject was carefully examined by John Dalton, who, in 1800, read a paper "on the heat and cold produced by the mechanical condensation and rarefaction of air."[3]

The science of thermodynamics had its origin in attempts

[1] *Naturforscher*, 1875, p. 400; *Journal de Pharmacie et de Chimie* (4), Vol. 22, p. 165; *Nature*, Vol. 23, 1881, p. 337.
[2] *Nature*, Vol. 23, p. 196; Vol. 41, p. 408; Vol. 44, 1891, p. 279; Vol. 45, p. 299; Vol. 49, 1893, p. 544.
[3] Rosenberger, III., p. 224.

to determine mathematically how much work can be gotten out of a steam-engine. The first impulse to this was given by **Nicolas Léonard Sadi Carnot** (1796–1832), who, in 1824, published his *Réflexions sur la puissance motrice du feu*.[1] Carnot introduced the consideration of cyclic operations, in which a working substance, after a series of changes, is brought back to its initial condition. He also advanced the principle of reversibility, by which the heat may be taken from the condenser and restored to the source by the expenditure of an equal quantity of work. Assuming perpetual motion to be impossible, he concluded that no engine can have a greater efficiency than a reversible engine. At this time Carnot was an adherent of the caloric theory; he believed in the doctrine of the conservation of caloric; he compared the motive power of heat with that of falling water. Both, he says, have a maximum power, independent, in one case, of the machine upon which the water acts, and, in the other case, of the nature of the substance receiving the heat. The motive power of water depends upon the amount of water and the height through which it falls; the motive power of heat depends upon the quantity of caloric and the difference in temperature between the source and the receiver. But some years later Carnot became convinced of the falsity of the caloric theory. His later writings, which long remained unpublished, prove that he was finally persuaded of the truth of the dynamical theory of heat. More than this, he had grasped the law of the conservation of energy. "Motive power is in quantity invariable in nature; it is, correctly speaking, never either produced or destroyed."

Though the importance of Carnot's work of 1824 was emphasized by B. P. E. Clapeyron, it did not meet with general recognition until it was brought forward by **William Thomson** (later Lord Kelvin), who pointed out the necessity of modifying Carnot's reasoning so as to bring it into accord with the new theory of heat. In 1848 Thomson showed that Carnot's

---

[1] Reprinted in German in *Ostwald's Klass.*, No. 37; an English translation by R. H. Thurston appeared in 1890.

principle of cyclic transformations leads to the conception of an absolute thermodynamic scale of temperature. In 1849 he published "an account of Carnot's theory of the motive power of heat, with numerical results deduced from Regnault's experiments." In February, 1850, **Rudolph Clausius** (1822–1888) communicated to the Berlin Academy a paper on the same subject, which contains the Protean second law of thermodynamics: "Heat cannot, of itself, pass from a colder to a hotter body." Clausius was at this time professor in Zürich; later he went to Würzburg, and, after 1869, was at Bonn. He was no great experimenter, but ranked very high as a mathematical physicist.[1] In the same month of February, 1850, **William John M. Rankine** (1820–1872), professor of engineering and mechanics at Glasgow, read before the Royal Society of Edinburgh a paper in which he declares heat to consist in the rotational motion of molecules, and arrives independently at some of the results reached previously by Clausius. He does not mention the second law of thermodynamics, but in a subsequent paper he declares that it can be derived from equations contained in his paper. His proof of the second law is not free from objections. In March, 1851, there appeared a paper by William Thomson which contained what was considered a rigorous proof of the second law. He obtained it before he had seen the researches of Clausius. The statement of this law, as given by Clausius, was much criticised, particularly by Rankine, Theodor Wand, P. G. Tait (1831–1901), and Tolver Preston. Repeated efforts to deduce it from general mechanical principles remained fruitless. The science of thermodynamics was developed with great success by Thomson, Clausius, and Rankine. As early as 1852 Thomson advanced the law of the dissipation of energy, deduced at a later period also by Clausius.

[1] During the Franco-Prussian War, his burning patriotism did not permit him to stay at home. He undertook the leadership of an ambulance corps, which he formed of Bonn students. See *Proc. of Roy. Soc. of London,* Vol. 48, 1890, p. II.

Conservation of Energy

The first law of thermodynamics is merely the application of the principle of the conservation of energy to heat-effects. This principle is the greatest generalization in physics of the nineteenth century. Its history is remarkable from various points of view. Several thinkers arrived at this great truth at about the same time; and, at first, all of them were either met with a very cold reception or were completely ignored. The principle of the conservation of energy was established by the Heilbronn physician, Robert Mayer, and again independently by Ludwig August Colding of Copenhagen, Joule in England, and Helmholtz in Germany.

Robert Mayer (1814–1878) was born in Heilbronn. In the gymnasium and the theological school he gave no evidence of great intellectual power. In 1832 he entered upon the study of medicine at Tübingen, and in 1838 began to practise, but he never found the work of a practising physician agreeable to his tastes. He travelled considerably and engaged in the study of physiology. An observation made in 1840, on the blood of a patient in a tropical climate, was the origin of his scientific writings. It led him to the study of those physical forces on which the phenomena of vitality depend. Thus, he was led from the contemplation of organic nature to the preparation of a paper, "On the Forces of Inorganic Nature," 1842. It was refused publication in Poggendorff's *Annalen,* but was accepted by Liebig for the May number of his *Annalen.* It attracted no attention, though containing the great principle that the energy of the world is constant. A second paper, 1845, could be published only at his own expense. Several other papers were published later.[1] The following story, related by Mach, shows Mayer's alertness of mind:[2] "During a hurried meeting with Mayer in Heidelberg

---

[1] See J. J. Weyrauch, *Robert Mayer,* Stuttgart, 1890. Consult also Weyrauch, *Die Mechanik der Wärme von* Robert Mayer, 3d ed., 1893; Weyrauch, *Kleinere Schriften und Briefe von Robert Mayer,* 1893.

[2] "On the Part played by Accident in Invention and Discovery," *Monist,* Vol. 6, 1896, p. 171.

once, Jolly remarked, with a rather dubious implication, that if Mayer's theory were correct, water could be warmed by shaking. Mayer went away without a word of reply. Several weeks later . . . he rushed into the latter's presence exclaiming: 'Es ischt so!' (It is so, it is so!) It was only after considerable explanation that Jolly found out what Mayer wanted to say.'' The mind of Robert Mayer became seriously affected by the lack of appreciation of his ideas, by controversies regarding his rights of priority, as well as by the death of two of his children. On May 28, 1849, he unsuccessfully attempted suicide by jumping from a second-story window. After a seeming recovery, he wrote a paper on the mechanical equivalent of heat. In 1851 he was placed in an insane asylum, where he was cruelly treated. In 1853 he was set free, but he never again regained complete mental equilibrium. In 1858 a few voices were heard in Germany in praise of Mayer, but the one who did most to bring him historical justice was John Tyndall, who in 1862 lectured before the Royal Institution on Robert Mayer and also translated several of Mayer's papers. William Thomson and Tait, placing a much lower estimate on Mayer's researches, brought the charge that Tyndall was belittling the work of Joule.[1]

James Prescott Joule (1818–1889) was born at Salford, near Manchester, where he was the proprietor of a large brewery. At an early age he engaged in electromagnetic researches. After laborious tests he succeeded in showing that during electrolytic action there was an absorption of heat equivalent to the heat evolved during the original combination of the constituents of the compound body. He studied the relations between electrical, chemical, and mechanical effects, and was led to the great discovery of the mechanical equivalent of heat. In a paper read before the British Association, in 1843, he gave the number as 460 kilogramme-metres. Friends who recognized the physicist in the young brewer persuaded him to become a candidate for the professor-

[1] Consult ''Notes on Scientific History'' by Tyndall in *Phil. Mag.*, July, 1864.

ship of natural philosophy at St. Andrews, Scotland, but his slight personal deformity was an objection in the eyes of one of the electors, and he did not receive the appointment. He remained a brewer, but continued scientific research throughout life. In April, 1847, Joule gave a popular lecture in Manchester, delivering "the first full and clear exposition of the universal conservation of that principle now called energy."[1] The local press would at first have nothing to do with it. One paper refused to give even a notice of it; the *Manchester Courier*, after long debate, published the address in full. In June, 1847, the subject was presented before the British Association meeting at Oxford. The chairman suggested that the author be brief; no discussion was invited. In a moment the section would have passed on to other matters without giving the new ideas any consideration, "if a young man had not risen in the section, and by his intelligent observations created a lively interest in the new theory. The young man was William Thomson." The result was that the paper caused a great sensation; Joule had attracted the attention of scientific men. After the meeting Joule and Thomson discussed the subject further, and the latter "obtained ideas he had never had before," while through him Joule heard for the first time of Carnot's theory.[2]

Joule experimented on the mechanical equivalent of heat for about forty years. By magneto-electric currents he got, in 1843, the value of 460 kilogramme-metres as the equivalent of the large French calorie. By the friction of water in tubes, he got 424.9; by the compression of air, in 1845, 443.8; by the friction of water he got, in 1845, 488.3; in 1847, 428.9; in 1850, 423.9; in 1878, 423.9.[3]

The mechanical equivalent of heat is such an important constant in nature that several physicists since Joule have

---

[1] A. W. Rücker in *Fortnightly Review*, 1894, p. 652. We are making considerable use of this article, entitled, "Hermann von Helmholtz." It is reprinted in *Smithsonian Report*, 1894.

[2] *Nature*, Vol. 49, 1893, p. 164.

[3] Consult *The Scientific Papers of James Prescott Joule*, in two volumes, London, 1884; *Nature*, Vol. 43, 1890, p. 112.

thought it desirable to redetermine it. One of the most accurate determinations was made in 1879 by Henry A. Rowland of Baltimore.[1] The part of the work which received greater attention than Joule had given it, was the subject of thermometry. Joule used mercury thermometers. Rowland, for convenience, used a mercury thermometer too, but compared it with an air thermometer and then reduced his data to the absolute scale. Rowland paid attention also to variations in the specific heat of water for different temperatures. Starting with the water at different temperatures, he obtained by friction of water in a calorimeter different values for the mechanical equivalent. This variation in the values he attributed to changes in the specific heat of water. The latter was found by him to reach a minimum at 30° C. Later, the mechanical equivalent of heat was measured by D'Arsonval, Miculescu, E. H. Griffiths, and others. Joule's estimate of this constant has been raised somewhat by the later determinations.[2]

The same year, 1847, in which Joule announced his views on energy, Helmholtz read before the Physical Society in Berlin a paper on the same subject. **Hermann von Helmholtz** (1821–1894) was born at Potsdam, studied medicine in Berlin, became assistant at the charity hospital there, then military surgeon in Potsdam (1843–1847), teacher of anatomy at Berlin, of physiology at Königsberg, later at Bonn and Heidelberg (1858–1871). In 1871 he accepted the chair of physics at the University of Berlin. He possessed an intellect of extraordinary breadth and depth. He was of the first rank as a physiologist, as a physicist, and as a mathematician. Many years ago W. K. Clifford, in his article "Seeing and Thinking," spoke of him as follows: "In the first place he began by studying physiology, dissecting the eye and the ear, and finding out how they acted, and what was their precise constitution; but he found that it was impossible to study the

[1] *Proc. of the Am. Acad. of Arts and Sciences,* N.S., Vol. 7, 1880.
[2] Consult E. H. Griffiths in *Science Progress,* Vol. 1, 1894, p. 127; *Johns Hopkins Circulars,* 1898, No. 135.

proper action of the eye and ear without studying also the nature of light and sound, which led him to the study of physics. He had already become one of the most accomplished physiologists of this century when he commenced the study of physics, and he is now one of the greatest physicists of this century. He then found it was impossible to study physics without knowing mathematics; and accordingly he took to studying mathematics and he is now one of the most accomplished mathematicians of this century.''

His famous paper on energy, entitled "Die Erhaltung der Kraft,"[1] which the youth of twenty-six read before the Physical Society of Berlin in 1847, was at first looked upon as a fantastic speculation. The editor of Poggendorff's *Annalen*, who in 1843 declined Mayer's paper, rejected Helmholtz's also. As Joule had been supported by William Thomson, so Helmholtz was defended by his fellow-student Du Bois-Reymond and by the mathematician C. G. J. Jacobi. Helmholtz's paper was published in pamphlet form in 1847. For a time it attracted little notice, but in 1853 it was vigorously attacked by Clausius. Later it subjected its author to virulent attacks from Eugen Karl Dühring and others, who accused him of being a dishonest borrower from his forerunner, Robert Mayer.[2] In 1847 Helmholtz, like Joule, had not heard of Robert Mayer, but later he cheerfully acknowledged Mayer's priority.

By the word *Kraft,* used by Mayer and Helmholtz, we must understand *energy.* For a time great confusion existed in text-books between the terms "force" and "energy." The two terms were frequently used synonymously. The use of the word "energy" to denote the quantity of work which a material system can do was introduced by Thomas Young in Lecture VIII. of his *Natural Philosophy.* With him it desig-

[1] Reprinted in *Ostwald's Klassiker,* No. 1. In Note 5 Helmholtz outlines the history of the new principle of energy.
[2] *Physical Review,* Vol. 2, 1894, p. 224.

nated mv^2; Lord Kelvin in 1849 used it for $\frac{1}{2}mv^2$. The expression "conservation of energy" is due to Rankine.[1]

ELECTRICITY AND MAGNETISM

BEGINNINGS OF ELECTROLYSIS

Electrical progress, both theoretical and practical, was so rapid that the nineteenth century was called the age of electricity.

After the discovery of current electricity by Galvani and the construction of the voltaic pile, Carlisle and Nicholson decomposed water by *low pressure currents*. This feat caused great excitement. In September, 1800, Johann Wilhelm Ritter (1776–1810), of Silesia, announced that he had succeeded in collecting the two gases separately and that copper could be precipitated from blue vitriol.

Sir Humphry Davy (1778–1829) was among the early workers in this line. While a poor boy, Davy attained notoriety for being "so fond of chemical experiments." After serving as assistant in the Pneumatic Institution at Bristol, he in 1801 became lecturer in chemistry at the Royal Institution in London. His lectures delighted the fashionable audiences. Said Coleridge, "I go to Davy's lectures to increase my stock of metaphors." It has been said that, if Davy had not been one of the first chemists, he would have been one of the first poets of his age.[2]

Davy showed that in the decomposition of water, the volume of hydrogen is double that of oxygen. His most striking discoveries were the resolution, by electrolysis, of the fixed alkalies, potash and soda. In 1807 the elements sodium

[1] Students desiring more detailed information on heat may consult, besides Rosenberger, Poggendorff, and Heller, Mach, *Principien der Wärmelehre*, Leipzig, 1896; Georg Helm, Lehre *von der Energie historisch-kritisch Entwickelt*, Leipzig, 1887; M. P. Desains, *Rapport sur les progrès de la théorie de la chaleur*, Paris, 1868; M. Berlin, *Rapport sur les progrès de la thermodynamique en France*, Paris, 1867; Joseph Peveling, *Gesch. d. Gesetze von d. Erhaltung d. Materie und Energie*, Aachen, 1891.

[2] *The Gallery of Portraits, with Memoirs*, London, 1883, Vol. I., p. 12.

and potassium were thus discovered, and the rapid advance of chemistry was aided by electricity.

The apparent migration of the products of electric decomposition called forth several curious theories, but the one which held its ground for over half a century was proposed by **Ch. J. D. von Grothuss** [1] (1785–1822). In his boyhood Grothuss was forbidden the study of chemistry, but later he pursued scientific courses at Leipzig, Paris (at the Polytechnic School), and Naples. After 1808 he lived on his estate in Lithauen, Prussia, giving his leisure time to chemical research. During his last years he suffered intensely from some organic trouble which finally drove him to suicide. He is best known by his paper, first published at Rome in 1805 when he was only twenty years old, "Mémoire sur la décomposition de l'eau et des corps, qu'elle tient en dissolution, à l'aide de l'électricité galvanique." [2] In a quantity of water (Fig. 17),

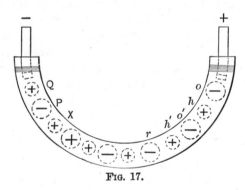

FIG. 17.

composed of oxygen (marked —) and hydrogen (marked +), electric polarity manifests itself as soon as an electric current is established in the water. All oxygen atoms in the path of the current receive a tendency to move toward the positive pole, while all hydrogen atoms in the same path tend toward

[1] Or Grotthuss.
[2] Reprinted in 1806 in *Annales de Chimie*, Vol. 58, pp. 54–74. A German translation in full is given in Ostwald, *Elektrochemie*, Leipzig, 1896, pp. 309–316.

the negative pole. Consequently, if the molecule oh gives off its oxygen o to the positive wire, then the hydrogen h soon gets oxidized by the arrival of another oxygen atom o', whose hydrogen h' combines with r, etc. The same action, in the opposite sense, occurs in the molecule QP. Thus, there is a progressive alternate separation and union of atoms. That such separation and recombination should go on, without the expenditure of work, is contrary to the laws of energy. As Ostwald put it, energy in a condition of rest cannot of itself become active; a stone lying on the ground cannot of itself rise and then fall again. Grothuss supposed "that at the moment of the segregated appearance of the hydrogen and oxygen, there takes place a division of their natural electricity, either by their contact or by mutual friction, so that the former assumes the positive, the latter the negative condition." On this point the first differences of opinion arose. Modified hypotheses were suggested by H. G. Magnus of Berlin, by the Swede chemist Jöns Jacob Berzelius (1779–1848), and by Auguste Arthur de la Rive (1801–1873) of Geneva. As to the mechanism of electrolytic conduction, the molecular chain of Grothuss was modified somewhat by Faraday and W. Hittorf (1824–1914), professor of physics at Münster. But the first radical modification of Grothuss's theory was made by Clausius in 1857.[1] He argued that, according to the electrolytic theories then held, the E. M. F. first turns the molecules, so that the positive ions face the kathode and the negative ions the anode, and then pulls asunder the ions which were previously firmly united in the molecule. Now, to separate these ions requires a force of definite intensity. Hence, if the electrolytic force acting upon the ions is less than the attraction between the ions, there can be no segregation whatever; if this force increases, many molecules will be broken up at once. This is contrary to fact. Experiment shows that the weakest E. M. F. causes decomposition, and that the action is proportional to the intensity of the current. To remove this difficulty,

[1] *Poggendorff's Annalen,* Vol. 101, p. 338.

Clausius assumed that the ions are not permanently united with each other; that part of them exist in the liquid in an uncombined state wandering about seeking partners. The electromotive force of the current acts upon these loose atoms. Some of the ions being free to begin with, the weakest current can act. Thus Clausius advanced the idea of dissociation to explain electrolysis. This dissociation hypothesis was modified by G. Quincke of Heidelberg to better explain the migration of ions. It was used by **F. Kohlrausch** to explain the facts of electrolytic conductivity. Yet Clausius's dissociation theory of the constitution of electrolytes met with little favor until 1887, when Svante Arrhenius in Stockholm brought new arguments to support it, based on the theory of solutions of J. H. van't Hoff (1852–1911) and the phenomena of osmotic pressure.[1] From certain new considerations the conclusion was reached that in solutions there exists a partial dissociation of the dissolved substances.[2] Important researches on this subject were carried on by Wilhelm Ostwald of Leipzig, and Walter Nernst of Göttingen.

In these researches there are exemplified the beneficial results arising from an intimate reunion of the two branches of science, physics and chemistry. At the beginning of the century many scientists contributed original researches in both sciences; they were chemists as well as physicists. But about 1835 a separation took place; men were known only as physicists or only as chemists. About 1885, after half a century of separation, a tendency to reunion became apparent in what is known as the "Leipzig School," with Ostwald, Nernst, and Arrhenius at the head.

The Voltaic Cell

One of the most interesting results achieved by this school is the solution of a problem which had been under discussion a

[1] Arrhenius, *Zeitschr. f. Physik. Chemie*, Vol. 1, p. 631.

[2] For a systematic and historical exposition of osmotic pressure and the theory of solutions, see W. Ostwald, *Allgemeine Chemie*, Vol. 1, 1891, Viertes Buch, or P. Muir's English translation of the same.

whole century, viz. the source or seat of the electromotive force in a voltaic cell. It will be remembered that Volta's contact theory did not meet with general acceptation. The theory that the origin and maintenance of the power of the voltaic pile resided in the contact of different metals was opposed by Giov. Val. Mattia Fabbroni (1752–1822) of Florence, Italy; by Wollaston in England, and by Ritter in Germany. They held that the real source of voltaic electricity was chemical action. This view was taken also by A. C. Becquerel in Paris, A. A. de la Rive of Geneva, and particularly by Faraday in London, who, in 1837 and 1840, published many experiments which seemed to disprove the contact theory. Volta's contact theory received strongest support in Germany. It was advocated by Fechner, Poggendorff, C. H. Pfaff, Ohm, and others. When the principle of the conservation of energy was established, this theory, as originally taught, had to be modified; the mere contact of metals could not give rise to an inexhaustible supply of electric energy. It became evident that in the voltaic cell there took place a transformation of energy. Nevertheless, the seat of the electromotive force might still be at the points of metallic contact. The question was cleared up in a paper by **Walter Nernst** on the electromotive action of ions.[1] The seat of the electromotive force coincides with the seat of the chemical phenomena, and lies in the surfaces of contact between the metals and the electrolytes. Nernst established the following fundamental formula:

$$E = K \text{ nat. } \log \frac{P}{p},$$

where E is the potential difference between the metal and electrolyte under consideration; p is the osmotic pressure of the metal ions in the solution; K is a constant depending on the units used; P is a constant of integration, to be physically interpreted as a pressure. This theory of the voltaic cell rests

[1] *Zeitschr. f. Physik. Chemie,* Vol. 4, 1889, p. 129.

on Van't Hoff's ideas of osmotic pressure and the views of Arrhenius on dissociation in electrolytes.[1] Nernst gives the following comparison with the action of a Daniell cell: "Given a reservoir containing liquid carbonic acid and another containing a substance, for instance, caustic potash, absorbing this one rapidly, and between the two a cylinder and piston contrivance to turn the difference in pressure into work. The machine does work until all the carbonic acid is absorbed; just so a Daniell cell acts till the zinc is used up."

Volta's pile and crown of cups, or slight modifications thereof, were for a long while the only means known for the generation of current electricity. They labored under the defect of a rapid diminution in current on account of polarization. The amalgamation of the zincs, first practised by Sturgeon in 1830, was a step in advance. A year previous A. C. Becquerel constructed a cell yielding a somewhat steadier current. A glass trough was divided into three partitions by two layers of gold-beater's skin. The middle portion between the two membranes was filled with a salt; into the outer portions containing appropriate solutions, dipped copper and zinc plates, respectively. With such a cell a tangent galvanometer deflection of 84° fell to 68° in half an hour. Better success in inventing a constant cell crowned the efforts of John Frederic Daniell (1790–1845), who was professor of chemistry at King's College, London. He contributed to science not only the "Daniell cell," but also "Daniell's hygrometer." The invention of the cell, in 1836, grew out of his contact with Faraday. In a letter describing the cell he wrote Faraday as follows: "You know how deep an interest I have taken in your *Experimental Researches in Electricity,* and how zealously I have availed myself of the opportunities which you have ever kindly offered me, of profiting by your oral explanation of such difficulties as occurred to me in the study of

[1] For an exposition of the theory see W. Ostwald, *Elektrochemie,* 1896, pp. 1133–1148; W. Ostwald, *Allg. Chemie,* Vol. 2, I., 1893; W. Nernst, *Theoretical Chemistry,* trans. by C. S. Palmer, 1895, pp. 609–616; A. Wüllner, *Experimentalphysik,* Vol. 3, 1897, pp. 909–919.

your last series of papers."[1] In his original cell the concentrated copper sulphate and dilute sulphuric acid were separated from each other by an animal membrane—the windpipe of an ox. Soon after J. P. Gassiot (1797–1877) suggested the use of an earthen porous cup in place of the windpipe. In 1839 Sir William Robert Grove (1811–1896) communicated to the British Association a paper, entitled "On a Small Voltaic Battery of Extraordinary Energy," and exhibited a battery "hastily constructed." In 1840 Grove was appointed professor of experimental philosophy at the London institution. Later he entered upon the practice of law,[2] but retained his interest in science. Still another battery,[3] in which the polarization was prevented mechanically by giving the electronegative plate a rough surface, was designed by the London surgeon, Alfred Smee[4] (1818–1877). In Grove's cell the great cost of the platinum was an objection; so Bunsen and others suggested the use of carbon in place of the platinum. Descriptions of "Bunsen's cell" appeared in 1841.[5] Among the numerous open circuit batteries was one brought forth in 1867 by Georges Leclanché (1839–1882), a Parisian chemist. A cell whose electromotive force is even more constant than that of the Daniell was suggested in 1873 by Latimer Clark, modified forms of which were used by Lord Rayleigh, Helmholtz, and Henry S. Carhart. The Clark cell was adopted as the international standard of electromotive force, and official specifications for its preparation were issued.

[1] *Phil. Trans.*, Part I., 1836, p. 107.
[2] *Electrician* (London), Vol. 37, 1896, p. 483; *Nature,* Vol. 54, 1896, p. 393.
[3] *Phil. Mag.* (3), Vol. 16, 1840.
[4] The reader may be interested in the following *jeu d'esprit*, being part of an electric valentine, written by Clerk Maxwell:

> "Constant as Daniell, strong as Grove;
> Ebullient through all its depths like Smee;
> My heart pours forth its tide of love,
> And all its circuits close in thee."

All four stanzas are given in L. Campbell and W. Garnett, *Life of J. C. Maxwell,* 1882, p. 630.
[5] *Poggendorff's Annalen,* Vol. 54, 1841, p. 417.

Storage Batteries

In 1803 Ritter described the first secondary or storage battery. He found that when two platinum wires were dipped in water and a battery current passed through so that hydrogen appeared at one wire and oxygen at the other, then, if the wires were disconnected from the battery and connected with each other by a conductor, the two wires acted like the plates of a battery, and a current passed for a short time in this new circuit. Its direction was opposite to that of the original current. The subject was studied in 1843 by Grove, who constructed a gas battery to illustrate the phenomenon of "polarization." In 1859 **Gaston Planté** (1834–1889), a pupil of A. C. Becquerel, made a thorough study of this method of storing energy, and devised a secondary cell consisting of two pieces of sheet lead rolled up and dipping into dilute sulphuric acid. The lead plates had to be "formed" (coated at the anode with a semi-porous film of dioxide of lead, and at the kathode with a spongy metallic surface) by sending a current through the cell, and reversing its direction several times. His cell had a higher electromotive force than any primary battery, nevertheless it hardly reached commercial efficiency on account of the tedious process of "forming." Little attention was paid to it. The operation of "forming" was avoided in 1881 by Camille A. Faure.[1] This was accomplished by coating the lead plates with red lead. Thereby the capacity of the cell was also increased. After this improvement commercial circles suddenly became interested. Four cells were sent from Paris to London in 1881 weighing only 75 pounds, yet it was said they were charged with 1,000,000 foot-pounds of energy! After all, this was no more than the energy stored up in a few ounces of coal. Filled with hope, inventors put forth extraordinary effort to make storage batteries, or "accumulators," commercially available. In recent years storage batteries have reached most extensive use in automobiles and in radio equipment

[1] Born 1840, died 1898.

OERSTED'S EXPERIMENT AND THE BEGINNING OF ELECTRO-MAGNETISM

The science of electromagnetism originated in 1819 in what is known as "Oersted's experiment." **Hans Christian Oersted** (1777–1851) was born at Rudkjöbing, Langeland, attended the University of Copenhagen, and later was professor at the university and polytechnic school there. Regarding Oersted's great discovery, Hansteen wrote Faraday in 1857 as follows:[1] "Already in the former century there was a general thought that there was a great conformity, and perhaps identity, between the electrical and magnetical force; it was only the question how to demonstrate it by experiments. Oersted tried to place the wire of his galvanic battery perpendicular (at right angles) over the magnetic needle, but marked no sensible motion. Once, after the end of his lecture, as he had used a strong galvanic battery in other experiments, he said: 'Let us now once, as the battery is in activity, try to place the wire parallel with the needle;' as this was made, he was quite struck with perplexity by seeing the needle making a great oscillation (almost at right angles with the magnetic meridian). Then he said: 'Let us now invert the direction of the current,' and the needle deviated in the contrary direction. Thus the great detection was made; and it has been said, not without reason, that 'he tumbled over it by accident.' He had not before any more idea than any other person that the force should be *transversal*. But as Lagrange has said of Newton on a similar occasion: 'Such accidents only meet persons who deserve them.' "

"Professor Oersted was a man of genius, but he was a very unhappy experimenter; he could not manipulate instruments. He must always have an assistant, or one of his auditors who had easy hands, to arrange the experiment; I have often in this way assisted him as his auditor."[2]

[1] B. Jones, *Life and Letters of Faraday*, London, 1870, Vol. II., p. 390.
[2] For Oersted's paper see Gilbert's *Ann.*, Vol. 66, 1820, p. 295; Ostwald, *Elektrochemie*, 1896, p. 367; Ostwald's *Klassiker*, No. 63. F. A. P. Barnard said of this discovery: "When Oersted, in 1819, ob-

Oersted placed different media between the needle and the wire carrying the current, and concluded that the current "acts upon the needle through glass, metals, wood, water, resin, earthen jars, stones; for when we placed between the two a plate of glass, or of metal, or a board, the result was not cancelled; indeed all three combined hardly lessened the effect."

Oersted's experiment was repeated everywhere. **Dominique François Jean Arago** (1786–1853), the noted Parisian astronomer and physicist, observed the following year (1820) that iron filings were attracted by the current. He concluded that the wire carrying the current must be considered a magnet, even if it is not of iron. In 1822 Davy proved that this apparent attraction of the filings was really due to their peripheral arrangement around the wire; opposite poles of the filings attracting each other and establishing a chain around the wire. The fact that the magnetizing force acts in a plane at right angles to the wire induced Ampère to twist the wire into a spiral in order to intensify the effect upon a needle placed inside. **André Marie Ampère** [1] (1775–1836) was born at Lyons, and early displayed mathematical power. During the Revolution his father was beheaded. In consequence, young Ampère was mentally crushed; hour after hour was passed in silence, while he was staring into the sky, or mechanically heaping sand into little piles. After a year he awoke from his mental stupor and his love for science was rekindled by his reading Rousseau's work on botany. After his marriage in 1799, his religious emotions became very strong. His

served the disturbance of the magnetic needle by the influence of a neighboring magnetic current, how wild and visionary would not that have been pronounced to be, who should have professed to read, in an indication so slight, the grand truth that science had, that day, stretched out the sceptre of her authority over a winged messenger, whose fleetness should make a laggard even of Oberon's familiar sprite, and render the velocity which could 'put a girdle round the earth in forty minutes' tardy and unsatisfactory?"

[1] Consult Arago, "Eulogy on Ampère," *Smithsonian Report*, 1872, p. 111.

intense catholicism, though weakened in the middle of his career, again asserted itself later in life. He became professor of physics and chemistry at Lyons. After his wife's death, Ampère, depressed and melancholy, wished to leave Lyons. Ampère, celebrated, overwhelmed with honorable distinctions, the great Ampère! apart from his mental labors, became once more hesitating and fearful, uneasy and troubled, and more disposed to place confidence in others than in himself."[1] In 1805 he became connected with the Polytechnic School in Paris, where for twenty years, he engaged in important researches.[2]

While Oersted had discovered simply the action of a current on a magnet, Ampère discovered the action of a current upon another current: parallel currents in the same direction attract each other; those in opposite directions repel each other.[3] In these beautiful phenomena some critics saw nothing more than the old electric attractions and repulsions. To this Ampère replied that while equal electric charges repel each other, conductors carrying parallel currents attract each other. Another critic aimed to belittle the discovery by asserting that, since it was known that two currents acted upon one and the same magnet, it was evident, to begin with, that they would act upon each other. Upon hearing this, Arago drew two keys out of his pocket and replied, "Each of these

[1] *The Story of his Love, being the journal and early correspondence of André Marie Ampère, edited by Madame H. C.*, London, 1873, p. 164.

[2] The following extract from a letter of 1805 gives a vivid picture of the man: "My life is a circle, with nothing to break its uniformity. . . . I have but one pleasure, a very hollow, very artificial one, and which I rarely enjoy, and that is to discuss metaphysical questions with those who are engaged in this science at Paris, and who show me more kindness than the mathematicians. But my position obliges me to work at the pleasure of the latter, a circumstance which does not contribute to my diversion, for I have no longer any relish for mathematics. Nevertheless, since I have been here I have written two treatises on Calculation which are to be printed in the journal of the Polytechnic School. It is seldom, except on Sunday, that I can see the metaphysicians, such as M. Maine de Biran, with whom I am very intimate, and M. de Tracy, with whom I dine occasionally at Auteuil, where he resides. It is almost the only place in Paris where the country reminds me of the banks of the Saône."—*Ibidem*, p. 322.

[3] *Annales de Chemie et de Physique*, Vol. 15, 1820.

keys attracts a magnet; do you believe that they, therefore, also attract each other?"

Ampère gave a rule—"Ampère's rule"—for the direction in which a magnet is deflected by a current. Faraday arrived at a more comprehensive conception of the relation, and devised experiments showing that current and magnet have a tendency to encircle each other. This result was extended by Ampère. Contrary to the opinion of Thomas Johann Seebeck, who looked upon the electric current as a magnetic action, Ampère considered a magnet as primarily due to the action of electric currents. Each particle in a magnet has an equatorial current, producing magnetic poles. To magnetize a magnet is to cause all these hypothetical molecular currents to flow in the same direction. Terrestrial magnetism, according to Ampère, is due to electric currents around the earth. In 1823 Ampère published a paper giving a mathematical theory of the new phenomena. Maxwell describes this research as "perfect in form and unassailable in accuracy."

OHM'S LAW

Georg Simon Ohm [1] (1789–1854) was an ingenious investigator who, although removed from the influence of personal contact with the great physicists of his time, yet working independently and alone, discovered the great law bearing his name. He was born in Erlangen, attended the university at his native place, then taught school at Gottstadt, Neufchâtel, and Bamberg. At the age of thirty he became teacher of mathematics and physics at the gymnasium in Cologne. He taught there nine years with great success. A pupil of that time, who attained great celebrity as a mathematician, was Lejeune Dirichlet. Ohm became ambitious to engage in research, but the want of leisure and books, as well as the lack of suitable apparatus, rendered progress difficult. The mechanical skill which he had acquired as a boy through his

[1] Consult Eugene Lommel, "The Scientific Work of Georg Simon Ohm" in *Smithsonian Report*, 1891, pp. 247–256.

father, a locksmith, enabled him to construct much apparatus for himself. His first experiments [1] were on the relative conductivity of metals. Taking wire of different material, but of the same thickness, he found that the following lengths possessed equal conductivities: copper 1000, gold, 574, silver 356, zinc 333, brass 280, iron, 174, platinum 171, tin 168, lead 97. Observe that his measurements made silver a much poorer conductor than copper, though it is actually a better conductor. Later, Ohm tried to verify his results and found the mistake. The silver wire first used, in being drawn, became covered with oily leather, so that, while both wires were drawn so as to be apparently of equal thickness, the first one was really much thinner. Further experiments with wires of the same material, but of different thicknesses yielded him the result that they have the same conductivity if their lengths are proportional to their cross-sections. In these tests he was greatly troubled by variations in his batteries ("Wogen der Kraft"). Finally, at the suggestion of Poggendorff, he adopted thermo-electric elements as the sources of current. These were free from this source of trouble.

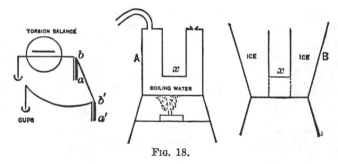

Fig. 18.

In the experiments by which Ohm established his law, he used two tin vessels A and B, Fig. 18. In A he kept boiling water; in B snow or ice. He prepared a bar of bismuth

[1] G. S. Ohm, "Bestimmung des Gesetzes, nach welchem Metalle die Contaktelectricität leiten, etc.," in *Schweigger's Journal f. Chemie u. Physik*, Vol. 46, 1826, p. 144. This article contains, among other things, the experimental proof of Ohm's law.

abb'a'; and to this he fastened by screws strips of copper, whose two free ends dipped into two cups filled with mercury. The thermo-electric couple was, therefore, bismuth and copper. To generate current, junction *ab* was placed in the hollow cylinder *x* of vessel *A*, while junction *a'b'* was placed in the corresponding position in vessel *B*. The difference in temperature gave rise to an electric current whenever the two mercury cups were connected with each other by a conductor, so as to complete the circuit. Ohm had a torsion balance constructed by a mechanic under his direction. A magnetic needle was suspended from a torsion-head by a flattened wire five inches long. When the needle was deflected by the current from its position of rest in the magnetic meridian, it was brought back to its original position by torsion. The angle through which the torsion-head must be deflected was measured in centesimal divisions of the circle. The force tending to deflect the needle from its initial position was proportional to this angle. Hence the strengths of currents could be compared by measuring the angles through which the torsion-head was turned, in each case, in order to bring the needle back to zero.

Ohm prepared eight copper wires of equal thickness (7/8 of a line) and, respectively, 2, 4, 6, 10, 18, 34, 66, 130 inches long. These were inserted as part of the electric current, one after the other. For each, measurements were taken on the strength of current. On January 8, 1826, he obtained the following data:

Number of conductor, 1, 2, 3, 4, 5, 6, 7, 8.
Angle of torsion in centesimal divisions, } 326¾, 300¾, 277¾, 238¼, 190¾, 134½, 83¼, 48½

On the 11th and 15th of the month he took, each day, two more sets of readings. He tabulates his readings and then says: "The above numbers can be represented very satisfactorily by the equation,

$$X = \frac{a}{b + x},$$

where X designates the intensity of the magnetic effect of the conductor whose length is x, a and b being constants depending on the exciting force and the resistance of the remaining parts of the circuit." He gave the quantity b the value 20 1/4, and, for the set of measurements given above, the quantity a the value 7285. These numbers reproduce very closely all the angular numbers given above. Take, for instance, the third conductor, for which $x = 6$, then, by computation, X becomes 277.53, its measured value being 277 3/4. The experiments were varied by selecting brass wire resistances, and again by taking for the two temperatures of the thermo-electric couples those of melting ice and of the room (7.5° C.). By this change in the range of temperature Ohm secured a variation in the electromotive force, which yielded a different value for a, but did not affect b. In all cases the above formula was satisfied. Thus, the new law was established, for a represents the electromotive force, $b + x$ the total resistance of the circuit, X the strength of current. Ohm then established experimentally the formulæ giving the strength of current for the cases when cells are grouped in series and when in multiple arc. These results were published in 1826. Ohm deserves great credit for introducing and defining the accurate notions of electromotive force, strength of current, and electric resistance.

The following year Ohm published a book, entitled *Die Galvanische Kette, mathematisch bearbeitet* (Berlin, 1827). It contained a *theoretic* deduction of Ohm's law, and became far more widely known than his article of 1826, giving the experimental deduction. In fact, his experimental paper was so little known that the impression long prevailed and still exists that he based his law on theory and never established it empirically. This misapprehension accounts, perhaps, for the unfavorable reception of Ohm's conclusions. Professor H. W. Dove (1803–1879), of Berlin, says that "In the Berlin *Jahrbücher für wissenschaftliche Kritik*, Ohm's theory was named a web of naked fancies, which can never find the semblance of support from even the most superficial observation of facts; 'he who looks on the world,' proceeds the writer, 'with the eye of reverence must turn aside from this book as the result of an incurable delusion, whose sole effort is to detract from the dignity of nature.' "[1]

As Ohm's great ambition was to secure a university professorship, we may readily imagine how this lack of appreciation affected him. In order to write his book of 1827, he had secured leave of absence and had gone to Berlin, where the library facilities were better than at Cologne. Not only did he fail to secure promotion by the publication of this book, but he incurred the ill-will of a certain school official (who was a supporter of Hegelianism and, therefore, opposed to experimental research) and, in consequence, he resigned his position in Cologne.

For six years Ohm lived in Berlin, giving three mathematical lessons a week in the *Kriegsschule*, at a yearly salary of 300 thaler. In 1833 he secured an appointment at the polytechnicum in Nürnberg. Gradually his electric researches called forth respect and appreciation. Poggendorff and Fechner in Germany, Lenz in Russia, Wheatstone in England, Henry in America expressed their admiration for his work. The Royal Society of London in 1841 awarded him the Copley medal. In 1849, at the age of sixty-two, the ambition of his youth was finally attained. He was appointed extraordinary professor at the University of Munich, and in 1852 ordinary professor. He died two years later.

MEASUREMENT OF ELECTRIC RESISTANCE

Wheatstone, the great admirer of Ohm, perceiving the necessity of more accurate means of measuring resistances, invented what is known as "Wheatstone's bridge." **Charles Wheatstone** (1802–1875) was born near Gloucester. He became a manufacturer of musical instruments, but in 1834 accepted the chair of experimental physics at King's College, London.

[1] *Memorial of Joseph Henry,* 1880, p. 489.

Later he retired to private life, living on the income from his inventions, particularly that of the telegraph. He was an experimentalist of extraordinary skill, but disliked to speak in public. "In fulfilment of the duties of his office at King's College he delivered a course of eight lectures on sound . . . but his habitual though unreasonable distrust of his own powers of utterance proved to be an invincible obstacle, and he soon afterwards discontinued his lectures, but retained the professorship for many years. Although any one would be charmed by his able and lucid exposition *in private,* yet his attempt to repeat the same process *in public* invariably proved unsatisfactory." [1] For this reason some of his more important investigations were brought before the public by Faraday in the theatre of the Royal Institution.

It is interesting to note that the measurement of resistance has been brought to perfection chiefly by those interested in the development of the telegraph. Wheatstone invented the rheostat, but this has been superseded by the resistance box, which was first used by Werner Siemens. The earlier methods of measuring resistance labored under the defect of depending on the constancy of the batteries used. This source of trouble was removed by Becquerel, who introduced the differential galvanometer, and by Wheatstone, who adopted a method suggested by Hunter Christie, and was led to the invention of "Wheatstone's bridge." In 1843 Wheatstone describes two forms, differing merely in the arrangement of the wires. [2]

THE DEVELOPMENT OF THE GALVANOMETER

The galvanometer was invented by **J. S. C. Schweigger** (1779–1857), professor at Halle, in 1820, immediately after Oersted's experiment became known. Schweigger increased the effective action of the current by carrying the wire many times round the magnetic needle. In 1825 Leopoldo Nobili (1784–1835) of Florence used the astatic multiplier, having

[1] *Proc. Roy. Soc. of London,* Vol. 24, p. xviii.
[2] *Phil. Trans.,* Vol. 133, pp. 303–327; *Scientific Papers of Sir Charles Wheatstone,* London, 1879, p. 127.

two needles rigidly connected with each other, and with the south pole of the one pointing the same way as the north pole of the other. In 1839 **Claude Servais Mathias Pouillet** (1790–1868) professor in Paris, invented the tangent and the sine galvanometers. Great improvements in the promptness and delicacy of action of galvanometers were effected by Sir William Thomson, who devised mirror galvanometers for signalling through submarine cables. A galvanometer designed by **A. D'Arsonval** met with great favor. In principle it is the same as the "siphon recorder" of Sir William Thomson, employed in submarine telegraphy, and as the suspended coil galvanometer, used as early as 1836 by Sturgeon. About 1890 C. Vernon Boys recommended the use of quartz fibres in place of silk for needle suspension in delicate experimentation.

Work of Faraday

Michael Faraday (1791–1867), the greatest experimentalist of the nineteenth century in the field of electricity and magnetism, was born at Newington in London, and was the son of a blacksmith. "My education," he says, "was of the most ordinary description, consisting of little more than the rudiments of reading, writing, and arithmetic at a common dayschool. My hours out of school were passed at home and in the streets."[1] In 1804 he served as errand boy at a bookstore and bookbindery near his home. The following year he became an apprentice to the bookbinder. At this time he liked to read scientific books which happened to pass through his hands. "I made such simple experiments in chemistry," he says, "as could be defrayed in their expense by a few pence per week, and also constructed an electrical machine." At the age of nineteen he sometimes in the evening attended lectures given by a Mr. Tatum on natural philosophy, his brother paying the admission fee for him. In 1812 he had the good fortune to hear four lectures delivered at the Royal Institution by Sir H. Davy, the great chemist. About this time Far-

[1] B. Jones, *Life and Letters of Faraday*, 1870, Vol. I., p. 9.

aday went as a journeyman bookbinder to a Frenchman in London. His new work was uncongenial. "My desire," he said later, "to escape from trade, which I thought vicious and selfish, and to enter into the service of science, which I imagined made its pursuers amiable and liberal, induced me at last to make the bold and simple step of writing to Sir H. Davy, expressing my wishes, and a hope that if an opportunity came in his way he would favor my views; at the same time, I sent the notes I had taken of his lectures." Davy replied, "I am far from displeased with the proof you have given me of your confidence. . . ." Faraday became Davy's assistant at the Royal Institution in 1813. In the autumn of that year Davy and his wife started on a tour abroad, Faraday going with them as amanuensis. After being with Davy in France, Italy, Switzerland, he returned to the Royal Institution in 1815. Soon after his return he began original researches, and published his first paper in 1816. He also commenced to lecture before the "City Philosophical Society." In a letter he wrote of "the glorious opportunity I enjoy of improving in the knowledge of chemistry and the sciences with Sir H. Davy." In 1821 Faraday married, and brought his wife to his rooms at the Royal Institution, where they lived together for forty-six years. In 1824 he was elected member of the Royal Society at a time when Davy was its president. It is sad to relate that jealousy on the part of Davy led him to oppose Faraday's election. Nevertheless, Faraday always spoke with respect and admiration for the talents of the man who had done so much to start him in his early scientific career. In 1825 Faraday became director of the Royal Institution.

Oersted's memorable experiment of 1820 was studied in England by Wollaston, who in 1821, in the presence of Davy in the laboratory of the Royal Institution, sought by experiment to convert the deflection of the needle by the current into a permanent rotation. He also hoped to produce the reciprocal effect of a current rotating around a magnet. His experiments failed. As previously noted, Faraday began to study magnetic rotations, and on the morning of Christmas Day, 1821, he showed his wife for the first time the revolution of a magnetic needle around an electric current.[1]   (See Fig. 19.)   Faraday was blamed for not mentioning Wollaston in his paper describing the experiments, but Faraday justly claimed that he was in no way indebted to Wollaston.[2]

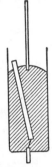

FIG. 19. **A magnet floats o n mercury.** Its lower end is held by a thread.   I t s upper end rotates around the wire carrying an electric current.

His next investigations were on the liquefaction of gases, on vibrating surfaces, and chemical subjects.   In 1831 came the discovery of magneto-electricity and induction currents.   As early as 1824 he had argued that as a voltaic current affects a magnet, so a magnet ought to react upon an electric current.   But he could obtain no experimental evidence of this effect.   Again, he knew that an electrified body acts upon an unelectrified body, that a wire carrying an electric current is electrified.   Could that wire excite in other wires a state similar to its own?   In 1825 he passed a current through one wire which was lying close to another wire connected with a galvanometer, but obtained no result.   The momentary existence of the phenomena of induction then escaped him.   In 1828 he again experimented without result.[3]

But Faraday persisted.   In August, 1831, he took a ring of soft iron (Fig. 20), and wound coils *A* and *B* around it.   Coil *B* was connected with a galvanometer.   When coil *A* was connected with a battery of ten cells, the galvanometer needle

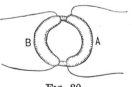

FIG. 20.

[1] John Tyndall, *Faraday as a Discoverer*, New York, 1877, p. 12. See also *Michael Faraday* by S. P. Thompson (1851–1916).

[2] Faraday explains all in his "Historical Statement respecting Electromagnetic Rotation," *Experimental Researches*, Vol. II., pp. 159–162.

[3] B. Jones *op. cit.*, Vol. II., p. 2.   What follows is taken from this source.

oscillated and settled at last in the original position. On dis-
connecting the battery the needle was again disturbed. Faraday did not at once grasp the full significance of this. On
September 23 he says in a letter, "I am busy just now again
on electromagnetism, and think I have got hold
of a good thing, but can't say. It may be a weed
instead of a fish that, after all my labor, I may at
last pull up." Next day he took an iron cylinder,
surrounded by a helix connected with a galvanometer. Then the cylinder was placed between
the poles of a bar magnet, as in Fig. 21. "Every
time the magnetic contact at N and S was made
or broken, there was magnetic motion at the
indicating helix [galvanometer]—the effect being, as in former cases, not permanent, but a
mere momentary push or pull. . . . Hence here
[was] distinct conversion of magnetism into electricity." This experiment is the converse of
Oersted's experiment; an electric current was excited by a magnet.

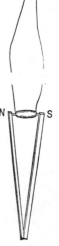

FIG. 21.

On October 1, 1831, Faraday discovered induced
electric currents. A helix, wound with insulated
copper wire 203 feet long, was connected with a galvanometer. Another coil of the same length and
wound around the same block of wood was joined
to the poles of a battery of ten cells. "A sudden
jerk was perceived when the battery communication was
made and broken, but it was so slight as to be scarcely visible.
It was one way when made, the other way when broken, and
the needle took up its natural position at intermediate times."
On October 17 he produced the same effects by merely thrust-
ing a permanent steel magnet into a coil of wire. The unexpected phenomenon in these experiments was that the induced
effect was not continuous; it was instantaneous "and partook
more of the nature of the electrical wave passed through from

the shock of a common Leyden jar, than the current from a voltaic battery."[1]

These epoch-making results threw light upon the mysterious experiment of Arago, who in 1824 had observed the motion of a magnet caused by rotating a copper disk in its neighborhood.

Faraday then, for a time, dropped electromagnetism and entered upon the study of electrolysis and the voltaic cell. He discovered the laws of electrolysis. The amount of water decomposed is proportional to the quantity of electricity passing through the liquid, no matter what the electric pressure or the area of the electrodes or the conductivity of the liquid may be. Thus, the amount of gas set free is an exact measure of the quantity of electricity passing through. He next ascertained that equal quantities of electricity decompose in different electrolytes equivalent amounts. In 1834 he introduced the terms "anode" and "cathode."

In 1834 William Jenkin observed that, if the wire which surrounds an electromagnet be used to join the plates of a single cell, a shock is felt each time contact is broken, provided the ends of the wire are grasped one in each hand. A. P. Masson in Paris had observed similar phenomena. Unaware of Henry's researches on self-induction, Faraday began in 1834 to study this action, and he recognized it as one of "induction of an electric current on itself"; he succeeded in showing the presence of an "extra current." The "extra current" at the "break" had the same direction as the original current and strengthened it; the "extra current" at the "make" flowed in the same direction and weakened the original current. This theory of the existence of an "extra current" met at first with considerable opposition, but was finally verified by other workers.

Sir Oliver Lodge recalls that Faraday's first magnetoelec-

[1] Faraday describes his tests in *Experimental Researches in Electricity*, London, 1839, Vol. I. See also *Ostwald's Klassiker*, No. 81. The order in which the experiments are described by Faraday is not quite the order of discovery.

tric apparatus, the forerunner of the dynamo, produced such insignificant results that Faraday after lecturing upon it, was asked what on earth was the use of it. A dignitary of the church had a conception of its dangerous possibilities in the hands of incendiaries, and deplored the discovery. Knowledge antedates understanding. A Danish thinker has well said, ''We live forward, but we understand backwards.'' In later years, contemplating Faraday's experiments on electromagnetism, Tyndall writes enthusiastically as follows: ''I cannot help thinking . . . that this discovery of magneto-electricity is the greatest experimental result ever obtained. It is the Mont Blanc of Faraday's own achievements. He always worked at great elevations, but higher than this he never attained.''[1]

The lofty heights which were scaled by the bold English explorer were at the same time reached by an American explorer, neither being conscious of the other's efforts until the summit was reached. In the discovery of magneto-electricity the name of Faraday must be accompanied by that of Joseph Henry.

RESEARCHES OF HENRY

Joseph Henry (1799–1878) was born at Albany, New York. At the age of fifteen he entered the shop of a watchmaker as an apprentice, although his chief ambition then was to excel as an actor and dramatic writer. Accidentally he came across Gregory's *Lectures on Experimental Philosophy,* the perusal of which created a love for science. He entered the Albany Academy as a pupil, and in 1826 became professor of mathematics there. He was appointed in 1832 professor of natural philosophy at Princeton College, and in 1846 secretary of the

[1] ''There is an aspect here of our physical research that is often lost sight of, namely, the small proportion of successful discoveries compared with the number of investigators. Certainly the number of unsuccessful attempts, even in the case of those fortunate individuals who make the great discoveries, is very much greater than the number of their successful attempts. Faraday's reputed satisfaction with 1/10 % return comes to mind.'' P. W. Bridgman, *The Logic of Modern Physics,* New York, 1927, p. 209.

newly established Smithsonian Institution in Washington. He first engaged in original investigation at Albany in 1827. Both as professor and as secretary his time was so largely taken up with teaching or routine work, that but little time was left for research. At the Albany Academy seven hours of daily teaching and the want of a room which could be used for experimentation prevented nearly all research, except during vacation time—the month of August. His researches were carried on in the large hall of the Academy, and invariably came to a stop with the first of September, the time when the Academy reopened.[1] Henry was the first to undertake important original electrical experimentation in the United States since the time of Franklin.

Henry's first improvements were in the electromagnet. We must here premise that in 1820 Arago and Ampère magnetized steel needles by placing them in a helix carrying an electric current, that in 1825 Sturgeon described the earliest electro-magnet worthy of the name. William Sturgeon (1783–1850), the son of an idle shoemaker in Lancashire, was a self-taught scientist, the founder of a monthly periodical, the *Annals of Electricity*.[2] Sturgeon's electromagnet of 1825 could lift nine pounds, or about twenty times its own weight. He used soft iron in place of steel, bent the iron in form of a horseshoe, and varnished the iron in order to insulate the single layer of naked copper wire wound around it in a loose spiral of eighteen turns. The current was obtained from a copper-zinc cell of small internal resistance. The fact that this horseshoe became a strong magnet as soon as the current started and lost its power the moment the current stopped made it the object of general interest. Professor Moll of Utrecht constructed a horseshoe magnet supporting 154 pounds. But the one who introduced radical improvements was Henry at Albany. Instead of varnishing the iron, he insulated the copper wire

[1] Mary A. Henry, "A Study of the Work of Faraday and Henry," *Electrical Engineer*, Vol. 13, p. 28.
[2] Consult a sketch of his life in S. P. Thompson, *The Electromagnet*, New York, 1891, pp. 412–418.

by covering it with silk; instead of a few turns of wire about the core, he put on many turns. His first magnet, having 400 turns, was exhibited in March, 1829. A further improvement consisted in winding the core with several coils, the ends of which were left free. Thereby the battery current could be made to subdivide, the coils being arranged in parallel. He experimented on the proper size of coil to be used with batteries of different kinds, and arrived at the highly important conclusion that one may use an "intensity" magnet with a long single wire, receiving current from an "intensity" battery, with cells grouped in series; or one may use a "quantity" magnet with many short wires, to be excited by a "quantity" battery of a single large pair of plates. The former magnet was to be preferred when the current was carried over considerable distances from the cell to the magnet, as in case of telegraphy. Henry's electromagnets were capable of sustaining fifty times their own weight under the stimulus of a single cell with plates hardly a hand's breadth in length and width.[1]

The originality of these results is the more conspicuous when we remember that Henry was at this time unacquainted with the law discovered by Ohm in 1826. In 1833 Henry asked Dr. Bache, "Can you give me any information about the theory of Ohm? Where is it to be found?" It was not till 1837, during his visit to London, that he became acquainted with Ohm's theory.[2]

In August, 1829, while he was testing the lifting power of magnets with different lengths of wire, and by means of his "intensity" magnet and battery had made the actual combination which constitutes the electric telegraph of to-day, he noticed an unexpected spark resulting from the break of a long coiled wire through which the battery current had been passing. "Nature . . . had lifted her veil for a moment to lure him in a different direction, and so it happened that when

[1] Henry published his results in the *Am. Jour. of Sci.*, Vol. 19, January, 1831, pp. 404, 405. Consult also the "Scientific Writings of Joseph Henry," in *Smithsonian Miscellaneous Collections*, Vol. 30, 1887, Part I., p. 37.

[2] Mary A. Henry, *op. cit.*, p. 30.

vacation came around again in August, 1830, he had taken up the investigation of this new pheomenon.'' He recognized its nature, and in 1832 published it under the heading ''Electrical Self-induction in a Long Helical Wire.''[1] Faraday's investigation on ''extra current'' was made in 1834 and published in 1835. The priority of the discovery of self-induction plainly belongs, therefore, to the American physicist.

Henry asked himself the question, if electricity can produce magnetism, cannot magnetism produce electricity? He took his ''quantity'' magnet at the Albany Academy, wound around the middle of its armature a coil of thin copper wire, the ends of which were connected with a galvanometer, forty feet away. The armature was placed across the ends of the magnet; the plates of the battery were dipped into the dilute acid, the magnet was excited, and the needle of the galvanometer swerved; the answer came, magnetism can produce electricity. Like Faraday, Henry was surprised to find only momentary effects, and that the deflection of the needle at ''break'' was in the opposite direction to that at ''make.'' There is almost conclusive evidence to show that this experiment was performed in August, 1830, or one year before Faraday made his first experiment on magneto-electricity.[2] Henry was enthusiastic, and was getting ready for an exhaustive series of experiments in August, 1831. He started to make a much larger electromagnet, also a great ''reel,'' aiming to secure a machine capable of powerful work—he was endeavoring to make a dynamo. But vacation drew to a close before it was completed.[3]

He resumed work, not in August, 1832, but in June! And why? By chance he had come upon a paragraph in a periodical, stating that Faraday had shown that magnetism can produce electricity. Faraday's experimentation was given only in outline. Henry could not tell to what extent he was anticipated. He immediately went to work. Using his old appara-

[1] *Am. Jour. Sci.*, Vol. 22, 1832, p. 408.
[2] Mary A. Henry, *op. cit.*, pp. 53 *et seq.*
[3] Mary A. Henry, *op. cit.*, p. 54.

tus, he repeated the experiments mentioned in the notice, and hastily prepared a paper, printed in the *American Journal of Science,* July, 1832. This paper contains tests made before he had heard of Faraday's work, and also tests made after that. Faraday had published his discovery of magneto-electricity in 1831. While it is almost certain that Henry's discovery antedated Faraday's Henry was anticipated in the date of publication. Hence the priority rightly belongs to Faraday. In 1837 Henry was in Great Britain, and became personally acquainted with England's great physicists. Henry loved to dwell on the hours he spent in Faraday's society. Faraday and Wheatstone expressed great esteem for the American physicist. At King's College, in London, Faraday, Wheatstone, Daniell, and Henry once tried to evolve the electric spark from the thermopile. The Englishmen attempted it and failed. Henry, calling in the aid of a discovery he had made of the effect of a long interpolar wire wrapped around a piece of soft iron, succeeded. Faraday became as wild as a boy, and, jumping up, shouted, "Hurrah for the Yankee experiment." [1]

Henry carried on original researches in various departments of physics, but of all his investigations the most finished are those of induced currents of different orders, made in the summer of 1838 at Princeton. As we have seen, currents induced by currents were observed by Faraday. As Faraday's secondary current was but momentary, it was by no means self-evident that it could act as a primary current and itself induce a current in a third circuit. Henry proved that induced currents of higher order are possible. "It was found that with a small battery a shock could be given from the current of the third order to twenty-five persons joining hands; also shocks perceptible in the arms were obtained from a current of the fifth order." [2]

[1] *A Memorial of Joseph Henry, Washington,* 1880, p. 506.
[2] *Trans. Am. Phil. Soc.,* Vol.. VI. (N.S.), p. 303. Quite full accounts of Henry's work on induced currents are given in J. A. Fleming, *The Alternate-current Transformer,* Vol. I.

An observation which has an important bearing on more recent electromagnetic theories was made by Henry in 1842. He showed that the discharge of the Leyden jar did not consist of a single restoration of the equilibrium, but of a rapid succession of librations back and forth, gradually diminishing to zero. That the Leyden jar discharge is oscillatory was shown again in 1847 by Helmholtz in his paper "Ueber die Erhaltung der Kraft." But both Helmholtz and Henry were anticipated by Felix Savary, who drew this conclusion from an experiment as early as 1827.[1] In 1853 Sir William Thomson, unaware of the earlier researches, concluded from theory and mathematical deduction that the discharge must be oscillatory.

DESIGNS OF TRANSFORMERS

Henry's "quantity" magnet and coiled armature of 1830 (?), and Faraday's ring (Fig. 20), used in 1831, may be looked upon as the first *transformers*. Inspired by Henry's researches, Charles Grafton Page (1812–1868), a native of Salem and graduate of Harvard College, after 1840 examiner in the patent office in Washington, invented what is now known as the Ruhmkorff's Coil. His earliest research was published in 1836. In 1838 he had constructed an induction coil [2] of a high degree of perfection. The primary was of thick copper wire; the secondary of very thin wire. The vibrations of an automatic hammer made and broke a mercury contact. To shorten the time of contact at break, Page poured oil or alcohol over the mercury. Later this device was suggested by others and is usually attributed to Foucault. The platinum contact, in place of the mercurial break, was first suggested in Germany in 1839 by J. P. Wagner and by Neef. Of Page's coil Uppenborn says: "The effects which Page produced by means of this instrument were much more

[1] *Memorial of Joseph Henry*, 1880, pp. 255, 396, 448.
[2] Described in *Am. Jour. Sci.*, Vol. 35, 1839, p. 259. A drawing of the coil is given there, also in Bedell, *Principles of the Transformer*, 1896, p. 291; in Fleming, *Alternate-current Transformer*, Vol. II., 1892, p. 26; and in F. Uppenborn, *History of the Transformer*, 1889, p. 7.

intense than those produced by Ruhmkorff with his, as Page succeeded with only a single Grove element in inducing in the second circuit such a high electromotive force as produced sparks $4\frac{1}{2}$ inches in length through a vacuum tube—a result which Ruhmkorff, although his invention created such a great and well-deserved attention, did not attain." In the year 1850 Page produced a coil yielding sparks through the air, eight inches in length. Says Uppenborn, "All things considered, it is not a little surprising that while the invention of the Ruhmkorff's coil was still in its infancy, the wonderful output of Page's apparatus was still, even in the year 1851, quite unknown in Europe." Evidently the coil should have been named after Page and not after Ruhmkorff.

Heinrich Daniel Ruhmkorff or **Rühmkorff** (1803–1877) was born at Hanover in Germany. In 1819 he went to Paris where, later, he started a manufactory of physical apparatus. A long series of experiments resulted in the appearance in 1851 of the famous "Ruhmkorff coil." It gave sparks in air two inches in length. In 1858 one of his coils received the first prize of 50,000 francs at the French Exposition of Electrical Apparatus.[1] Jamin says that Ruhmkorff died almost a poor man, because he had spent all his earnings in behalf of science and in works of benevolence.[2]

The Ruhmkorff coil is a transformer of the "open magnetic circuit" type, while the commercial transformer of our day, like Faraday's original ring (Fig. 20), has a "closed magnetic circuit"; that is, in the latter the magnetic lines of force nowhere pass through air, but follow the easier iron path throughout. The transformer or converter used in systems

---

[1] It has been claimed by some that this prize should have been awarded to **Edward Samuel Ritchie** (1814–1895), the American philosophical instrument maker, who improved on Ruhmkorff's instrument of 1851 by dividing the secondary coil into sections for the purpose of better insulation. This division had been previously suggested by Poggendorff. One of Ritchie's instruments was exhibited in England in 1857. It is alleged that Ruhmkorff secured one of these and, copying it successfully, captured the grand prize. See A. E. Dolbear in *Proc. Am. Acad. of Arts and Sciences*, N. S., Vol. 23, 1895–1896, p. 359.

[2] Nature, Vol. 17, 1877, p. 169.

of electric lighting or long-distance power transmission, has been developed by Cromwell Fleetwood Varley, Paul Jablochkoff, C. W. Harrison, C. T. and E. B. Bright, S. Z. de Ferranti, Carl Zipernowsky, Max Déri, Otto Titus Bláthy, Gaulard and Gibbs, William Stanley, and others. Thus, the theoretical researches of Faraday and Henry, carried on out of pure love for science have become the foundation of one of the most extensive commercial developments of modern times, and are contributing vastly toward the progress of civilization and the comfort of mankind.

ELECTROSTATIC INDUCTION

Returning to Faraday at the Royal Institution in London, we find him soon after 1835 working on electrostatic induction. Coulomb and others had assumed the theory of "action at a distance"; electric charges were supposed to attract and repel each other at a distance without being affected in any way by the intervening medium. Faraday had an idea that this view was erroneous, that electric attraction and repulsion are propagated by means of molecular action among the contiguous particles of the insulating medium, which thereby participates in the propagation of the electric forces. Hence Faraday termed such medium "dielectrics." Faraday satisfied himself by experiments that induction does not always take place in straight lines, as the theory of an action at a distance without the aid of an intervening medium would lead us to believe; on the contrary, induction takes place along curved lines, and by the action of contiguous particles. These curved lines he termed "lines of force." His experiments showed that the intensity of the electric force between two charged bodies varies with the nature of the insulating medium. He was thus led to the capital discovery of what is now termed "specific inductive capacity." Henry Cavendish had arrived at the same results long ago, but had allowed these pearls of scientific truth to be hidden away. Faraday's apparatus, by which he compared specific inductive capacities, was in principle a Leyden jar in which the dielectric could be changed. It consisted of two concentric spheres. The hollow space between their surfaces could be filled with any desired material. Taking air as the standard dielectric, he found the electric attraction or repulsion for sulphur 2.26 times greater; for shellac, 2.0 times; for glass, at least 1.76 times greater. Faraday's experiments were published in 1837; since 1870 large additions to our knowledge of this subject have been made, but owing to electric absorption the values assigned by different observers for the specific inductive capacity of various substances show a most perplexing disagreement.

In these researches Faraday created a symbolism which has since been universally adopted in teaching physics. We refer to his "lines of force." He used this term for the first time in 1831 in connection with the lines exhibited by iron filings, but the concept of "lines of force" was held by others before him; for instance, by T. J. Seebeck.[1] In Faraday's reasoning "lines of force" took the place of mathematical analysis, a knowledge of which he had had no opportunity to acquire. Being debarred from following the course of thought which had led to the achievements of the French mathematical physicists, Poisson and Ampère he invoked the aid of "lines of force," which, in his mind's eye, he saw as distinctly as the solid bodies from which they emanated.[2] Faraday's ingenous symbolism found its way not only into the technique, but also into elementary instruction. Even in Germany, where the theory of action at a distance in electricity and magnetism had the strongest hold, Faraday's notions found acceptance; for Hertz's experiments added support to the fundamental hypothesis in Maxwell's developments of Faraday's theory of the dielectric.[3]

[1] See Seebeck's paper in *Ostwald's Klassiker*, No. 63.
[2] See Clerk Maxwell, "Action at a Distance," *Nature*, Vol. 7, 1872–1873, p. 342.
[3] See A. Schülke in *Zeitschr. f. Math. Unterricht*, Vol. 25, p. 403.

LIGHT AND ELECTRICITY

Faraday was led by speculation to the belief that there existed some direct relation between light and electricity or magnetism. Many experimental attempts to prove this yielded purely negative results, but in 1845 his strong conviction was finally supported by actual experiment. "I have at last succeeded in illuminating a magnetic curve or line of force, and in magnetizing a ray of light."[1] Faraday caused a polarized beam to pass through a piece of "heavy glass," lying in a strong magnetic field, due to a large electromagnet. By means of a Nicol prism, it was found that the wave of light was twisted round by the action of the magnet so that its vibrations were executed in a different plane. He says: "Not only heavy glass, but solids and liquids, acids and alkalies, oils, water, alcohol, ether, all possess this power." Commenting on this relation between light and magnetism, Whewell wrote Faraday: "I cannot help believing that it is another great stride up the ladder of generalization, on which you have been climbing so high and standing so firm."

Faraday's powerful magnets and heavy glass led him to the verification of another of his prophecies. That magnetic properties should be confined to iron and nickel appeared to him too extraordinary to be probable. Knowing that the magnetic strength of iron lessens at very high temperatures, he suspected that other metals might show magnetism at lower temperatures. As early as 1836 he experimented on metals cooled to — 50° C., but without results. In 1839 he repeated these experiments at — 80° C., again without result. In 1845 he added cobalt to the list of magnetic substances. In 1846, at last, he published the general result. On November 4, 1845, he suspended by silk a bar of heavy glass between the poles of his new electromagnet. When the magnet was excited the heavy glass was repelled from the poles so as to assume an equatorial position. Faraday experimented with

[1] B. Jones, *op. cit.*, Vol. II., p. 195. See also *Experimental Researches*, 19th Series.

other substances and found that all liquids and solids were attracted or repelled, provided that sufficient magnetic power was used. Sulphur, india-rubber, asbestos, tissue of the human body, were repelled—were shown to be diamagnetic. Says Faraday, "If a man could be in the magnetic field, like Mohammed's coffin, he would turn until across the magnetic line."[1] Diamagnetic phenomena had been observed before, but the experiments were not known to Faraday. Brugmans, A. C. Becquerel, Le Baillif, Saigey, and Seebeck had indicated the existence of repulsive force exercised by a magnet on two or three substances. Wheatstone called Faraday's attention to Becquerel's research on the magnetic condition of matter, and Faraday replied, "It is astonishing to think how he could have been so near the discovery of the great principle and fact, and yet so entirely miss them both, and fall back into old and preconceived notions."[2]

[1] In 1853 the London public was greatly excited over the "table-turning" of three skilful performers. Without due inquiry, the effects were referred to electricity, to magnetism, or to some unrecognized physical power able to affect inanimate bodies. Faraday looked into the matter and wrote in part as follows: "I have not been at work except in turning the tables upon the table-turners, nor should I have done that, but that so many inquiries poured in upon me, that I thought it better to stop the inpouring flood by letting all know at once what my views and thoughts were. What a weak, credulous, incredulous, unbelieving, superstitious, bold, frightened, what a ridiculous world ours is, as far as concerns the mind of man." Faraday complains of the great body of men who refer the results "to some unrecognized physical force, without inquiring whether the known forces are not sufficient, or who even refer them to diabolical or supernatural agency rather than suspend judgment or acknowledge to themselves that they are not learned enough in these matters to decide on the nature of the action. *I think the system of education that could leave the mental condition of the public body in the state in which this subject has found it must have been greatly deficient in some very important principle.*"—B. Jones, *op. cit.*, Vol. II., pp. 300–302.

[2] In coining the words "diamagnetic" and "paramagnetic" Faraday consulted Whewell, who wrote in 1850 in a letter as follows: "I am always glad to hear of your wanting new words, because the want shows that you are pursuing new thoughts. . . . The purists would certainly object to the opposition, or coördination, of 'terromagnetic' and 'diamagnetic.' Hence it would appear that the two classes of magnetic bodies are those which place their length *parallel* or *according* to the terrestrial magnetic lines and those which place their length *transverse* to such lines. Keeping the preposition *dia* for the latter the preposition

ELECTROMAGNETIC THEORY OF LIGHT

Beginning about the time of Ampère, several new electric theories came to be advanced.[1] The early theories neglected the action of the dielectric, but assumed the existence of one or two electric fluids and took no account of the principle of the conservation of energy. The recognition by Faraday of the influence of the dielectric medium "is, perhaps, the most important step that has ever been made in the theory of electricity." We have seen that he was led to this by his desire to get rid, as far as possible, of the idea of action at a distance, which was very prevalent in his time, but to which his researches have given the death-blow. Faraday's ideas were expressed in mathematical language and were more fully developed, so as to culminate in the electromagnetic theory of light, by the genius of Maxwell.

James Clerk Maxwell (1831–1879) was born in Edinburgh, enjoyed good opportunities for early development, and soon displayed power for mathematical and physical research. At the age of fifteen he published a paper on oval curves. He attended meetings of the Royal Society of Edinburgh. In 1847 he met William Nicol, the inventor of the polarizing prism, and became interested in the phenomena of polarized light. Professor Campbell[2] says that, to keep their education at the Edinburgh Academy "abreast of the requirements of the day," etc., it was thought desirable that they should have lessons in "Physical Science." So one of the classical masters gave them out of a text-book. The only thing I distinctly remember about these hours is that Maxwell and P. G. Tait

para or *ana* might be used for the former; perhaps *para* would be best, as the word 'parallel,' in which it is involved, would be a technical memory for it." See I. Todhunter, *William Whewell*, London, 1876, Vol. II., p. 363.

[1] Consult J. J. Thomson, "Report on Electrical Theories," *Report of the Brit. Association*, 1885, pp. 97–155; Helmholtz, "On Later Views of the Connection of Electricity and Magnetism," *Smithsonian Report*, 1873.

[2] L. Campbell and W. Garnett, *Life of James Clerk Maxwell*, London, 1882, p. 85; we are using also R. T. Glazebrook, *James Clerk Maxwell and Modern Physics*, New York, 1896.

seemed to know much more about the subject than our teacher did. In the fall of 1847 Maxwell entered the University of Edinburgh, learning mathematics from Kelland, physics from J. D. Forbes, and logic from Sir Wm. Hamilton. Forbes gave him free use of the class apparatus for original experiments, and he worked without any assistance or supervision with physical and chemical apparatus, and devoured all sorts of scientific works in the library. In 1850 Maxwell entered the University of Cambridge, where he obtained the position of second wrangler. At this time, and later, Maxwell was fond of writing quaint verses which he brought round to his friends, "with a sly chuckle at the humor, which, though his own, no one enjoyed more than himself." [1] Maxwell became professor of physics at Marischal College, Aberdeen, in 1856; at King's College, London, in 1860; at Cambridge University, in 1871.

In papers on "Physical Lines of Force," published in 1861 and 1862, and in later papers, he translated Faraday's theories into the language of mathematics, and developed the theory according to which the energy of the electromagnetic field resides in the dielectric as well as in the conductors. Faraday had said that "induction appears to consist in a certain polarized state of the particles into which they are thrown by the electrified body sustaining the action, the particles assuming positive and negative points or parts. . . . This state must be a forced one, for it is originated and sustained only by a force, and sinks to the normal or quiescent state when that force is removed." Maxwell changed Faraday's nomenclature; instead of the polarization of the dielectric, he speaks of the change as consisting of an "electric displacement." He looked upon the action in the dielectric as analogous to that of an elastic solid which springs back to its original position when the external force is removed. The change in electric displacement is an electric current, called a "displacement current," to distinguish it from a current in conductors,

---

[1] Read verses in L. Campbell and W. Garnett, *op. cit.*, pp. 577–651, particularly his parody of Tyndall's Belfast Address.

designated as "conduction current." (Hertz proved the ex
istence of these "displacement currents" by experiments which
are quite free from objection.) In a medium supposed to be
subject to such electric displacement, waves of periodic displacement could be set up. The velocity of such a wave was
very nearly equal to that of light. Hence, "the elasticity of
the magnetic medium in the air is the same as that of the luminiferous medium if these two coexistent, coextensive, and
equally elastic media are not rather one medium." That electromagnetic phenomena and the phenomena called light have
their seat in the same medium, and are, in fact, identical in
nature, is the theory elaborated by Maxwell in his great
Treatise on Electricity and Magnetism,[1] published in 1873.
While this theory did not contradict any observed facts, Maxwell himself had only few and indecisive criteria in support
of it, but his great prophecy was experimentally confirmed by
the illustrious Hertz.

Hertz's Experiments in Electromagnetic Waves

Heinrich Rudolf Hertz [2] (1857–1894) was born at Hamburg. After leaving the gymnasium, he fitted himself for
civil engineering. At the age of twenty, he came to a turning-
point in his career; he was converted from a man of practice
to one of learning. He went to Berlin, and, under Helmholtz,
advanced rapidly. He became in 1880 assistant to Helmholtz, in 1883 privat-docent at Kiel, in 1885 professor of
physics at the Technical High School at Karlsruhe. There

[1] This epoch-making book has always been found difficult of comprehension. H. Poincaré (1854–1912) writes this: "A French *savant*,
one of those who have most completely fathomed Maxwell's meaning,
said to me, 'I understand everything in the book except what is meant
by a body charged with electricity.'" Hertz expresses himself as
follows: "Many a man has thrown himself with zeal into the study
of Maxwell's work, and, even when he has not stumbled upon unwonted
mathematical difficulties, has nevertheless been compelled to abandon
the hope of forming for himself an altogether consistent conception of
Maxwell's ideas. I have fared no better myself."—*Electric Waves*,
trans. by D. E. Jones, p. 20.

[2] H. Ebert in *Electrician* (London), Vol. 33, 1894, p. 272. See also
a sketch by H. Bonfort, in *Smithsonian Report*, 1894, p. 719.

he performed his memorable experiments on electromagnetic waves. In 1889 he succeeded Clausius at Bonn, and
thus, at the age of thirty-two, occupied a position usually
attained much later in life. In 1892 a chronic blood-poison-
ing began to undermine his health, and he died in the prime
of life.

In 1888 Hertz found means of detecting the presence of
electromagnetic waves arising from Leyden jar or coil sparks.
This was an accomplishment which Maxwell had feared would
never be realized. During the oscillatory discharge of a Leyden jar, or of a Holtz machine, electromagnetic waves radiate
into space. Such a wave is called "electromagnetic" because
it has two components—an electric wave and a magnetic wave.
Hertz was able to observe each separately. If electromagnetic waves fall upon a reflector (a large sheet of tin, for instance), then they are thrown back, and the interference of
the two trains of waves, moving in opposite directions, gives
rise to places of least and of maximum disturbance (nodes and
antinodes). Hertz's detector consisted simply of a circular
wire, the ends terminating in brass knobs, which were ad-
justed at small distances apart. A wave falling upon the wire,
under suitable conditions, causes minute sparks to pass between the knobs. Hertz succeeded in reflecting, refracting,
diffracting, and polarizing these waves. "The object of these
experiments," says Hertz, "was to test the fundamental
hypotheses of the Faraday-Maxwell theory, and the result of
the experiments is to confirm the fundamental hypotheses of
the theory." [1] Electricity has thus annexed the entire terri-
tory of light and "radiant heat."

After Hertz had published his results, he learned that
English experimentalists had been working in similar lines.
He says: "I may here be permitted to record the good work

[1] Hertz's papers are collected in a book, *Electric Waves*, trans. by
D. E. Jones, London, 1893. A full account of Hertz's experiments is
given in Fleming, *Alternate-current Transformer*, Vol. I., in Preston,
Theory of Light. See also O. J. Lodge, "The Work of Hertz" in *Na-
ture*, Vol. 50, 1894, pp. 133–139, 160, 161; Poincaré "On Maxwell and
Hertz," in *Nature*, Vol. 50, 1894, pp. 8–11.

done by two English colleagues who at the same time as myself were striving toward the same end. In the same year in which I carried out the above research, Professor Oliver Lodge, in Liverpool, investigated the theory of the lightning conductor, and in connection with this carried out a series of experiments on the discharge of small condensers which led him on to the observation of oscillations and waves in wires. Inasmuch as he entirely accepted Maxwell's views, and eagerly strove to verify them, there can scarcely be any doubt that if I had not anticipated him he would also have succeeded in observing waves in air, and thus also in proving the propagation with time of electric force. Professor Fitzgerald, in Dublin, had some years before endeavored to predict, with the aid of theory, the possibility of such waves, and to discover the conditions for producing them. My own experiments were not influenced by the researches of these physicists, for I only knew of them subsequently." [1]

Since the publication of Hertz's experiments, several new detectors of electromagnetic radiation from Leyden jar or coil sparks were found. The frog's leg, to which we owe the discovery of current electricity, was tried, but gave poor results. Small Geissler tubes were used in place of the minute air-gap in Hertz's receiver or resonator. But the most useful and delicate of the contrivances was the "coherer," the invention of which rests on observations made independently by Edouard Branly, of the Catholic Institute in Paris,[2] and Oliver J. Lodge, of University College, Liverpool.[3] As usually constructed, it consisted of a tube of filings (iron filings are good), placed in circuit with a voltaic cell and a galvanometer. The filings offer a high resistance, but as soon as an electric wave reaches the coherer, the resistance breaks down through a process of electric welding between the filings, the battery current increases and gives a larger galvanometer deflection. Improvements on Hertz's vibrator, or wave-

---

[1] Hertz, *Electric Waves*, trans. by D. E. Jones, p. 3.
[2] *Comp. Rend.*, Vol. 111, p. 785; Vol. 112, p. 90.
[3] *Nature*, Vol. 50, pp. 133–139.

radiator, have been made by Augusto Righi (1850–1920) of Bologna.[1]

THEORIES OF MAGNETISM

We have seen that Ampère, observing that solenoids act like magnets, proposed a theory of magnetism according to which all magnets were simply collections of currents. He supposed that around every molecule a minute current is flowing ceaselessly. As such an assumption cannot be experimentally verified, and as it savors somewhat of the fantastic, later theorists were content to assume with Siméon Denis Poisson (1781–1840), that each molecule becomes magnetized when the field begins to act, or with Wilhelm Weber, that the individual particles are permanently magnetic. Weber made no attempt to explain the origin of this magnetism. He advanced the view that in hard steel there was some kind of friction between the molecules, which prevented the molecules of magnetized steel from turning back into higgledy-piggledy positions. Then J. A. Ewing, of the University of Cambridge, somewhat modified Weber's theory and showed that a complete explanation of the phenomena can be given by merely considering the forces which the magnetic molecules necessarily exert on one another. He prepared groups of little magnets, pivoted like compass needles, so that each was free to tuin, except as each was restrained by the presence of the others. An electromagnet, whose strength could be varied at will, was used as the external magnetizing force. With the aid of this model Ewing was able to imitate the phenomena of the magnetization of iron—how, with a weak magnetizing force, magnetism is acquired slowly, then, as the external force increases, the iron is gaining magnetism fast for a while, but is approaching a third stage in which the rate of increment of magnetism falls off and the iron approaches satura-

[1] *Electrician* (London), Vol. 39, 1897, p. 686; consult also O. Lodge, "History of the Coherer Principle," *Electrician*, Vol. 40, 1897, pp. 87–91.

tion.[1] If now the magnetizing force is gradually diminished, then the model again simulates a piece of iron; at first the reduction in the magnetization is slow, then instability begins and the magnetization diminishes rapidly. When the external force is entirely removed, a little residual magnetism remains. As the magnetizing force is applied in the opposite direction, the reversal of the polarity occurs with a rush. "We thus find," says Ewing, "a close imitation of all the features observed when iron or any of the other magnetic metals is carried through a cyclic magnetizing process. The effect of any such process is to form a *loop* in the curve which expresses the relation of the magnetism to the magnetizing force. The changes of magnetism always lag behind the changes of magnetizing force. This tendency to lag behind is called magnetic *hysteresis*." When iron is magnetized, energy is given to it; when it is demagnetized, energy is taken from it. When the magnetization is cyclically altered, there is a net loss, or rather a waste of energy (a transformation into heat), the amount of which is proportional to the area of the loop. This heating Ewing explains thus: "When the molecule becomes unstable and tumbles violently over, it oscillates and sets its neighbors oscillating." Heat is due to these oscillations. When heated, iron is found to be more permeable to magnetization, until a stage is reached, at a high temperature, when the magnetic quality vanishes almost suddenly. This increase in permeability seems to be due to expansion, so that the molecular centres lie further apart, and also to the fact that the molecules are thrown into vibration. Thereby the molecules tumble more easily from one group arrangement into another. As to the loss of magnetic property, Ewing says: "It is at least a conjecture worth consideration whether the sudden loss of magnetic quality at a higher temperature is not due to the vibrations becoming so violent as to set the

[1] Consult Ewing, "The Molecular Process in Magnetic Induction," *Nature*, Vol. 44, 1891, pp. 566–572. Reprinted in *Smithsonian Report*, 1892, pp. 255–268.

molecules spinning, when, of course, their polarity would be of no avail to produce magnetization.''

The study of the magnetic properties of iron and steel has received a powerful stimulus from the demands of the designers of dynamos, motors, and transformers. The accurate measurement of the relation of various magnetizing forces to the magnetization produced in a given piece of iron or nickel was first undertaken by Rowland. We digress to sketch the life of this foremost American physicist of his day.[1]

Henry Augustus Rowland (1848–1901) was born at Honesdale, Pennsylvania. As a boy he displayed a love for science and a dislike for Latin and Greek. In 1870 he graduated as civil engineer from the Rensselaer Polytechnic Institute at Troy, New York. A year later he returned to the Institute as instructor in physics. After publishing a few minor papers, he undertook an investigation of the magnetic properties of iron from which he expected, as he wrote to his sister, ''good substantial reputation.'' But the ideas were then so novel that the paper was more than once rejected because it was not understood. The appearance at this time of Maxwell's wonderful *Treatise on Electricity and Magnetism* induced Rowland to send his paper to Maxwell who surely would be a competent judge of its value. Maxwell received it with enthusiasm and at once had it published in the *Philosophical Magazine* for August, 1873. The experiments of Rowland were the first research of magnetism in which the results were expressed in absolute measure; the reasoning is carried out in the language of Faraday's theory of lines of magnetic force. Rowland pointed out that the flow of magnetic lines of force through a magnet admitted of accurate calculation, and that the law ''is similar to the law of Ohm.'' The word ''permeability,'' denoting the ratio between the magnetizing force and the resulting magnetization, was proposed by Lord Kelvin. Rowland's paper was appreciated abroad. When President D. C. Gilman was organizing the Johns Hopkins

[1] See the Sketch by Thomas C. Mendenhall in the *Report of the Smithsonian Institution for 1901*, p. 750.

University, he sought the advice of Maxwell on filling the post of physics. Maxwell recommended Rowland. When Gilman went to West Point as a member of a visiting Board, Michie of that institution spoke highly of Rowland. He was called to West Point by telegraph, and on the banks of the Hudson Gilman and Rowland walked and talked, "he telling me," Gilman said, "his dreams for science and I telling him my dreams for higher education." Rowland was appointed, but was allowed to go to Europe for a year. He spent several months in the laboratory of Helmholtz at Berlin. While there he carried out a very difficult experiment on the magnetic effect of a moving electrostatic charge. The theoretical interest of this experiment has been growing with the advent of the electron theory. The rotating electrostatic charge affected a magnetic needle and acted like a current. His conclusions have been held in question, some experimenters reaching negative results. Rowland himself repeated the experiment in 1889 and again in 1900. By that time its accuracy was accepted. At the Johns Hopkins University he trained a number of young physicists. He was unfit for the ordinary routine work of the class room. Graduate students were placed largely upon their own resources. When asked at one time with reference to graduate students—"What do you do with them?" "Do with them?" replied Rowland, "I shall neglect them." Nevertheless, he was an inspiration, as his former pupils testify. He had no patience with pretense and sham. The physicist George F. Barker once told Lord Rayleigh [1] of a visit he and Rowland paid to the workshop of Keely in Philadelphia, who claimed to be able to run a motor by powerful mystic forces known only to himself. Some apparently remarkable effects were exhibited, but Rowland suspected that what purported to be a wire was really a hollow tube conveying compressed air. He stepped forward to satisfy himself by cutting it. But Keely flew at him to prevent this, and they

[1] R. J. Strutt, Fourth Baron Rayleigh, *John William Strutt, Third Baron Rayleigh*, London, 1924, p. 146.

rolled together on the floor. After Keely's death it was shown that he produced his effects by trickery.

THE CONCEPT OF POTENTIAL

A concept which is finding wide application in theoretical physics is that of *potential*. Its origin we owe to the mathematicians, Lagrange and Laplace, who applied it to gravitation problems. The first to apply the potential function to a different class of problems was **George Green** (1793–1841), who introduced it into the mathematical theory of electricity and magnetism. His paper of 1828 escaped the notice even of English mathematicians until 1846, when Lord Kelvin had it reprinted. Meanwhile all of Green's general theorems had been rediscovered by Lord Kelvin, Michel Chasles, J. C. F. Sturm, and Gauss. The mathematicians defined *potential* as that function whose differential coefficient with respect to an axis of coördinates is equal to the force acting along that axis. When the ideas of energy and work came to occupy a more central position in the minds of physicists, the term "potential" was interpreted as signifying work done or energy acquired. For instance, "electric potential at any point is the work that must be expended upon a unit of electricity in bringing it to that point from an infinite distance." The notion has been made use of in elementary instruction, and has often been explained by its analogy to temperature or difference of level.

THE EARTH'S MAGNETISM

After the time of Halley, charts showing terrestrial declination were published by Mountain and Dodson, Bellin, and John Churchman (Philadelphia, 1790; London, 1794). The question as to the number of the earth's magnetic poles continued to be agitated. **Christopher Hansteen** (1784–1873), director of the astronomical observatory at Christiania, in 1812 attempted to answer the prize question of the Royal Danish Academy of Sciences, viz. "Is it necessary, in order to explain facts in the earth's magnetism, to suppose more than one magnetic axis in the earth?'' He held the affirmative view. Making terrestrial magnetism his life study, he endeavored to subject to mathematical analysis all observations, with the view of testing rigorously Halley's speculations as to the existence of four magnetic poles in the earth. From secular changes in the lines of equal declination he inferred that there were two northern magnetic poles, moving obliquely toward the west, and two southern poles, moving toward the west; that the shortest time in which all the poles return to the same relative position agreed closely with the period of revolution in the precession of the equinoxes. "By the liberality of the Norwegian government he was enabled to go to Siberia, in company with Due and Erman, to search for the ideal point of the Asiatic pole of magnetism. They started from Berlin, April 25, 1828. . . . Ten magnetic observatories were established in the Russian empire by the recommendation of Humboldt, and great results were reached by Gauss, Sabine, Lamont, and others from the materials collected by Hansteen and Erman. Hansteen ascertained beyond dispute the existence of a magnetic pole in Siberia supplementary to that in British America, and also the biaxial character of the earth's magnetism."[1] The fact that the earth's magnetism in the northern hemisphere reaches a maximum in two places, viz. in the north of Canada and in the north of Siberia, proves conclusively that the earth is not a single magnet. But neither Hansteen's theory nor that of Sir Edward Sabine (1788–1883) seem to be in accordance with observations of more recent years. The cause of the earth's magnetism and its secular changes continues to be a mystery.[2]

Absolute Units of Measurement

An important step toward the accurate study of terrestrial magnetism was taken in Germany by **Carl Friedrich Gauss**

[1] *Proc. Roy. Soc. of London*, Vol. 24, 1875–1876, p. v.
[2] Consult further A. W. Rücker, "Recent Researches in Terrestrial Magnetism," *Nature*, Vol. 57, 1897, pp. 160 *et seq.*

(1777–1855), who, in conjunction with **Alexander von Humboldt** (1769–1859), organized the German Magnetic Union. Its object was to take continuous observations of the magnetic elements (dip, declination, intensity) at fixed points. Observations were begun in 1834 and were mostly concluded about 1842. Gauss and **Wilhelm Weber** (1804–1891) of Göttingen designed the instruments used in these measurements. Gauss's theory does not aim to investigate the cause of terrestrial magnetism and its changes, but is simply a mathematical presentation of the distribution of magnetism over the earth's surface.

Speculations have frequently been indulged in as to the magnetic and electric relationship between the sun and the earth. But nothing very conclusive was then adduced.[1]

In a paper on terrestrial magnetism, read in 1832, Gauss proposed a system of *absolute units*. Since all forces may be measured by the motions they produce, only three fundamental units are necessary, viz. a unit of length, of time, of mass. The advantage to be gained is this: If all practical units are derived from these three, then all results of measurement are comparable with each other. Gauss took as the unit of force that which gives to unit mass in unit time a unit velocity. As the unit of magnetic intensity he chose that quantity which, acting upon an equal quantity at unit distance, exerts unit force. Gauss's use of absolute units in the measurement of terrestrial magnetism led his colleague at Göttingen, Wilhelm Weber, to introduce absolute units in electricity. His first papers on the subject were published in 1846, 1852, 1856. As practical units of resistance, Moritz Hermann Jacobi at St. Petersburg recommended a copper wire of given dimensions, the resistance of which Weber determined in absolute units. As a copper resistance was found to vary in time, **Werner Siemens** (1816–1892) of Berlin, in 1860, proposed as a practical unit the resistance of a mercury prism one metre long and

---

[1] Consult the "Abstract of a Report on Solar and Terrestrial Magnetism" by Frank H. Bigelow, *Bulletin No. 21, U. S. Department of Agriculture,* 1898.

one square millimetre in cross-section, at 0° C. ("Siemens's unit"). Weber determined this in absolute units. In 1861 the British Association and Royal Society of London appointed a committee, with Lord Kelvin at its head, to recommend a unit ("B. A. unit"). Weber's absolute unit of resistance was a *velocity*. The British committee adopted this unit in principle. In 1881, at an international congress of electricians in Paris, Weber's absolute system was adhered to; only, the *centimetre, second,* and *gramme* were selected as primitive units, in place of the *millimetre, second,* and *milligramme,* used by Weber and Gauss. As the *ohm* the congress selected 10^9 times the velocity of one centimetre per second. At this time definitions were given also to the *volt, ampère, coulomb,* and *farad,* along the lines previously marked out by Weber.[1] The subject of "dimensional equations" was first systematically presented by Clerk Maxwell.

The securing of a convenient, invariable resistance, equal to 10^9 absolute units, has been a difficult task. The B. A. unit was a little too small. The "legal ohm" was provisionally adopted in 1883 by a committee appointed by the congress of 1881. It was the resistance at 0° C. of a column of mercury 1 square millimetre in cross-section and 106 centimetres long. Competent investigators like Rayleigh and Mascart contended that this column was a little too short, but some smaller values obtained by certain experimenters led to the adoption of the mean value 106 centimetres. The "legal ohm" satisfied no one and failed to become legal in any country.[2]

Henry A. Rowland, after pointing out errors in some of the determinations previously made, found the length of the mercury column in question to be 106.32 centimetres. At the meeting of the British Association in 1892, German, French, and American physicists were invited to take part in the consideration of electrical units. The "B. A. unit" and the

[1] Rosenberger, III., pp. 302, 514–519; A. Kiel, "Geschichte der Absoluten Masseinheiten," *Jahresb. d. Königl. Gymnasiums zu Bonn,* 1890.
[2] H. S. Carhart in *Science,* Vol. 21, 1893, pp. 86, 87.

"legal ohm" were abandoned. The ohm was defined as the resistance offered by a column of mercury at the temperature of melting ice 14.4521 grammes in mass, of constant cross-sectional area, and of the length of 106.3 centimetres. By specifying the mass of the mercury, instead of the cross-section of the column, any error arising from the uncertainty as to the exact volume of a gramme of mercury at 0° C. was avoided. A system of *international* units was adopted at the congress held in Chicago in 1893 during the World's Fair. The ohm, as defined in 1892, became the *international ohm*. The other units were defined, including the *joule* as a unit of work, the *watt* as a unit of power, and the *henry* as a unit of self-induction.

ELECTRIC DISCHARGES THROUGH PARTIAL VACUA

The electric discharge through partial vacua was carefully investigated after the middle of the century. In 1853 A. Masson, of Paris, sent the discharge from a powerful Ruhmkorff coil through the Torricellian vacuum. J. P. Gassiot thereupon constructed for experimental study tubes containing a trace of different gases. A few years later, **Heinrich Geissler** (1814–1879), a glass-blower in Tübingen, later proprietor of a manufactory of physical and chemical apparatus in Bonn, began to prepare such tubes with so great skill that they have since been named "Geissler tubes." This designation was proposed by Plücker, who said, "I give them this name and justly so, although the first tubes were not prepared by himself." [1] The discharges through these tubes were of great beauty, but hardly afforded a deeper insight into electricity or the theory of gases. With the improvements in mercury air-pumps and the attainment of higher degrees of rarefaction, the phenomena assumed a wider range. W. Hittorf, of Münster, in 1869 noticed that the dark space separating the negative pole from the negative glow increased in width, as exhaustion was carried further and finally filled the entire tube; that the discharge from the kathode caused

[1] Rosenberg, III., p. 521.

considerable fluorescence against the glass. More striking and impressive were the experiments which **William Crookes** began to publish in 1878. His experiments on high vacua began in 1873, when, in course of an investigation of the atomic weight of thallium, he attempted to perform the delicate weighings in a vacuum, in order to avoid the effect of the buoyancy of the air. When heated bodies were weighed in his exhausted metallic box, the balance showed irregularities in action which he could not explain by currents of air resulting from differences in temperature. Crookes undertook a thorough investigation of the phenomenon, and was led in 1875 to the invention of the famous radiometer. At first Crookes and others inclined to the opinion that the rotation of the vanes was due to the direct impact of ether-waves. But Crookes succeeded in carrying the exhaustion of the bulb to such a degree that the vanes no longer rotated. Hence Tait, Dewar, and himself invoked the aid of the modern kinetic theory of gases, and attributed the effect to the molecules of the residual gas. The molecules impinging upon the heated black surface of the vane rebounded with increased momentum, and by their reaction propelled the vanes. A mathematical investigation of this action, based on the kinetic theory of gases, was given by Clerk Maxwell. In 1878 Crookes touched the line of Hittorf's researches, which were apparently unknown to him. The thickness of the dark space observed by him and Hittorf he took to be the "measure of the mean free path between successive collisions of the molecules of the residual gas." In his highly exhausted tubes "the molecules of the gaseous residue are able to dart across the tube with comparatively few collisions, and radiating from the pole with enormous velocity, they assume properties so novel and so characteristic as entirely to justify the application of the term borrowed from Faraday, that of "Radiant Matter." By beautiful experiments he proved that "Radiant Matter" proceeds in straight lines, casts shadows when intercepted by solid matter, is capable of turning a small wheel, is deflected by a magnet (shown previously by Hittorf and others). The state and behavior of the residual gas in Crookes's highly exhausted tubes were such that he thought himself justified in calling this an "ultragaseous state," or a "fourth state" of matter, differing as much from the gaseous as does the gaseous from the liquid state. The theory of the "fourth state" was much criticised, particularly by the Germans.

RÖNTGEN RAYS

While in the days of Gassiot the discharge from the anode was the subject of greatest attention, that from the cathode later monopolized the interest. Hertz found that the "cathode rays" will pass through metal foil. His assistant, P. Lenard, prepared a vacuum tube with a small window of aluminium foil, through which he passed the "cathode rays" out into the air. They still retained their power of exciting phosphorescence, but could not be made to travel through air but a short distance. Lenard held that his rays were not flying particles but "phenomena in the ether."[1] While the discussion over the nature of these mysterious rays was in progress, **Wilhelm Konrad Röntgen** (1845–1923)[2] of Würzburg, in 1895 discovered a new kind of rays which at once caused a sensation throughout the world. He found that a Crookes tube in action emits a radiation which causes a paper screen washed with barium-platino-cyanide to light up brilliantly or to fluoresce. Paper, wood, aluminium, and a great many other substances which are opaque to ordinary rays were found transparent to the new radiation. The fact that animal tissues are transparent and bones somewhat opaque, makes it possible for the skeletons of human beings to be photographed, the resulting negatives being of the nature of shadow pictures. The nature of the new rays being unknown, Röntgen called them "X-rays" but they are usually and more

[1] See Lenard's papers in *Electrician* (London), Vol. 32, March 23, 1893; Vol. 33, 1894, p. 108.
[2] Röntgen, "On a New Form of Radiation," *Electrician* (London), Vol. 36, 1896, pp. 415–417, 850, 851.

appropriately called "Röntgen rays." They showed no perceptible refraction, nor regular reflection and polarization. J. J. Thomson made an experiment which seemed to prove that Röntgen rays and kathode rays were different, inasmuch as kathode rays inside a vacuum had no power of exciting the photographic plate. He also found that these rays make insulators conduct and consequently are able to discharge electrified bodies. Improved tubes—the so-called "focus-tubes" —were designed for radiography. An important discovery which appeared to be a link towards establishing continuity between the old and the new forms of radiation was made in 1896, in Paris, by **Henry Becquerel** (1852–1909), of the Conservatoire des Arts et Métiers. He was the son and successor of Edmond Becquerel and the grandson of A. C. Becquerel. He observed that certain uranium compounds, after exposure to sunlight, emitted radiations which, like Röntgen rays, could pass through plates of aluminium or of cardboard, but which could also be refracted and polarized. Allied to both of these are the rays emitted by thorium and its compounds, which were discovered almost simultaneously by Sklodowska Curie and G. C. Schmidt. Thorium rays could be refracted, but could not be polarized by transmission through tourmaline.

ELECTRICAL INFLUENCE MACHINES

There existed two methods for producing very high differences of electric potential: one is by induction coils like Ruhmkorff's, the other is by electrical influence machines. These machines were evolved from the electrophorus of Volta, through the improvements due to Georg Christoph Lichtenberg (1742–1799) of Göttingen, Abraham Bennet, Tiberius Cavallo (1749–1809) of London, William Nicholson (1753–1815, editor of *Nicholson's Journal of Natural Philosophy, Chemistry, and the Arts,* London), Belli, Varley, Kelvin, Töpler, Holtz, Wimshurst, and others.

The first marked advance in the design of these machines was made in 1865. In that year machines were brought out by A. Töpler (1836–1912) of Dorpat, later professor at the Polytechnicum in Dresden, and by W. Holtz. The latter soon improved his machine, while Töpler, in 1879, united the principles of the two machines into the "Töpler-Holtz machine." A similar one was constructed in 1880 by the mechanic, J. R. Voss, of Berlin. The machine with radial strips of tin-foil and contact brushes was described by Holtz in 1881,[1] and again in 1882 and 1883 by James Wimshurst,[2] who made his improvements independently of Holtz.[3]

THERMO-ELECTRICITY

Thermo-electricity was discovered in 1821 by **Thomas Johann Seebeck** (1780–1831). He was born in Reval (Esthonia, Russia). At the age of seventeen he left his native country, never again to return. He studied medicine in Berlin. Being well off, he was free to devote himself to science. From 1802 to 1810 he lived in Jena, and had a personal acquaintance with Schelling, Hegel, Ritter, Göthe, and other prominent men. Unfortunately he allowed himself to be completely dominated by the erroneous anti-Newtonian views on color, so elaborately and confidently set forth by Göthe in his *Farbenlehre*. Being elected a member of the Berlin Academy of Sciences in 1818, Seebeck took up his residence in that city. Oersted's experiment induced him to enter upon a long series of electric investigation. With the view of verifying certain speculations regarding the magnetic character of the electric current, he established an electric circuit consisting partly of copper and partly of bismuth. One metallic junction he held in his hand. He satisfied himself that the resulting deflection of the galvanometer needle arose from the difference in temperature of the metallic junctions, brought about by the heat from his hand. He found similar effects by cooling one of the

[1] Uppenborn's *Zeitschr. f. angewandte Elektr.*, 1881, p. 199.
[2] *Engineering*, Vol. 35, 1883, p. 4.
[3] Consult articles on the theory of recent types of machines, written by Holtz, Wimshurst, and V. Schaffers, in *Electrician* (London), Vol. 35, 1895, pp. 382–388. See also John Gray, *Electrical Influence Machines*, Whittaker & Co.

junctions; the effects varied for different metals, and were greater for greater differences of temperature. He used the expression "thermomagnetic" currents, and later objected to the term "thermo-electric."

Thirteen years after Seebeck's discovery, **Jean Charles Athanase Peltier** [1] (1785–1845), a Parisian watchmaker, who devoted the latter part of his life to scientific pursuits, demonstrated that, conversely, an electric current may produce not only heat but also cold. In copper-antimony junctions he found a heating of 10° where the current went from antimony to copper, and a cooling of 5° where it went in the opposite direction. Greater differences were found for bismuth-antimony joints. **Heinrich Friedrich Emil Lenz** (1804–1865), well known for his law of electromagnetic induction, succeeded in freezing water by the Peltier effect.

EVOLUTION OF THE DYNAMO AND ELECTRIC LIGHTING

After the principles of electromagnetism were established by Faraday and Henry, constant efforts were made in the way of practical application. The early dynamo machines labored under two defects: the magnetic intensity was not adequate or properly applied, and the electric current generated was not sufficiently steady. The concentration of the magnetic lines of force in a powerful field between the magnetic poles was effected in 1856 by Werner Siemens in Berlin through his improved shuttle armature, with its coils of wire wound upon a grooved iron core. Ten years later Henry Wilde of Manchester substituted electromagnets for the permanent steel magnets previously employed. He took three Siemens machines, two of which had electromagnets. The machine with steel magnets generated a current which was used to excite the field magnets of the second machine; the armature current from the second excited the field magnets of the third. The current from the last was used in experimentation. An electric lamp was made to give an intense light, which caused

[1] See "Memoir of Peltier" in *Smithsonian Report,* 1867, pp. 158–202.

great astonishment among the populace. When passed through a convex lens, the light ignited paper. The electric arc melted not only iron wire, but a rod of platinum 6 millimetres thick and 61 centimetres long. The arc was still a novelty to people, notwithstanding the fact that sixty-six years earlier, in 1800, it was noticed by Sir Humphry Davy, and at a still earlier date by J. W. Ritter. Davy used in his experiments a battery of 2000 cells and rods of charcoal.

In 1866 Werner Siemens demonstrated by the operation of a new machine of his own construction that electromagnets can be used without separate exciters, and that the field magnets may be excited by the current from the armature of the machine itself. This idea appears to have been in the air; for, about the same time and independently, it was advanced by Murray, Cromwell Fleetwood Varley (1828–1883), C. Wheatstone, and others. In Siemens's armature the coils are wound around a cylindrical core. Another typical armature is that in which the coils are wound upon a ring. This was invented in 1861 by Antonio Pacinotti (1841–1912) of Florence, and again independently in 1868, by **Zénobe Théophile Gramme** (1826–1901), of Paris. Through Gramme this armature came to be extensively used. Since their day the construction of dynamos for various purposes has been carried to great perfection. Machines of high merit were produced by the Siemens brothers, Charles F. Brush, Thomas A. Edison, and others.[1]

The design of practical dynamos made electric lighting possible. Arc-lighting was never a success until means were thought out for rendering lights placed in series automatic in action and somewhat independent of each other. Such a regulator was invented in 1847 by W. E. Staite; later Werner Siemens and others worked out designs. Among the patterns are clockwork lamps, solenoid lamps, and clutch lamps.

For house illumination arc-lights were not well adapted.

[1] For details see S. P. Thompson (1851–1916), ''Historical Notes,'' in *Dynamo Electric Machinery.*

A less brilliant light was needed. In the years 1877–1880 inventors arose to the emergency by the production of the incandescent lamp. The names associated with this development of applied electricity are Joseph Wilson Swan and Lane-Fox in England, Hiram S. Maxim, William Edward Sawyer, Albon P. Man, and Thomas A. Edison.

In early experiments platinum wire was tried as the substance to be heated to whiteness by the passage of the electric curent. In 1878 Edison was thus engaged, but neither platinum nor iridium could be kept from the risk of fusing. In the same year Sawyer and Man of New York tried to prepare carbon fibres from vegetable tissue. They endeavored to prevent combustion of the fibre by filling the globe with nitrogen, but the process was not successful. Lane-Fox, in 1879, being convinced that platinum and iridium were useless as bridges in lamps, used carbonized vegetable fibres. Swan, in February, 1879, made a public exhibition of a lamp with a carbon filament in a vacuous bulb. Swan's success led Edison to abandon platinum and iridium, and, in October, 1879, he had constructed a vacuum lamp with a filament of lampblack and tar carbonized. In January, 1880, Swan prepared filaments from cotton twine, prepared by immersion in sulphuric acid and then carbonized. Edison sent out explorers into South America and into the far East in quest of suitable fibres for lamps, and in 1880 employed a flat strip of carbonized bamboo for a filament. Most of the modern lamps have filaments prepared from parchmentized cellulose, afterwards carbonized. The race between the several experimenters was indeed close and exciting; numerous lawsuits over the validity of patents followed the commercial introduction of the new lamps.[1]

The discovery that the action of the dynamo is simply the converse of the electric motor, so that the same machine can be used either as dynamo or motor, was made by M. H. Jacobi in 1850. The principle of transmitting power from one dynamo as a generator to another used as a motor was first

[1] For a fuller account see F. L. Pope, *Evolution of the Electric Incandescent Lamp*, 1889.

pointed out and demonstrated at the Vienna Exhibition in 1873 by Fontaine and Gramme. Since then great progress has been made in the details of design of motors. Two Gramme machines, made in Paris, were on exhibition at the Centennial Exposition of 1876 in Philadelphia, one of them was afterwards bought by the University of Pennsylvania, the other by Purdue University.

After much experimentation in the United States and elsewhere on the design of electric railways, the first electric railway was put in operation by the firm of Siemens and Halske in 1879 at the Industrial Exhibition in Berlin.[1]

Up to 1883 the progress made in electric roads was mainly due to Werner Siemens in Germany, but at this time substantial advances were made in the United States by the labors of C. J. Van Depoele, Leo Daft, F. J. Sprague, and others.

The first polyphase motor was exhibited to the Royal Society of London in 1879 by Walter Baily. It was a mere toy and received no further attention. A two-phase motor was constructed and used by Galileo Ferraris (1847–1897) in his laboratory at Turin in 1885. He used two independent alternate currents of the same period, but differing in phase and thus producing a rotary magnetic field. Thinking that no motor requiring more than two wires could interest any one but the theoretical physicist, he did not publish his results till 1888.[2] Only a few months later, commercial motors based on the same principles were brought out by Nikola Tesla, then at Pittsburgh, who had made the discovery independently. A remarkable rotary-field motor, devised by Dolivo Dobrowolsky, was used at the Frankfort Exposition of 1891. Many forms of such motors have been constructed since and are meeting with extended application in both Europe and America.

[1] In the United States, at this time, Edison, Stephen D. Fields, and Wellington Adams were experimenting on electric roads, and applying for patents. See W. Adams, ''The Evolution of the Electric Railway,'' p. 9, reprinted from the *Jour. of the Ass. of Eng. Societies*, of September and October, 1884.

[2] See translation of paper in *Electrician* (London), Vol. 36, 1895, p. 281; see also Nature, Vol. 44, 1891, p. 617.

The Electric Telegraph and Cable

After the principles of electromagnetism were made known through the epoch-making researches of Faraday and Joseph Henry, telegraphy seemed a comparatively easy matter. So many investigators busied themselves with this idea, and performed experiments which were more or less successful, that it is difficult to assign the invention of the telegraph to any one individual. The transmission of signals by electromagnetic apparatus was suggested by Ampère in 1821. Gauss and Weber at Göttingen in 1833 had a crude telegraphic line between the Observatory and the Physical Cabinet, a distance of 9000 feet. Joseph Henry at Albany, in 1831, by the attraction of an electromagnet produced audible signals at a distance. In 1837 Morse of New York devised a telegraph in which the attraction of an armature produced dots and dashes upon a moving strip of paper. Karl August Steinheil of Munich discovered that the earth may take the place of a wire for the return circuit. The first commercial line in the United States was erected between Washington and Baltimore through the efforts of Morse. **Samuel Finley Breese Morse** (1791–1872) was educated as an artist, and is the founder of the National Academy of Design in New York. He studied art in the schools of the Continent. While on his ocean voyage homeward, in 1832, the first thought of the telegraph suggested itself to him. He experimented for several years with some success. Finally, his assistant, Dr. Gale, applied the principles discovered by Henry to render Morse's machine effective at a distance.[1] After many discouragements, Morse established, by aid of the American government, the telegraphic line between Washington and Baltimore. On May 24, 1844, the message was sent from the rooms of the United

[1] See "Statement of Professor Henry in Relation to the History of the Electromagnetic Telegraph," *Smithsonian Report*, 1857, pp. 99–106; "Henry and the Telegraph," by William B. Taylor, in *Smithsonian Report*, 1878, pp. 262–360, containing much detailed information on the history of the telegraph.

States Supreme Court, "What hath God wrought!" Morse's apparatus is now the most extensively used of all.

Experimentation on submarine telegraphy began as early as 1837. After some successes with shorter lines, the first Atlantic cable expedition was started in 1857. One of the questions debated some years before was the probable speed of signalling through a cable 2000 miles long. Great vagueness then existed as to the way in which electricity travelled. Wheatstone had proved in 1834 with aid of revolving mirrors that electricity travelled with a velocity of 288,000 miles per second; but Latimer Clark, from experiments made in the presence of Airy and Faraday on 800 miles of underground wire, came to the conclusion that it took half a second before the current appeared at the other end. Other experimenters obtained intermediate results.

The explanation of these discrepancies was given by a young man, William Thomson, later Lord Kelvin, in a correspondence with Sir Gabriel Stokes. This correspondence formed the basis of Thomson's very important paper, published in the Proceedings of the Royal Society in 1855. One of the first conclusions theoretically deduced by him was that electricity has no velocity at all. Just as the time for the flow of heat through a rod depends only on the rod, so the time before the current begins to appear at the other end depends only on the cable—that is, upon the product of its resistance and its electrostatic capacity. The opinion of well-known engineers of the time was opposed to this. Thomson also tried to make it plain that it would take so long for the current to reach its steady state at the end of an Atlantic cable that, if they ever wanted the cable "to pay," they must not wait for the current, but must send messages with currents at the very beginning of their growth. Another important conclusion reached by him was that the retardation of signals was proportional to the square of the length. Thomson estimated the probable speed of the proposed cable at three words per minute, Wer-

[1] For details consult W. E. Ayrton, "Sixty Years of Submarine Telegraphy," *Electrician* (London), Vol. 38, 1897, pp. 545–549.

ner Siemens at one word per minute, Sir Charles Bright at ten or twelve words per minute. The results gave for ordinary recording instruments 1.8 words per minute. On August 5, 1858, England and America had the first cable communication. The President of the United States sent a message containing the prayer, "May the electric telegraph, under the blessing of Heaven, prove to be a bond of perpetual peace and friendship between the kindred nations." One hundred and fifty words were transmitted in thirty hours. As time went on the signals grew weaker, and in a month the Atlantic cable ceased to speak. William Thomson calculated what would be the best proportions for the new Atlantic cable, which was successfully laid in 1866. He designed apparatus to be used in signalling. The astatic reflecting galvanometer was a much improved form of the mirror galvanometer originally devised by Gauss and Weber, and employed on their telegraph line in Göttingen. Thomson's galvanometer raised the speed of cable telegraphy from two or three to twenty-two or twenty-five words per minute. On account of the great fatigue to the eye in following the motion of a spot of light in the mirror galvanometer, it was discarded in signalling through cables, and Thomson's "siphon recorder" adopted. The researches of Thomson, as continued by Cromwell F. Varley, showed that the speed can be increased still further by sending a positive current, and then a negative one for a short time.

INVENTION OF THE TELEPHONE

The earliest record of a theoretical telephone was contained in Du Moncel's *Exposé des Applications,* Paris, 1854, when Charles Bourseul, a French telegraphist, conceived a plan of transmitting speech by electricity. The author says, "Suppose a man speaks near a movable disk sufficiently flexible to lose none of the vibrations of the voice; that this disk alternately makes and breaks the currents from a battery, you may have at a distance another disk which will simultaneously execute the same vibrations.'' Bourseul did not work out his ideas to a practical end.

The next step in the history of the telephone is told by D. E. Hughes, as follows: ''I was invited by his Majesty the Emperor Alexander II. (of Russia) to give a lecture before his Majesty, the Empress, and court at Czarskoi Zelo, which I did; but as I wished to present to his Majesty, not only my own telegraph instrument, but all the latest novelties, Professor Philipp Reis, of Friedericksdorf, Frankfort-upon-Main, sent to Russia his new telephone, with which I was enabled to transmit and receive perfectly all musical sounds, and also a few spoken words—though these were rather uncertain, for at moments a word could be clearly heard, and then, for some unexplained cause, no words were possible. This wonderful instrument was based upon the true theory of telephony. . . . Its unfortunate inventor died in 1874, almost unknown, poor and neglected; but the German government has since tried to make reparation by acknowledging his claims as the first inventor, and erecting a monument to his memory in the cemetery of Friedericksdorf.'' [1] Reis's experiments were made in 1861.

For fifteen years electric telephony was neglected, then, in 1876, **Alexander Graham Bell** (1847–1922) invented his wonderful telephone, which is still used at the present time as the ''receiver.'' It was first exhibited publicly, but in an imperfect form, at the *Centennial Exhibition*, at Philadelphia, in 1876. Bell was born at Edinburgh, in Scotland, and took up his residence in the United States in 1872. In a lecture delivered at Cambridge in 1878, Clerk Maxwell said that when the news of Bell's invention reached England, he expected the new instrument to surpass the siphon recorder in delicacy and intricacy as much as that excels a common bell-pull. But when the instrument appeared, ''consisting, as it does, of parts, every one of which is familiar to us, and capable of being put together by an amateur, the disappointment arising from

[1] *Electrician* (London), Vol. 34, p. 637. See also S. P. Thompson, *Philipp Reis*, London, 1883.

its humble appearance was only partially relieved on finding that it was really able to talk."[1]

Strange to say, on the very same day (February 14, 1876) on which Bell patented his telephone, Elisha Gray applied for a patent for an instrument of a similar kind. Later one company took up the patents of both inventors.

While Bell's instrument seemed perfect as a "receiver," it was defective as a "transmitter." The first step toward remedying this defect was the invention of the carbon transmitter by **Thomas A. Edison** and of the microphone by David Edwin Hughes. Edison's invention was brought out in 1877 and consisted of a vibrating plate abutting against a carbon button. The transmitters used in more recent telephony, such as Blake's, Berliner's, Hunnings's, and others are all constructed on the principle of loose contact involved in Edison's instrument.[2]

Hughes's microphone is the same in principle as Edison's transmitter, but its arrangement and action are quite different. In 1865 Hughes had experimented on Reis's telephone. On hearing of Bell's success, he resumed his investigation and produced the microphone. It was first exhibited in 1878 at his rooms to a company including Huxley, Lockyer, and W. H. Preece. The new apparatus was of the most primitive character, "consisting of a child's half-penny wooden moneybox for a resonator, on which was fixed by means of sealing-wax a short glass tube, filled with a mixture of tin and zinc, the ends being stopped by two pieces of charcoal to which were attached wires, having a battery of three small Daniell cells—consisting of three small jam-pots—in circuit. The wires were led away to a Bell telephone placed in an adjoining apartment. The money-box, which had one end knocked out, served as a mouthpiece or transmitter, while a Bell telephone was used a receiver. Sounds scarcely audible . . .

[1] *Nature*, Vol. 18, p. 160.
[2] Consult W. H. Preece, *The Telephone*. The reader will find much information in Thomas Gray's article, "The Inventors of Telegraph and Telephone," *Smithsonian Report*, 1892, pp. 639–657.

to the unassisted ear were . . . delivered with startling loudness through the Bell telephone."[1]

SOUND

Experimental Study of Vibrations and Waves

In the eighteenth century sound was studied mainly by the musicians and mathematicians; in the nineteenth century it became a regular branch of research for the physicist. The "father of acoustics" is **Ernst Florens Friedrich Chladni** (1756–1827), born in Wittenberg. His father educated him for law, but after the death of his father he devoted himself to science. His reading of several papers on sound brought him to the conviction "that in that more remains to be discovered, because the mathematico-physical assumptions are far more meagre than is usual in science." Euler's and D. Bernoulli's mathematical papers led him to investigate sounding plates. The necessity of earning a livelihood induced him to travel in order to give art performances and scientific lectures. He invented a new musical instrument, the euphonium, on which he performed during his travels in Germany, France, and Italy. He also made a collection of meteorites. "Inventive power, ready wit, and good nature distinguished him above all."[2]

Chladni experimentally studied the vibrations of strings, rods, and plates. "Chladni's figures" are celebrated; they are formed by the sand collecting at the nodal lines of vibrating plates. When Chladni, in 1809, exhibited his figures before the French Institute, they created great interest among the members, including Laplace. Napoleon had the experiments repeated for him at the Tuileries, and gave Chladni 6000 francs for the purpose of enabling the latter to translate his *Akustik* (first published in 1802) into French. Chladni dis-

covered the longitudinal vibrations in a string or rod, as well
as their application to the determination of sound velocity in
solids; he first investigated torsional vibrations in rods, and
determined the absolute rate of vibration of bodies. He determined the velocity of sound in other gases than air by filling
organ pipes with the gas and then determining the resulting
pitch. An elegant method of comparing velocities in gases
or in solids was invented in 1866 by A. Kundt. "Kundt's
method" has been generally introduced into elementary instruction.

A far-reaching discovery, as important in light as in sound,
was the *principle of interference of waves,* which we owe to
Thomas Young. He explained it in a paper of 1800, and later
again in his *Lectures on Natural Philosophy.* Wave motion
was made the subject of careful study on the part of Wilhelm
Weber and his brother, **Ernst Heinrich Weber** (1795–1878),
who published, in 1825, their work, entitled *Wellenlehre.*

It was long believed that in liquids, sound waves, consisting
of condensations and rarefactions, could not travel at all, for
the reason that liquids appeared to be incompressible. The
compressibility of water had been the subject of experimentation on the part of the *Accademia del Cimento* in Florence,
sometime between 1657 and 1667. Hollow spheres of silver
were filled with water, closed tight, and then disfigured by
hammering. The water was forced through the pores of the
metal. Apparently water is incompressible. Boyle believed
that water was elastic, but could not establish his view by
conclusive experiment. In 1762 John Canton demonstrated
before the Royal Society that water is compressible, but his
test received little attention. More accurate figures on the
degree of compressibility were obtained by Oersted about 1822.
Like Canton, he experimented by subjecting the vessel containing the water to the same pressure outside as inside, thereby
preventing a change in its capacity. His results indicated a
diminution of the .000047th part of the original volume when
the pressure was increased by one atmosphere. A somewhat

larger value—.0000513—was obtained in 1827 by Jean Daniel Colladon, professor of mechanics in Geneva, and Jacob Carl Franz Sturm (1803–1855) of Geneva, who, after 1830, was professor of mathematics in Paris. These co-workers determined also the velocity of sound in water. The experiments were made on Lake Geneva, between Thonon and Rolle, a distance of 13,487 metres. At one station a bell was placed under water and struck with a hammer; at the other station a specially prepared ear trumpet was dipped into the water. The velocity was found to be 1435 metres per second. Felix Savart (1791–1841), a teacher in Paris, and later conservator of the physical cabinet at the Collège de France, showed in 1826 that sound waves are propagated in water in the same way as in solids. Cagniard-Latour succeeded in imparting sound vibrations to water by means of the siren. This ability of the instrument to cause audible sounds in water led Cagniard-Latour to name it a "siren." He greatly improved the siren and its mechanism for counting vibrations. This apparatus, together with other devices, was used by Savart in determining the limits of audibility. He could hear tones of bodies vibrating at the rate of 24,000 or 48,000 per second. The lower limit he placed at 14 or 16 per second.

HELMHOLTZ'S THEORY OF HARMONY

A new epoch in the history of the science of sound was created by Helmholtz, who in 1863 published the first edition of his *Lehre von den Tonempfindungen*. The third German edition of 1870 was translated into English by Alexander J. Ellis in 1875. New German and English editions have appeared since. Helmholtz attributes musical tones to periodic motions in the air; he distinguishes musical tones by their Intensity, Pitch, and Quality. The Quality of a sound he found to be determined by the "upper partial tones," which are called by Tyndall "overtones." Nearly all musical tones possess these overtones, the number and relative intensity of which determine the Quality. G. S. Ohm was the first to point out that there is only one form of vibration which will give rise to no harmonic upper partial tones, but consists only of the prime tone, viz. the form of vibration peculiar to the pendulum and tuning-fork. Helmholtz made experiments showing the direct composition of vowel qualities, which were "essentially distinguished from the tones of most other musical instruments by the fact that the loudness of their partial tones does not depend solely upon their numerical order, but preponderantly upon the absolute pitch of those partials." "If only the unevenly numbered partials are present (as in narrow stopped organ pipes, pianoforte strings struck in their middle points, and clarinets), the quality of tones is *hollow,* and, when a large number of such upper partials are present, *nasal.* When the prime tone predominates, the quality of tone is *rich;* but when the prime tone is not sufficiently superior in strength to the upper partials, the quality of tone is poor." [1] Helmholtz devised spherical resonators by which he analyzed the human voice and musical tones in general. He also, by synthesis of sounds from tuning-forks, operated by electromagnetic apparatus, succeeded in producing artificial vowels, which were close imitations of the vowels of the human voice. In the same way he simulated the quality of tone of organ pipes, although the "whizzing noise, formed by breaking the stream of air at the lip, is wanting in these imitations."

The study of "beats" led Helmholtz to a new theory of harmony. Pythagoras had made the discovery that the simpler the ratio of the two lengths into which a string is divided, the more perfect is the harmony of the sounds produced by these two parts of the string. Later it was shown by investigators that the strings act in this way because of the relation of their lengths to the rate of their vibrations. Why simplicity should give pleasure remained an enigma, even after Euler had declared that the human soul takes a

[1] Helmholtz, *Sensations of Tone,* trans. by Ellis, London, 1885, pp. 118, 119.

constitutional delight in simple calculations. Helmholtz, by means of a costly polyphonic siren, which he had constructed, experimented on beats. In the case of two simple tones, the number of beats in unit time is equal to the difference in the rates of vibration. If the number of beats is 33 per second, then the dissonance is intolerable; if the number is smaller or larger, the effect is less disagreeable; if it exceeds 132, then the unpleasantness totally disappears. If each sound has its overtones, then the question of harmony or dissonance is more complicated. Beats arising between fundamentals and overtones, or between the overtones themselves, must be brought into consideration. It is found in a general way that as the difference in pitch of two musical tones is so varied that the disturbing action of beats becomes more and more pronounced, the number expressing the ratio of the vibrations of the two fundamentals becomes larger and larger. Thus, Helmholtz's theory explains how it is that the simpler ratios in music are the more agreeable.

Helmholtz's theory of harmony met with much criticism on the part of musicians and philosophers, but the attacks were unsuccessful, and the opposition to it has disappeared.

When two simple musical tones are sounded together, there occur two sound phenomena: (1) the *beats* discussed above, (2) *combinational sounds*. The latter are of two kinds: the *summational tones,* discovered by Helmholtz, and the *differential tones,* discovered in 1744 by the German organist, Andreas Sorge, and again by the celebrated Italian violinist, Giuseppe Tartini. Suppose the two simple tones have, respectively, m and n vibrations per second, then the rate of vibration of the differential tone is $m - n$, and of the summational tone $m + n$. To produce the differential tones it is necessary that the primary tones be of considerable intensity. Helmholtz used for this purpose the siren. The summation tones are much more difficult to observe. They were predicted and discovered by Helmholtz. Rudolf König (1832–1901), the celebrated acoustic instrument maker in Paris, entertained views which in some respects were contrary to those of the great German investigator. König held the opinion that when rapid beats set in they themselves give rise to new tones. This theory was not new; it had been held by Lagrange and Thomas Young, but was rejected by Helmholtz. With aid of large tuning-forks of his own make, König endeavored to demonstrate the correctness of his view. König was not sure that he could detect with his tuning-forks the presence of summational and differential tones, but he claimed to hear tones of the rate of vibration indicated by $m - vn$ and $(v + 1)n - m$, where $m > n$ and v is a whole number, so that vn and $(v + 1)n$ are rates of vibration of those harmonic overtones of the lower tones which immediately enclose the higher tone. W. Voigt (1850–1919),[1] in 1890, concludes that both the combinational tones of Helmholtz and the beat tones of König can theoretically be produced, and that the one system or the other will predominate according to circumstances. If the energy of the two vibrations approaches equality, combinational tones are more prominent; otherwise the beat tones will be more easily heard.

König improved an invention by E. Léon Scott of the year 1859, and brought forth the well-known manometric-flame apparatus for the analysis of sound. The phonograph of Edison, first described in 1877, has been found serviceable for the same purpose.

To study the composition of vibrations, **Jul. Ant. Lissajous** (1822–1880), professor at the Collège Saint Louis, in Paris, devised, in 1855, a very elegant method. The two vibrating bodies (tuning-forks, for instance) were supplied with small mirrors. A ray of light was reflected from one mirror to the other, and then to a screen. Usually the bodies were so placed that their planes of vibration were perpendicular to each other. The curves thus traced by the spot of light on the screen are known as "Lissajous's figures," but they had been discovered long before in the United States by

[1] *Wiedemann's Annalen*, N. F., Vol. 40, pp. 652–660.

Nathaniel Bowditch of Salem, Massachusetts. In 1815 Professor Dean of Burlington, Vermont, published a memoir, on "the motion of the earth as seen from the moon," and devised the compound pendulum for illustration, which is supposed to have been introduced into science twenty-nine years afterwards by Blackburn. This paper induced Bowditch to examine the theory of the motions of a pendulum suspended from two points, and to make a few experiments to test his theory. He drew figures which are the same as the curves of Lissajous.[1]

[1] Consult J. Lovering, "Anticipation of the Lissajous Curves," in *Proc. of the Am. Acad.*, N. S., Vol. 8, pp. 292–298; for Dean's and Bowditch's papers see *Memoirs of Am. Acad. of Arts and Sciences*, 1st Series, Vol. III., 1815, pp. 241, 413.

THE TWENTIETH CENTURY

THE first quarter of the twentieth century may fitly be designated as the age of fundamentalism, in which the very foundations of physics and chemistry are being re-examined and extended. The constitution of matter, the possibility of the transmutation of chemical elements, the fundamental laws of mechanics are being examined anew.

RADIOACTIVITY

Few subjects in experimental physics have made as wide a popular appeal and effected as deep a reconstruction of fundamental theory, as has radioactivity. It has found extended application in medical and surgical practice; it has brought a partial realization of the dreams of medieval alchemists.

H. BECQUEREL AND RADIOACTIVITY

We have already spoken (p. 271) of the discovery of X-rays in 1895 by W. K. Röntgen (1845–1923), and (p. 272) of the detection of radioactivity by Henri Becquerel (1852–1908) of Paris. Becquerel, who was studying the phenomena of phosphorescence, ascertained the fact that uranium salts gave out radiation, not only after being exposed to light, but also after having been kept several months in the dark. He found that this radiation impressed a photographic plate and discharged from a distance electrified bodies—properties giving two methods for studying the new rays.

MME. CURIE, POLONIUM, RADIUM

Marie Sklodowska,[1] who later became **Mme. Curie,** was born in 1867 at Warsaw where her father was professor of

[1] *Marie Curie, Pierre Curie,* trans. by Charlotte and Vernon Kellogg, New York, 1923, ''Autobiographical Notes,'' pp. 155–242.

physics and mathematics in one of the lyceums. In private schools, she acquired a knowledge of French, German, Russian and English. At the age of seventeen she became a governess, but continued her studies, evenings. In 1891 she left for Paris, where her eldest sister had gone for courses in medicine. Living in a garret she devoted herself to the study of physics at the Sorbonne, which called for great effort, partly because of her insufficient preparation in mathematics. In 1893 she graduated in first rank as "licenciée en sciences physiques," and in 1894 in second rank as "licenciée en sciences mathématiques." Thereupon she began experimental research in one of the physics laboratories at the Sorbonne in preparation for a doctor's thesis. There she met **Pierre Curie** (1859–1906) who had just been made professor in the School of Physics and Chemistry in Paris; they were married in 1895. She began research work with him in the laboratory of that institution. In 1897 she completed an investigation of the magnetic properties of steel. At this time she and her husband became excited by H. Becquerel's discoveries on uranium. Mme. Curie resolved to undertake a further study of this subject. She found that thorium (p. 272) behaved as did uranium. Working with the electrometer as the chemist works with the spectroscope, she observed also that certain minerals exhibited much greater radioactivity than that due to the amount of uranium and thorium contained in them—indicating the presence of some very active unknown substance. In July, 1898 [1] Pierre Curie, Mme. Curie, and G. Bremont, through their joint labors, were able to announce the existence of a new element which they named polonium [2]—after Mme. Curie's native country. It was found associated with compounds of bismuth obtained from the pitchblende, that black shiny ore of uranium from St. Joachimsthal in Bohemia. While working on polonium they discovered radioactivity accompanying not only the compounds of bismuth that were extracted from the pitchblende, but also compounds of barium

[1] *Comptes Rendus,* Vol. 127, 1898, pp. 12, 15.
[2] *Comptes Rendus,* Vol. 127, 1898, p. 175.

which were likewise extracted from pitchblende. Moreover, they found that ordinary barium compounds are not at all radioactive and that the radioactivity which they observed in the extracts from pitchblende must be due to new substances. On December, 1898 they were able to announce the separation of a salt of this new substance which they called "radium," and which proved to be much more important than polonium. But that polonium and radium were chemical elements was not yet demonstrated nor generally admitted.[1] The most difficult part of the research had yet to be done—the determination of the atomic weight of radium and other properties, and the separation of radium as a pure element. This required the continuous and heroic effort of years. The Curies were without a suitable laboratory, without funds and laboratory assistants. They knew that the treatment of pitchblende at the uranium plant at St. Joachimsthal was such that the radium was left behind in the discarded residues. With the permission of the Austrian government which owned the plant, they secured several sacks of these residues—"brown dust mixed with pine needles." Later they secured several tons of these residues. They treated this material in an abandoned shed near the School of Physics at Paris, which had been used at one time as a medical dissecting room. It had a leaky roof and afforded no adequate protection against the heat of summer and the cold of winter. Nevertheless the Curies persisted, and in 1902 they possessed one decigram of pure radium chloride; they studied its characteristic spectrum and announced the first determination of its atomic weight as 225.

In 1900 Pierre Curie was made assistant professor at the Sorbonne, and Mme. Curie professor at the Superior Normal School for girls at Sèvres near Paris. She finished her doctor's thesis in 1903. That year the Nobel prize was awarded jointly to H. Becquerel, Curie and Mme. Curie. In 1906 Pierre Curie was struck and killed by a truck in a street in Paris. Upon Mme. Curie alone devolved the task of bringing

[1] *Nature*, Vol. 62, 1900, p. 152.

up and educating her two young daughters. She succeeded her husband at the Sorbonne. In 1907 Andrew Carnegie provided funds for research fellowships. She prepared several decigrams of pure radium chloride, made a new determination of the atomic weight as 226.2, and in 1910 isolated pure radium metal. The next year she was awarded a Nobel prize and, though suffering from illness, she travelled to Stockholm to receive it. The use of radium salts in medicine and industry made it necessary to have a standard for measuring the quantity of radium. She prepared a standard consisting of a glass tube, a few centimeters in length, containing 21 milligrams of radium chloride, which was deposited in the International Bureau of Weights and Measures at Sèvres. She was active in the design of laboratories in Paris for a Radium Institute that was being organized. During the Great War, Mme. Curie was very active in relief work through radio-therapeutic service. In 1921 she came to the United States to receive from the women of America a gram of radium which had been extracted from 500 tons of Colorado carnotite ore. This is used in the Radium Institute in Paris, of which she is the head and where her daughter Irene is a research worker and teacher.

ACTINIUM, IONIUM

A third radioactive substance in pitchblende was found by A. Debierne, in 1900, and independently by F. O. Giesel. An uncertainty as to their identity was cleared away by Bertram Borden Boltwood (1870–1927) of Yale University, who split Debierne's substance into two elements, namely Giesel's substance, now called "actinium" and a new element named "ionium."

AVAILABILITY OF SALTS OF RADIUM

The extraordinary radioactivity of radium caused a sensation, but experimentation was at first limited by the difficulty of obtaining the radium salts. About 1900, under the direction of F. O. Giesel, working in coöperation with Julius

Elster (1854–1920) and Hans Geitel (1855–1923), both of the gymnasium at Wolfenbüttel, the firm of E. de Haën of List, near Hanover, undertook the preparation in small quantities of radioactive barium containing radium, and also placed on the market cheaper radioactive byproducts.[1] Before this, in France, the Société Centrale de Produits Chimiques, under the direction of Debierne, had arranged for the sale of barium containing radium.[2]

Attack on the Principle of the Conservation of Energy

A property of chlorides or bromides of radium which early impressed scientists was their ability to give off radiation without any apparent physical or chemical change. At first this was attributed to the extreme minuteness of the quantities of energy in question.[3] But more accurate measurements of the energy radiated rendered this explanation untenable. **E. Rutherford** and R. K. McClung of McGill University in Montreal found, in 1900, that a gram of uranium oxide radiated 10^{-11} calories per second and that radium was 100,000 times more radioactive than uranium.[4] Other estimates yielded a still higher figure for radium. Every hour radium generates sufficient heat to raise the temperature of its own weight of water from the freezing point to the boiling point, yet according to early observations, this steady stream of energy showed no sign of failing. Giving out rays and heat, like Aladdin's lamp, radium apparently defied the principle of the conservation of energy as a general law of nature.[5] Said Gustave Le Bon: "If the principle of the conservation of energy —which by-the-by is simply a bold generalization of experiments made in very simple cases—likewise succumbs to the blows which are already attacking it, the conclusion must be arrived at that nothing in the world is eternal. This great

[1] *Nature,* Vol. 62, 1900, p. 152.
[2] E. Rutherford, *Radioactive Substances,* 1913, p. 17.
[3] *Nature,* Vol. 61, 1900, p. 547.
[4] *Nature,* Vol. 63, 1900, p. 51.
[5] *Nature,* Vol. 62, 1900, p. 154.

divinity of science would also be condemned to submit to that invariable cycle which rules things—birth, growth, decline and death."[1]

Adherents to the principle of the conservation of energy sought other explanations. Thus W. Crookes[2] made the suggestion that uranium and thorium compounds absorbed energy from surrounding gas molecules and transformed it into radiant energy. Mme. Curie[3] believed that the world was filled with rays of even greater penetration than X-rays, which could be absorbed only by substances of heavy atomic weight like uranium and thorium. J. Elster and H. Geitel[4] opposed both of these hypotheses and later made the happy suggestion[5] "that the atom of a radioactive substance giving off energy passes, in the manner of a molecule, from an unstable combination into a stable condition." This same idea was developed by Rutherford and Soddy[6] in their basic article on the disintegration of atoms. They showed experimentally, in 1902 and 1903, that radium, while radiating energy, does change, does undergo transformation. They held to the view that the radium atom changes, that intra-atomic energy is converted into energy of motion outside the atom. Thus the law of the conservation of energy survived the terrific storm which uprooted some other scientific ideas of the nineteenth century. In the words of Crookes: "A few decigrammes of radium have undermined the atomic theory of chemistry, revolutionized the foundations of physics, revived the ideas of alchemists, and given some chemists a bad attack of swelled head."[7]

[1] Gustave Le Bon, *Evolution of Matter*, transl. into English by F. Legge, London, 1907, p. 18.
[2] *Nature*, Vol. 58, 1898, p. 438.
[3] *Comptes Rendus*, Vol. 126, 1898, p. 1101.
[4] *Wiedemann's Annalen*, Vol. 66, 1898, p. 735.
[5] *Wiedemann's Annalen*, Vol. 69, 1899, pp. 83, 88.
[6] *Phil. Mag.*, 6. S., Vol. 4, 1902, pp. 376, 569.
[7] E. E. F. D'Albe, *Life of Sir William Crookes*, 1924, p. 286.

Spectrum of Radium

Tracing the course of events somewhat more minutely, we find that the earliest determination of the spectrum of radium was made by Eugène Demarçay (1852–1904), from ore specimens supplied by Mme. Curie. He found in the spectrum of impure radium chloride, besides the lines of barium, lead, calcium and platinum, a strong new line, $\lambda = 3814.7$ Å., which in his opinion confirmed the existence of a new element.[1]

Ionization Produced by Radioactivity

The radiation from uranium, polonium and radium received much attention from different experimenters and led at first to some contradictory results.[2] Rutherford, in 1899, reached the important conclusion that the conductivity set up in gases by uranium was due to the phenomenon of ionization, identical with that provoked by X-rays according to the experiments of **J. J. Thomson.**

Properties of Radium Radiation

Another important observation made in 1899 simultaneously by several observers, was that some of the radiations from active bodies were deviated by a magnetic field. This was observed by F. O. Giesel, also by St. Meyer and E. v. Schweidler, and by Becquerel and P. Curie. Preparations of radium gave out some rays which were bent by a magnetic field in a manner similar to the cathode rays in a vacuum tube. P. Curie found that the rays from radium were of two kinds, one apparently non-deviable (now known as α-rays) the other deviable and more penetrating (now known as β-rays). The identification of some of this radiation with cathode rays required two verifications,—one made by P. and Mme. Curie that there is a transport of electric charges, the other made by H. Becquerel that there is a deviation in an electrostatic field.[3]

[1] *Comptes Rendus*, Vol. 127, 1898, p. 1218; Vol. 129, 1899, p. 716; Vol. 131, 1900, p. 258.
[2] *Nature*, Vol. 62, 1900, p. 153.
[3] H. Becquerel, *Nature*, Vol. 63, 1901, p. 398.

As the result of repeated effort Rutherford was able, finally, to detect by most powerful magnets a slight bending of α-rays, but in the opposite direction to that of β-rays. This was shown by the electric method, and verified by Becquerel by the photographic method.[1]

A third type of radium rays (now called γ-rays), found by P. Villard,[2] by the photographic method, proved to be more penetrating than the most penetrating X-rays produced in a vacuum tube; these γ-rays are not bent by a magnetic field.

EMANATIONS

In 1900 Rutherford investigated a mysterious "emanation" from thorium compounds and found it to ionize the gas in the neighborhood, to retain its radioactive power for some minutes and gradually to lose it. Was this emanation simply a vapor of thorium?[3] The specimen of impure radium then in his possession gave out no emanation. In 1901, Mme. Curie and A. Debierne obtained a radioactive gaseous substance from radium by placing radium in a globe and exhausting the air. The vacuum steadily decreased, due to the gaseous substance given off, which was strongly radioactive. With a specimen of radium from Haën of List near Hanover, Rutherford found later that by heating the radium, the amount of emanation from it is increased ten thousand times the amount for ordinary temperatures. Were these emanations vapors of the radioactive substances, or radioactive gases, or radiating particles large compared with molecules? Rutherford in 1901 examined the rate of diffusion of radium emanation into air and found it to be more rapid than it could be for a vapor of radium, on account of the heavy atomic weight of radium; hence he concluded that the gaseous substance was not the *vapor* of radium.[4] Later Rutherford and Soddy found that the thorium emanation behaves like an inert gas.[5]

---

[1] *Phil. Mag.*, S. 6, Vol. 5, 1903, p. 481.
[2] P. Villard, *Comptes Rendus*, Vol. 130, 1900, pp. 1010, 1178.
[3] E. Rutherford, *Phil. Mag.*, Vol. 49, 1900, p. 1; *Nature*, Vol. 62, 1900, p. 154.
[4] E. Rutherford, *Nature*, Vol. 64, 1901, pp. 157, 158.
[5] *Phil. Mag.*, S. 6, Vol. 5, 1903, pp. 484, 485.

Apparent chemical changes producing new types of matter were found in 1902 by Rutherford and Soddy; thorium from which the radioactive substance which they called thorium X had been separated, regained its activity after a time, while that of thorium X slowly disappeared.[1] Soddy obtained uranium X from uranium which gives off no α-rays, only β-rays. As previously stated, in the fall of 1902 Rutherford and Soddy put forward the view that the radioactivity of the elements is a manifestation of *subatomic chemical change,* and that the radiations accompany the change.[2]

HELIUM OBTAINED FROM RADIUM

Ramsay and Soddy announced experiments which seemed to indicate that radium breaks down into helium.[3]   This conclusion was received "with a chorus of wonder."   Helium, it will be remembered, was discovered in the sun by Pierre Jules César Janssen (1824–1907) and Norman Lockyer (1836–1920).   Lockyer gave it the name "helium."   In 1895, Sir William Ramsay (1852–1916) and Lockyer found helium in the gas liberated from the mineral clevite.   The almost invariable presence of helium in minerals containing uranium led Rutherford and Soddy to suggest "that possibly helium is an ultimate product of the disintegration of one of the radioactive elements."[4]   The uncertainty regarding helium was removed by an experiment performed by Ramsay and Soddy in July, 1903.[5]   An emanation from radium bromide was introduced into a spectrum tube.   No helium could be detected spectroscopically at first, but after four days the characteristic spectrum lines of helium appeared.   Thus helium was produced by the transformation of radium emanation.

In the fall of 1903, Rutherford [6] presented before the Brit-

---

[1] *Nature,* Vol. 66, 1902, p. 119.

[2] *Phil. Mag.,* S. 6, Vol. 5, 1903, p. 485.

[3] Ramsay and Soddy, *Nature,* Vol. 68, 1903, p. 246.

[4] Rutherford and Soddy, *Phil. Mag.,* S. 6, Vol. 5, 1903, p. 453; Vol. 4, 1902, p. 582.

[5] *Nature,* Vol. 68, 1903, p. 355.

[6] *Nature,* Vol. 68, 1903, p. 610.

ish Association his and Soddy's hypothesis which we have already noticed, that the atoms of radioactive substances break up and that this disintegration is the cause of radioactive properties. The electrically neutral atom of the radioactive substance throws off positively charged bodies which constitute the α radiation. What remains of the atom constitutes the emanation. This again throws off a positively charged body, and the process repeats itself until the positively charged bodies are exhausted and the substance no longer possesses radioactive properties. In the case of radium the store of energy in the atom was estimated to be enormous, not less than 10^6 ergs per gram. Oliver Lodge and Joseph Larmor viewed this hypothesis sympathetically. Lord Kelvin,[1] in a letter, advanced another theory based on his conception of the atom, according to which "the large amount of energy radiated is derived from without the atom, where it exists in a form which we have not yet found means of detecting." A year later Kelvin repeated that if the high rate of emission of heat by radium "can go on month after month, energy must somehow be supplied from without."[2] In 1904 he described models of radium atoms to give out α- and β-rays, respectively.[3]

In 1903 the designation of the radiation from radium by the names "α-rays," "β-rays," "γ-rays" was finally established. In 1904 appeared the first edition of E. Rutherford's book, *Radio-Activity*,[4] which contained a full summary of results reached up to that time. The book advances the hypothesis that the heat given off by radium is due to the spontaneous disintegration of radium atoms into matter possessing less energy; the process is apparently non-reversible. The α particle is positively charged and was thought to have a mass twice that of the hydrogen atom. The rest of the radium atom constitutes Radium X. This disintegrates into an α particle and the gaseous emanation. The latter in turn

1 *Nature*, Vol. 68, 1903, p. 611.
2 *Nature*, Vol. 70, 1904, p. 107.
3 *Nature*, Vol. 70, 1904, p. 516.
4 *Nature*, Vol. 70, p. 241.

disintegrates, and so on. The final product is perhaps polonium. A radium atom appears therefore to consist of a polonium atom and about six α particles. But there is reason to believe that the α particles become helium atoms. Therefore, Rutherford argued at that time, the radium atom would seem to be really a compound of polonium and helium, a molecule, and not an elementary atom. And yet, the velocity of radioactive processes being independent of the temperature would seem to indicate that the changes are purely atomic. Rutherford gives reasons for suspecting that radium itself evolves from uranium. He estimates the average life of the radium atom to be not less than 1500 years.

KELVIN'S OPPOSITION TO THE THEORY OF DISINTEGRATION

A dramatic incident was the controversy on radium during August, 1906, in the London *Times*. Lord Kelvin made the opening challenge immediately after the meeting of the British Association at which F. Soddy had discussed the evolution of the elements and stated that uranium gradually changes to radium, radium to its emanation and several other successive products, until in all probability it became lead; lead in turn suffers a gradual transmutation into silver.[1] Kelvin almost single-handed started his campaign against the transmutational and evolutionary doctrines framed to account for the properties of radium. He argued that the production of helium from radium no more proves transmutation than does the discovery of helium in cleveite prove transmutation. It is enough to suppose that both radium and cleveite contain helium. Kelvin denied that there was experimental evidence that solar heat is due to radium; he ascribed this heat to gravitation. Oliver Lodge, H. E. Armstrong, R. J. Strutt and A. S. Eve [2] were among those participating in the discussion. Kelvin quoted Rutherford as regarding radium a chemical

[1] *Nature*, Vol. 74, 1906, p. 453.
[2] *Nature*, Vol. 74, 1906, pp. 516–518 contains an account of the controversies.

compound and suggested that radium might be made up of one atom of lead and four of helium. Soddy attributed to Rutherford the remark that when a single experimental fact is established which does not conform to the disintegration theory it will be time to abandon it. Kelvin again argued against the transmutation theory at the British Association in August, 1907. He thought it very improbable that all the different chemical and other properties of the many chemical elements could be explained merely by differences in the grouping of primitive atoms which are all equal and similar. At the same meeting, Rutherford expressed the opinion that the electron had come to stay, although at the time it was impossible to decide whether the electrons which are set free in radioactivity or are revealed by the optical properties of an atom are merely an outer circle or are a revelation of an internal constitution of the inner core of the atom.

DEATH OF KELVIN [1]

A few months later on December 17, 1907, Lord Kelvin passed away, at the age of 83 years. Death resulted from a chill contracted while experimenting in a corridor of his country house. Lord Kelvin (William Thomson) was born in 1824 at Belfast, Ireland, but was of Scotch descent. He and his brother James studied in Glasgow. From there he entered Cambridge and was graduated as second wrangler, in 1845. Clerk Maxwell and J. J. Thomson were other physicists of first rank who took second place at Cambridge in the competitive wrangler examinations. W. Thomson was elected professor of natural philosophy in the University of Glasgow, at the age of twenty-two, a position which he held until his death. For his brilliant, mathematical and physical achievements he was knighted in 1866 and in 1892 was made Lord Kelvin. He was greatly influenced by the mathematical physics of Joseph Fourier (1768–1830) and other French mathematicians. It was Fourier's mathematics on the flow of heat

[1] S. P. Thompson, *Life of William Thomson*, London, 1910.

through solids which led him to his treatment of the diffusion of the electric current through a wire and of the difficulties encountered in signaling through the Atlantic cable (p. 280). Reference to his enthusiasm for laboratory instruction is made in our account of the evolution of physical laboratories.

SUCCESSIVE TRANSFORMATIONS OF RADIUM

On January 31, 1908, E. Rutherford described the progress in radioactivity [1] and the confirmation of the disintegration theory put forward five years earlier by himself and Soddy. Rutherford said: "A large amount of work has been done in tracing the remarkable succession of transformations that occur in the various radioactive substances . . . a large list of unstable bodies are now known. . . . The analysis of the transformations of the radium emanation has yielded results of great importance and interest. After passing through three stages, radium A, B, and C, of short period, a substance, radium D, of long period, makes its appearance. This is transformed through two stages, E and F, of short period into radium G, of a period of 140 days. St. Meyer and Schweidler have conclusively shown that radium D is the primary constituent of the radioactive substance separated by K. A. Hoffmann and called by him radio-lead. Radium G is identical with the first radioactive substance separated from pitchblende by Mme. Curie, viz., polonium. We are thus sure that these bodies are transformation products of radium. . . . I have added another product of period 4.5 days between radium D and polonium. The presence of such a product has been shown by Meyer and Schweidler. In the case of thorium, a very long list of products is now known."

THE PARENT OF RADIUM

The search for the substance from which radium immediately descends is described by Rutherford thus: "The search for this elusive parent of radium has been one of almost

[1] *Nature*, Vol. 77, 1908, p. 422.

dramatic interest, and illustrates the great importance of the theory as a guide to the experimenter. . . . The most probable parent of radium appeared to be uranium, which has a period of transformation of the order of 1000 million years. If this were the case, uranium, initially freed from radium, should in the course of time grow radium, i.e., radium should again appear in uranium. This has been tested independently by Soddy and Boltwood, and both have shown that . . . there is no appreciable growth of radium in the course of several years. . . . There is, however, another indirect, but very simple method of attack to settle the parentage of radium. If radium is derived from the transformation of uranium . . . the ratio between the amount of radium and uranium in old minerals should be a definite constant. This is obviously the case, provided sufficient time has elapsed for the amount of radium to have reached its equilibrium value. The constancy of this relation has been completely substantiated by the independent work of Boltwood, R. J. Strutt, and H. N. McCoy. It has been shown that the quantity of radium corresponding to 1 gram of uranium is 3.8×10^{-7} gram.'' A substance intervening between uranium and radium, named actinium, was found in 1906, experimentally by Boltwood;[1] but Rutherford showed that actinium itself was not responsible for the growth of radium, but another substance separated with it. This result was confirmed by Boltwood, who isolated a new substance from uranium minerals which was slowly transformed into radium. This substance he named ''ionium.''[2] It is the long-looked for parent of radium. Thus the main previsions of the theory of transformation were experimentally verified; ''we are able to link uranium, ionium, radium, and its long line of descendants, into one family, with uranium as its first parent.''[3]

[1] *Nature*, Vol. 75, 1906, p. 54.
[2] *Nature*, Vol. 76, 1907, p. 589.
[3] *Nature*, Vol. 77, 1908, p. 423.

WORK AND DEATH OF CROOKES

Nineteenth century scientists entertained no hope that an individual atom could ever be observed. Seeing a single atom of matter! And yet in 1903 **Sir William Crookes**,[1] by means of an instrument—his spinthariscope, purchasable for a few shillings and containing only an infinitesimal amount of radium bromide—showed momentary flashes of light caused by α particles of radium upon a screen of zinc sulphide. The effect resembles a shower of shooting stars, a distinct discontinuity of scintillating effects, each impact of an α particle giving rise to a tiny flash. In fact Rutherford and Geiger have actually counted the number of α particles expelled from a given quantity of radium every second.[2]

Crookes' researches on radium mark the last important scientific work of a long career. He died in 1919. He[3] was born in 1832 in London, the son of a tailor. He had very little regular schooling. As a boy, he fitted up a sort of laboratory and was always trying experiments and reading any book on science he could find. He had no university education, nor did he hold a professorship. In 1870 he began a four years' investigation of spiritual phenomena. His researches on "radiant matter," his radiometer and "Crookes tubes" are noted on pages 270 and 271. His "radiant matter" is similar to β-rays. He is the discoverer of the element thallium.

RANGE OF α PARTICLES

Of importance in studying the structure of the atom was the scattering of α particles. **William Henry Bragg** (during 1886–1908 professor at Adelaide University in South Australia, during 1909–15 at Leeds University, during 1915–23 at University of London), about 1904, discovered that α particles have a definite *range;* when emitted by polonium the range is 38 mm. through air. Bragg gives a vivid picture of

[1] C. W. Crookes, *Nature*, Vol. 68, 1903, p. 303.
[2] F. Soddy, *The Interpretation of Radium*, New York, 1920, p. 45.
[3] E. E. F. D'Albe, *Life of Sir William Crookes*, New York, 1924.

the flight of an α particle: "Each α particle pursues a rectilinear course, no matter what it encounters; it passes through all the atoms it meets, whether they form part of a solid or a gas . . . suffering no deflection on account of any encounter until, at any rate, very near the end of its course. . . . A thin metal plate may be placed in the way of the stream, and so rob every particle of some of its energy, but not a single one is brought to rest by collision with the atoms of the metal, and the number of particles in the stream remains unchanged."[1] Later experimentation did show that some of the α particles are more or less deflected in their passage through matter. Rutherford made extensive use of this scattering.

α Particle a Charged Helium Atom

Rutherford proved that the α particles consisted of positively charged atoms; he gave their mass at first as twice that of hydrogen, on the assumption that they carried one atomic charge. But as a sequel of experiments on counting the α particles, it appeared, in 1908, that each of them carries two atomic charges of positive electricity. Rutherford ascertained this by measuring the total charge carried by a known number of α particles.[2] Hence the mass of the α particle is 4 and is the same as the mass of an atom of helium. Rutherford and T. D. Royds proved also by direct experiment that the α particle after losing its charge is a helium atom.[3]

Photographing Tracks of α and β Particles

Further study of the paths of α particles was due to C. T. R. Wilson of Cambridge, England, who succeeded in photographing the tracks of the α particles.[4] When moist air in a

[1] F. Soddy, *The Interpretation of Radium*, 4. Ed., New York, 1920, p. 62. W. H. Bragg, *Phil. Mag.*, Vol. 8, 1904, p. 719; Vol. 10, 1905, p. 600; Vol. 11, 1906, p. 617. W. H. Bragg and R. D. Kleeman, *Phil. Mag.*, Vol. 8, 1904, p. 726; Vol. 10, 1905, p. 318.
[2] Rutherford and Geiger, *Proc. Roy. Soc.*, London, Vol. 81, 1908, pp. 141–173.
[3] Rutherford and T. Royds, *Phil. Mag.*, Vol. 17, 1909, p. 281.
[4] C. T. R. Wilson, *Proc. Roy. Soc.*, London, A, Vol. 87, 1912, p. 277.

closed space is suddenly expanded, it is cooled. If pure air, when thus cooled, is traversed by an α particle, causing ionization, moisture condenses upon the ions, and under suitable illumination, the tracks of the α particles can be momentarily seen, and can be photographed, as long spider-threads of mist. Wilson says: [1] "The α particle has thousands of encounters with atoms of the gases of the air in each millimeter of its course by which ionization is brought about, . . . and in accordance with this the cloud particles (which are simply ions magnified by condensation of water) are so closely packed that they are not separately visible in the photograph." Almost all tracks of α particles are straight, but a very few show abrupt deflections. The β particles, on the other hand, give zigzag tracks.

DISRUPTION OF THE NITROGEN NUCLEUS

A spectacular achievement was the breaking up artificially of one of the "stable elements". We premise that permanent change in an atom requires the disruption of the nucleus itself. The nucleus was supposed to be an association of simpler parts which are the same in all atoms. In 1922 Rutherford and J. Chadwick were able to break up the nucleus of a substance that was not radioactive, that contained stable atoms, namely, nitrogen gas. The forces binding the components of the nucleus of such a stable atom are very great, but they yielded to the swift α particles expelled from radium. As a result, hydrogen nuclei (protons) were liberated from the nucleus of the nitrogen atom. This was a startling achievement of fundamental importance. The era of modern alchemy had indeed arrived. Other atoms were tried out. With the exception of helium, neon and argon, all the elements up to the atomic weight 40 were examined in 1922. Hydrogen particles were successfully liberated also from atoms of boron, fluorine, sodium, aluminum and phosphorus (all of them, elements of odd atomic number), but not

[1] Quoted by Soddy, *op. cit.*, p. 64.

from the nuclei of other elements. The α particles were used in measuring nuclear charges of atoms on the supposition that the law of inverse squares holds (if not very close to the nucleus) over the greater part of the space in the atom, for the forces acting between the α particle and the nucleus. When it was found that protons can be expelled from the nucleus of some of the lighter elements, the question arose, what becomes of the α particle which caused the disintegration? In 1925 H. H. Plaskett, in the Cavendish laboratory, under the direction of Rutherford, photographed the tracks of more than 400,000 α particles in nitrogen and found the tracks of the proton and of the recoiling nucleus, but not of the escaping α particle. He concluded that the α particle was captured by the nitrogen nucleus and that the nucleus may increase, rather than diminish, in mass, as the result of collisions in which a proton is expelled.[1] On the other hand, different experimental results were obtained at the University of Chicago by William D. Harkins and R. W. Ryan.[2] They photographed tracks of α particles in air, using the Shimizu method, and recorded a collision in which the track of the α particle broke up into three branches—the tracks of the proton, the nucleus and the α particle. In that case the α particle had not penetrated the nucleus and united with it, perhaps because before the collision the α particle had already lost a good bit of its energy. Other experiments on the transmutation of elements, in 1926, are the conversion of hydrogen into helium, effected not by electric discharges but by simple catalytic action, announced by Fritz Paneth and Walter Peters of Berlin,[3] and the change of nitrogen into fluorine and then into hydrogen and oxygen, when hit by the nucleus of an atom of helium, reported by William C. Harkins of the University of Chicago to the National Academy of Sciences in Washington.

[1] Rutherford, *Science*, Vol. 62, 1925, pp. 210, 211.
[2] *Journal Am. Chem. Soc.*, Vol. 45, 1923, p. 2095; *Nature*, Vol. 115, 1925, p. 493.
[3] *Science*, Vol. 64, 1926, p. 416.

N-RAYS

Psychologically interesting is the incident of *n*-rays. A French experimenter, R. Blondlot, at Nancy, persuaded himself that he had observed a new kind of rays, emitted by solids in a state of strain, such as hardened steel. These rays were claimed to brighten a screen of phosphorescent paint, which was already faintly luminous.[1] A few experimenters reported success, but experienced observers in France, Germany, and England tried but failed to observe the alleged phenomenon. Finally the original observer could not comply satisfactorily with objective tests, such as photography, and general incredulity resulted. The changes in brightness seem to have arisen from a purely subjective source, from processes in the retina,[2] and to have been purely psycho-physiological phenomena.

HEAT

EXPERIMENTS ON "BLACK BODIES"

The "black bodies" of Stewart and Kirchhoff suggested experimentation, but nothing was achieved in this difficult line of laboratory research before 1895–1901, when Otto Lummer (1860–1925), Ernst Pringsheim (1859–1917) and Ferdinand Kurlbaum (1857–1927) of the Reichsanstalt in Charlottenburg, began their experiments. They determined curves indicating the intensity of radiation for different wave-lengths for any given temperature. These curves indicated that for any given temperature the radiation of some one wave-length exceeded in intensity the radiation of other wave-lengths. We call this one the "optimal" wave-length. It was found that these experimental curves closely verified the "displacement law" which Wilhelm Wien (1864–1928)[3] had advanced on theoretical grounds, namely the law that the product of the

---

[1] *Nature*, Vol. 69, 1903, pp. 47, 72, 119, 167 (p. 182, a good general account).

[2] *Nature*, Vol. 69, 1904, p. 378; Vol. 70, 1904, pp. 198, 530 (by R. W. Wood); Vol. 72, 1905, p. 195.

[3] W. Wien, *Sitzungsb. d. Akad. d. Wissensch.*, Berlin, 1893, p. 55.

absolute temperature and the optimal wave-length is a constant. For example, for the absolute temperature $T = 1000°$, the intensity of radiation was greatest for $\lambda = 3.1\mu$; for $T = 2000°$, the intensity was a maximum at a shorter wavelength $\lambda = 1.5\mu$. This is in close accordance with Wien's displacement law, for $1000 \times 3.1 = 2000 \times 1.5$ (nearly). The experiments of Lummer, Pringsheim and Kurlbaum served as guides to Planck, in his theoretical investigations.

RAYLEIGH'S THEORETICAL FORMULA

Experimental and theoretical studies abounded. Lord Rayleigh (John William Strutt, 1842–1919)[1] refers in his paper of 1900 to the formula for the radiation from a "black body" due to Boltzmann, W. Wien and Planck (earlier results), and says that "viewed from the theoretical side the result appears to me to be little more than a conjecture," that "the question is one to be settled by experiment, but in the meantime I venture to suggest a modification . . . which appears to me more probable *a priori.*" He then alludes to the "doctrine of the partition of energy" according to which "every mode of vibration should be alike favored; and although for some reason not yet explained, the doctrine fails in general, it seems possible that it may apply to the graver modes." This doctrine of equipartition received the attention of the mathematical physicists, Clerk Maxwell, **Ludwig Boltzmann** (1844–1906), and **Josiah Willard Gibbs** (1839–1903). These great leaders were far apart geographically, at Cambridge (in England), Vienna, and New Haven in Connecticut, respectively. They instituted "statistical mechanics," resting it on the theory of probability. These statistical methods began to play an important rôle in theories of radiation.

In deriving his formula, Rayleigh first considers the transverse vibration of a stretched string of length l. If a is the velocity of propagation, p the number of subdivisions in any

[1] Lord Rayleigh, *Phil. Mag.,* Vol. 49, 1900, p. 539; *Nature,* Vol. 72, 1905, p. 54.

mode of vibration, λ the wave-length and ν the frequency, then since $\nu \cdot \lambda \times a$ and $l/p = \lambda/2$, we have $\nu = ap/(2l)$. The passage from one mode to the next in order involves a change of unity from p to $p + 1$, or $2l/a \cdot d\nu$. If e denotes the kinetic energy of a single mode, the law of equipartition requires that the kinetic energy corresponding to the interval $d\nu$ shall be $2le/a \cdot d\nu$. This expression applies to all parts of the string and represents therefore the longitudinal *density* of the kinetic energy.

Passing to three dimensions, consider the vibrations inside a cube of side l. Here subdivisions may occur in three directions. Let the subdivisions be represented by the integers p, q, and r respectively. We may regard p, q, r as coordinates of a point. The whole system of points thus obtained constitutes a cubic array of volume-density unity. If R be the distance of any of these points from the origin, we have $R^2 = p^2 + q^2 + r^2$. For the frequency ν one obtains now a formula similar to the one for a vibrating string, namely, $\nu = aR/(2l)$. Neglecting the higher powers of dR, the volume of the spherical shell between R and $R + dR$ is $4\pi R^2 dR$. This expression gives also the number of the points in this interval. But our expression for ν yields $d\nu = a/(2l) \cdot dR$. Substituting for dR its value, the number of points is given by $4\pi (2l/a)^3 \nu 2 \cdot d\nu$. This value represents the number of modes corresponding to $d\nu$. If in place of ν we introduce λ, and remember that $\nu\lambda = a$ and $\nu \cdot d\lambda + \lambda \cdot d\nu = 0$, we obtain for the number of modes $32\pi l^3 \lambda^{-4} \cdot d\lambda$. If now we introduce the assumption that each mode has the same amount of kinetic energy e, according to the principle of *the equal distribution of energy* in radiation, we obtain $32\pi e \lambda^{-4} \cdot d\lambda$ as the kinetic energy corresponding to $d\lambda$ and to the unit volume ($l^3 = 1$). If we take the whole energy (kinetic plus potential) to be double the kinetic energy and remember that e is proportional to the absolute temperature T, we obtain

$$C_1 \, T\lambda^{-4} \cdot d\lambda$$

(where C_1 is a constant) as representing the total energy of radiation per unit volume corresponding to the interval from λ to $\lambda + d\lambda$. Rayleigh knew that this formula agreed fairly well with experimental data involving long wave-lengths λ, but failed for short wave-lengths. The derivation of Rayleigh's formula was re-examined by J. H. Jeans and others. It seemed to be a necessary consequence of the law of equal distribution of energy, and the laws of classical thermodynamics (relating to energy) and of electrodynamics (relating to radiation as an electromagnetic phenomenon). And yet, Rayleigh's formula does not correctly represent the observations published about this time by O. Lummer, E. Pringsheim, and F. Kurlbaum. The divergence is wide for very short rays. According to this formula, the energy for any given temperature T would reside mainly in the part of the spectrum where the wave-lengths are very short, because where λ is very small the factor λ^{-4} increases rapidly as the wave-length λ decreases. Where is the error? If the process of absorption and emission of energy is a continuous one, as it has always been assumed to be, then the law of the equipartition of energy has been shown to follow as a necessary consequence. Is this law true for the case of radiation?

PLANCK'S QUANTUM THEORY

Rejecting the law of the equipartition of energy, Planck deduced a theoretical formula which agrees with observation. In the derivation of this formula he boldly resorted to a new and startling assumption which is now reconstructing many of the very foundations of physical science. **Max Planck** was born at Kiel in 1858. He studied for some years in Munich, and spent one year in Berlin attending lectures by Helmholtz, Kirchhoff and Weierstrass. He spent some years as privat docent at Munich, and in 1889 he succeeded Kirchhoff in Berlin. In 1912 he became permanent secretary of the Prussian Academy of Sciences at Berlin. His publications on radiation began in 1896, but not until 1900 did he suggest the quantum theory.

In his earlier studies Planck was much impressed by W. Wien's radiation formula which involved the factor λ^{-5} where Rayleigh had the factor λ^{-4}. Planck labored under the erroneous impression for some time that Wien's formula was the only one which harmonized with the second law of thermodynamics. The experiments on "black bodies" due to O. Lummer and E. Pringsheim in Charlottenburg, H. Rubens (1865–1922) and F. Kurlbaum forced him from that position. Planck's speculations proceeded as follows: Not knowing the exact structure of the atom, he assumed the existence of hypothetical "oscillators," vibrating with frequencies ν. An oscillator emits radiation and in consequence itself loses energy. It will come to rest unless new energy is supplied to it. If radiation falls upon it which is of the same frequency as that which it itself emits, this radiation will be absorbed. If a radiating body which is kept at a constant temperature by receiving radiations from its surroundings has a large number of oscillators of the same frequency ν, the emissions and absorptions among these oscillators of frequency ν must be in equilibrium; the energy of emission must equal that of absorption. Planck assumes that there are in the body many different groups of oscillators, each group having its own frequency which is different from the frequency of every other group. The radiation of such a body is the same as that of a "black body." Let N_ν be the number (assumed large) of oscillators of frequency ν; let their combined energy be E_ν. The energy of any one oscillator is a variable quantity, increasing during absorption and decreasing during emission. Its average energy is evidently the total energy of the group divided by the number of oscillators, or $E_\nu \div N_\nu$. Planck is led to the inquiry, what is the number of ways of partitioning the energy E_ν among the N_ν oscillators of any frequency ν? If E_ν is taken to be divisible into parts in any manner whatever, without restriction, then the number of ways is infinite.

If, however, E_ν be supposed to be made up of a definite number P of parts that are indivisible, finite and equal, then the number of ways of partitioning is finite, and can be ascertained by the arithmetical theory of combinations.

Of the two hypotheses the one assuming unrestricted and unlimited divisibility of the energy among the oscillators leads to the doctrine of the equipartition of energy and to radiation formulas which Planck found to be at variance with observation.

Planck then proceeded to the alternate hypothesis, that strange assumption, that energy is composed of indivisible units (quanta) which can be distributed in only a finite number of ways among the individual oscillators of a group which have the same frequency ν and among the different groups of oscillators having each a distinct frequency. This finiteness renders the mode of distribution amenable to the theory of probability. Regarding this audacious hypothesis, H. A. Lorentz remarked: "We must not forget that the good fortune to have such inspirational ideas comes only to those who have earned it by arduous work and deep cogitation."[1]

With the aid of W. Wien's "displacement law" for radiation from "black bodies," Planck concluded that quanta for oscillators of different frequency are not of the same size, that their sizes are proportional to the frequency ν, and may be represented by $h\nu$, where h is a constant, now called "Planck's constant." Thus energy quanta of high frequency are larger than those of low frequency. Using the observations of Lummer and others, Planck found $h = 6.5 \times 10^{-27}$ erg sec.[2]

If the kinetic energy E of a group of oscillators N_ν is made up of P indivisible parts or quanta, then the number of ways in which that energy can be distributed among the os-

[1] H. A. Lorentz, *Die Naturwissenschaften*, Vol. 13, 1925, p. 1081.
[2] Max Planck, *Verhandl. d. deutsch. physikal. Gesellschaft*, Vol. 2, 1900, p. 237. Planck's leading early papers on radiation are republished in *Ostwald's Klassiker*, No. 206.

cillators is given by the theory of combinations as

$$\frac{(N + P - 1)!}{(N - 1)!\,P!}.$$

Suppose, for example, the number of oscillators of frequency ν were 2, and the number of quanta were 3; that is, $N_\nu = 2$ and $P = 3$. By the formula or by trial we find that there are four ways of partitioning the three quanta among the two oscillators, namely, $1, 2$; $2, 1$; $0, 3$; $3, 0$. If, for another group of oscillators of, say, double frequency, we had $N_{2\nu} = 3$ and $P = 5$, the number of possible partitions for that group would be 21. Hence the number of ways of partitioning among the oscillators of both groups taken together would be $4 \times 21 = 84$.

Let now the same total kinetic energy of the two groups be divided differently among the two groups, so that, for example, for the first group $N_\nu = 2$, $P = 5$, for the second group $N_{2\nu} = 3$, $P = 4$, then the number of partitions of energy among the oscillators is for the first group 6, and for the second group 15. For both groups the number of partitions would be $6 \times 15 = 90$, as against 84 in the first count.

It appears therefore that the total number of ways of distributing a fixed amount of kinetic energy of a body in thermal equilibrium among its oscillators varies with the mode of distributing that energy among the *groups* N_ν of oscillators having the same frequency. There is a definite mode of distribution of the total energy among the various groups, for which the total number of possible ways of partitioning the energy among the oscillators of the body is a maximum. This maximum number represents the actual condition of the body in equilibrium, and yields the energy of each group of oscillators N_ν. Knowing the energy E_ν of each group N_ν, we can find the average kinetic energy of each oscillator by the division $E_\nu \div N_\nu$. From these data we can get per unit volume the kinetic energy lying in the frequency interval ν and $\nu + d\nu$, or, if we prefer, in the interval of wave-lengths from λ to $\lambda + d\lambda$.

The radiation formula which Planck finally obtained is complicated. It gives the intensity of the wave-length λ, and it may be written,

$$hc^2\lambda^{-5} \Big/ \left(exp\,\frac{hc}{\lambda kT} - 1 \right),\qquad\text{I}$$

where h is Planck's constant, k is another constant, called Boltzmann's constant, and $ch/k = 1.436$ cm. grad. He published several somewhat different modes of approach to his formula I.

In Planck's formula the factor λ^{-5} increases rapidly as λ diminishes. Nevertheless, the formula does not labor under the difficulty of Rayleigh's formula, which yields excessive energies for the shorter waves. The quantity in the denominator increases also, and does so at a rate sufficiently great so that the entire expression is in agreement with the known experimental results.

For small values of λT (i.e., small compared with ch/k) Planck's Formula I goes over into the formula of W. Wien. For large value of λT, it goes over into Rayleigh's formula. It reduces to Rayleigh's formula for any value of λT when Planck's constant h is allowed to approach the value of 0; that is, when the assumption of the existence of quanta of energy is dropped.

At first Planck assumed both absorption and emission to be discontinuous. In the second edition of his *Wärmestrahlung*, 1912, he made only emission discontinuous, in order to lessen the difference between the classical and the quantum theory. Later he returned to his original assumptions.

In giving Rayleigh's and Planck's formulas in considerable detail, we have been prompted by a desire to set forth to the reader the impassable stone wall which physics had encountered, and to indicate a great turning point in the onward march of this science.

According to Planck's quantum theory, energy does not *flow* from radiating bodies; it goes off in distinct separate parcels. Energy is granulated, but different frequencies of radiation have granules of different sizes $h\nu$.

Planck's formula commanded the attention of physicists, not because of the compelling force of his logic (his arguments were involved and far from conclusive), but because it was in startling agreement with observation. Between the quantum ideas and the laws of orthodox physics lies at present an unbridged gulf.

THE VALUE AND IMPORTANCE OF h

Planck estimated the numerical value of h to be 6.5×10^{-27} erg sec. The second decimal place proved to be difficult to determine. Some later measurements are as follows: W. Duane[1] and F. L. Hunt, $h = 6.51 \times 10^{-27}$; D. L. Webster,[2] $h = 6.53 \times 10^{-27}$; E. Wagner,[3] $h = 6.49 \times 10^{-27}$; Raymond T. Birge,[4] $h = (6.5543 \pm 0.0025) \times 10^{-27}$ erg sec. On the importance of h, J. H. Jeans[5] remarks: "Small though the value of h is, we must recognize that it is responsible for keeping the universe alive. If h were strictly zero the whole material energy of the universe would disappear into radiation in a time which would be measured in thousand-millionth part of a second. For instance, the normal hydrogen atom, owing to continuous emission of radiation, would begin to shrink at the rate of over a meter a second, and after about 10^{-10} seconds the nucleus and electron would fall together and would probably disappear in a flash of radiation. The quantum theory, by prohibiting any emission of radiation less than $h\nu$, prohibits in actual fact any emission at all except from those atoms which have a quite exceptionally large amount of energy to emit."

[1] *Phys. Rev.*, Vol. 6, 1915, p. 166; Vol. 10, 1917, p. 624.
[2] *Phys. Rev.*, Vol. 7, 1916, p. 587.
[3] *Physik. Zeitschr.*, Vol. 18, 1917, p. 440.
[4] *Phys. Rev.*, Vol. 14, 1919, p. 368.
[5] J. H. Jeans, *Atomicity and Quanta*, Cambridge, 1926, p. 21.

SPECIFIC HEAT AND THE QUANTUM THEORY

Molecular heat or atomic heat (for monatomic substances) is defined as the product of the specific heat and molecular or atomic weight. According to measurements made by Dulong and Petit in 1819, the atomic heat of solids is a constant value close to the number 6. Later it was found by observation that the specific heat diminished rapidly when the temperature falls. In 1907 several fruitless attempts were made to find a theoretical explanation of this fact on the theory of the equipartition of the energy of molecules along the three directions x, y, z. Abandoning equipartition, Einstein [1] in that year developed a theory on the assumption of the existence of quanta distributed among oscillators in a manner yielding the greatest probability. Atomic heat appears here as a function of the absolute temperature and $h\nu$. By his theory, atomic heat diminishes more rapidly for low temperatures than is indicated by experiment. His formula was modified by **Peter Debye** [2] at Zurich who, instead of assuming a definite frequency characteristic of every particular substance, imagined the solid capable of vibrating so as to yield a whole spectrum of frequencies from zero up to an assigned maximum. Still better agreement was secured by a modification of Debye's theory, proposed by M. Born and Theodor V. Kármán,[3] in Göttingen. They took into consideration the crystalline structure of the body, that is, the space-lattice arrangement of the atoms,[4] instead of resting the development upon the classical theory of elasticity as Debye had done.

AN EXTENSION OF THE QUANTUM THEORY

The original Planck oscillator was conceived as possessing only one degree of freedom; it swings back and forth in one

[1] A. Einstein, *Annalen d. Phys.*, Vol. 22, 1907, p. 180.

[2] P. Debye, *Annalen d. Phys.*, Vol. 39, 1912, p. 789.

[3] M. Born und Th. V. Kármán, *Physik. Zeitschr.*, Vol. 13, 1912, p. 297.

[4] F. Reiche, *Quanten theorie*, 1921, Chapter IV.

direction. But the application of the quantum theory to the kinetic theory of solids and gases calls for the extension of this theory to bodies possessing several degrees of freedom. The need of considering the manner of partitioning the quanta among the various possible degrees of freedom was emphasized by **Henri Poincaré** (1854–1912) in 1911 at the Solvay Congress in Brussels. How this extension may be effected was indicated in 1915 and 1916 independently by Planck[1] and Sommerfeld.[2] Further studies along this line were undertaken by W. Wilson,[3] P. S. Epstein,[4] **K. Schwarzschild**[5] (1873–1916) and P. Ehrenfest.[6] In 1916 Einstein[7] gave an important new derivation of Planck's radiation formula.

AN ESTIMATE OF THE QUANTUM THEORY

In 1925 **Hendrik Antoon Lorentz** (1853–1928), professor in the University of Leyden, evaluated the quantum theory as follows: "That the theory of elements of energy could be developed into a general quantum theory, is owing to its wonderful power of adaptability, in consequence of which it could associate itself with general theorems of theoretical mechanics. As long as one dealt with simple harmonic vibrations, the original conception of elements of energy was sufficient in its applications. Later we learned to 'quantize' also other motions which are completely or conditionally periodic or even non-periodic, in the consideration of the values of 'phase integrals' or the size of bounded regions in 'phase space.' The quantum conditions set up in such cases consist always in this, that the quantity in question shall be allowed only values which are multiples of some unit value, and in these unit values there occurs always the constant h. We have now progressed so far that this constant is depended upon, not only

[1] M. Planck, *Annal. d. Physik.*, Vol. 50, 1916, p. 385.
[2] A. Sommerfeld, *Annal. d. Physik.*, Vol. 51, 1916, pp. 1, 125.
[3] W. Wilson, *Phil. Mag.*, Vol. 29, 1915, p. 795.
[4] P. S. Epstein, *Annal. d. Physik.*, Vol. 50, 1916, p. 489.
[5] K. Schwarzschild, *Berl. Akad. d. Wiss.*, 1916, p. 548.
[6] P. Ehrenfest, *Annal. d. Physik.*, Vol. 51, 1916, p. 327.
[7] A. Einstein, *Phys. Zeitschr.*, Vol. 18, 1917, p. 121.

for explaining the intensity of radiation and the wave-length for which it is a maximum, but also for explaining the quantitative relations existing in many other cases. In conjunction with other physical quantities it determines, to mention only a few, the specific heat of solids, the photochemical effects of light, the orbits of electrons in the atom, the wave-lengths of spectral lines, the frequency of Röntgen rays which are brought forth by the impact of electrons of given velocity, the velocity with which gas molecules can rotate and indeed also the distances of the little parts which make up a crystal. We do not exaggerate when we say that in our view of nature it is the quantum conditions which hold matter together and prevent it from completely losing its energy by radiation. That in all this we are dealing with real relations is convincingly evident from the agreement of the values of h derived from different phenomena, values which differ little from the number which Planck computed 25 years ago from the experimental data then available to him. . . . To be sure, the fusion of the new ideas with the classic mechanics and electrodynamics is still a dream of the future and we are still far remote from having a quantum mechanics which admits the discontinuous among its fundamentals."[1]

Low Temperatures

The physical properties of bodies at low temperatures have been investigated assiduously by Sir James Dewar (1842–1923), who was connected for forty-six years with the Royal Institution in London. He liquefied hydrogen in 1893 (p. 213) and in 1899 solidified it. His discovery of the marvelous power of charcoal to absorb gases at low temperature rendered the period 1900 to 1907 ever memorable.[2] He conducted experiments at low temperatures on the electric constants of metals and other substances, also on chemical and photographic action. He found that bacteria survived at very low tempera-

[1] H. A. Lorentz, *Die Naturwissenschaften*, Vol. 13, 1925, p. 1082.
[2] *Smithsonian Report* for 1923, p. 550.

tures, that phosphorescent organisms ceased to emit light in liquid air, but resumed their luminosity on being thawed out.

LIQUEFACTION AND SOLIDIFICATION OF HELIUM

The liquefaction of helium at an absolute temperature of only 4.3° was accomplished by H. Kamerlingh Onnes (1850–1926) at Leyden in Holland in the year 1908. After that, lower temperatures were reached by making helium boil at low pressure. It was ascertained that at very low temperatures some metals become supremely conductive. It seems as if at absolute zero the atoms settle to rest in some form which leaves absolutely free paths through which electrons may travel without hindrance. In 1919 the United States government gave Onnes 30 cubic meters of helium for use in experimentation. In 1923 Onnes made an unsuccessful attempt to solidify helium. He then reached a temperature of 272.18° C. below zero, or .82° absolute, by evaporating the liquid helium in the most perfect vacuum he could obtain (one sixty-five thousandth of an atmosphere) with the aid of a battery of twelve glass and six iron Langmuir vacuum pumps connected in parallel.[1] In 1926, four months after the death of Onnes, helium was solidified at last, in his laboratory, by W. H. Keesom,[2] who accomplished it by subjecting liquid helium to high pressure as well as low temperature. The helium was solidified within a narrow brass tube placed in a liquid helium bath. When the helium in the brass tube was subjected to a pressure of 86 atmospheres and a temperature of 3.2° absolute, or to a pressure of 50 atmospheres and a temperature of 2.2° absolute, the helium was solidified. The solidification curve of helium was observed by varying the temperature and pressure. Of all gases, helium was the last to resist liquefaction and solidification.

[1] *Science,* Vol. 57, March 30, 1923, p. VII.
[2] *Science,* Vol. 64, 1926, p. 132.

THIRD LAW OF THERMODYNAMICS

The researches of H. Le Chatelier (1888) and others, regarding free energy, were brought to a focus by W. Nernst in 1906 in what is sometimes called the third law of thermodynamics, namely, the impossibility of actually reaching absolute zero temperature. As stated by Planck the law is, that the entropy of solids and liquids has the value 0 at the zero point of absolute temperature. Certain limitations are observed in the version given by G. N. Lewis: "If the entropy of each element in some crystalline state be taken as zero at the absolute zero temperature: every substance has a finite positive entropy, but at the absolute zero of temperature the entropy may become zero, and does so become in the case of perfect crystalline substances."[1]

THERMODYNAMICS AND STATISTICS

Doubt concerning the validity of the first law of thermodynamics has been cast by N. Bohr, H. A. Kramers and J. C. Slater, as being only a statistical law, when applied to electrons.[2] For large bodies this law has withstood all onslaughts, but has been merged with the principle of the conservation of mass in a new formulation due to Einstein[3] in his special theory of relativity, which requires that the law of conservation of energy hold with reference to every system of coordinates. The second law of thermodynamics has continued to be the subject of much speculation. If the world is a finite, isolated system, then according to the first and second laws its energy is constant, while its phenomena are irreversible and its entropy tends to a maximum. If that maximum is reached, then the world's available energy is zero, all motion ceases and all bodies have the same temperature. This final state will be reached in a finite time. "This picture of the universe mov-

[1] G. N. Lewis and M. Randall, *Thermodynamics*, 1923, p. 448.
[2] D. L. Webster and L. Page, *Bulletin Nat. Research Council*, Washington, 1921, p. 353.
[3] A. Einstein, *Relativity, The Special and General Theory*, New York, 1921, p. 54.

ing toward old age and ultimate death has seemed to many a gloomy one," says G. N. Lewis;[1] the statement that the world's entropy increases toward a maximum "must be challenged." That we live in a world of irreversible phenomena would not be true if Maxwell's "little demon"[2] existed who could separate individual molecules. But may this separation not happen without the intervention of the "little demon"? May it not happen simply by chance? It has been shown by the statistical mechanics of W. Gibbs and L. Boltzmann, that the reversal of the so-called irreversible phenomena is not impossible, but simply improbable. This idea, says G. N. Lewis,[3] "has grown to be an important, and almost the most important, guiding principle in modern physics." We shall see the theory of probability applied to the explanation of the Brownian movements; it appeared in the derivation of Planck's radiation formula. If the second law of thermodynamics is not absolute, but is simply a highly probable law, then in the course of time exceptions to it will arise and it is not proved that entropy will increase toward a maximum. Take for example the "irreversible phenomenon" of the mixing of two gases, oxygen and nitrogen. A container with a partition in the middle has oxygen on one side and nitrogen on the other. The number of molecules is finite. If a hole is made in the partition, the two gases will mix by diffusion. There will be a probability—very small to be sure, nevertheless a probability— that by the laws of chance, the oxygen and nitrogen will for a moment become separated again, just as, in a pack of cards, one particular arrangement of the cards is sure to arise again upon repeated shuffling.

LIGHT

The Fitzgerald and Lorentz Contraction

The Michelson and Morley experiment of 1887 seemed to indicate that in the place where the experiment was performed

---

[1] G. N. Lewis, *The Anatomy of Science*, New Haven, 1926, p. 142.
[2] J. C. Maxwell, *Theory of Heat*, 7. Ed., 1883, Chap. 22, pp. 328, 329.
[3] G. N. Lewis, *The Anatomy of Science*, New Haven, 1926, p. 148.

(a cellar in Cleveland, Ohio), there was no "ether-drift"; that is, the earth in its motion dragged the ether along with it. Such a conclusion created all sorts of embarrassments to physicists. What is the mode of escape? In 1895 **George Francis Fitzgerald** (1851–1901) [1] of Dublin and H. A. Lorentz,[2] independently, made the audacious assumption that a moving body contracts along the line of its motion. A yard stick is shorter when moving in the direction of its length than when it is at rest. On this assumption the Michelson and Morley experiment could be explained, even though the ether be taken to be stationary, not moving with the earth. The strangeness of this contraction hypothesis was partly removed by an explanation of it on the electric theory of matter. Lorentz went further and, on this hypothesis, deduced mathematically addition-theorems for distances and for time, which deviate from the Newtonian mechanics and are generally known as the "Lorentz transformations." He made a close approach to the modern special theory of relativity.

TWENTIETH CENTURY EXPERIMENTS ON ETHER DRIFT

Dayton C. Miller and E. W. Morley constructed an interferometer about four times as sensitive as the one used by Michelson and Morley in 1887, and in 1902–1904 made experiments at Cleveland with the view of ascertaining whether the Fitzgerald contraction was greater for some materials than for others. The observations indicated no such difference.

In 1905 **Albert Einstein,** then at Zurich, advanced his special theory of relativity, and in 1915 his general theory of relativity, based in part on the assumption that the ether drift experiments of Michelson and Morley had given a nul result. Miller felt that this nul effect interpretation was unwarranted and that the experiment should be repeated at a

---

[1] *Scientific Writings of G. F. Fitzgerald*, Dublin, 1902, pp. LX, 562; O. Lodge, *Philos. Trans.* A, Vol. 184, London, 1894, p. 749.

[2] H. A. Lorentz, *Verslagen d. Zittingen d. k. Akademie van Wetenschappen*, Amsterdam, Vol. 1, 1893, p. 74.

high altitude. Accordingly he moved his instruments to the observatory at Mount Wilson in California and began observing in 1921. In that year Miller obtained an effect there such as would be produced by a real ether drift, corresponding to the relative motion of the earth and ether, of ten kilometers per second. Much time was then given to the study of possible experimental errors and to the explanation of the phenomena on certain assumed motions of the earth in space. But none of the motions, assumed at first, agreed with the results of experiment. However, all observations extending over a period of several years pointed to "a constant and consistent small effect which has not been explained."[1] He found also that the "direction and magnitude of the observed ether drift is independent of local time and is constant with respect to sidereal time." This implies, says Miller, "that the effect of the earth's orbital motion is imperceptible in the observations. . . . In order to account for this fact it is assumed that the constant motion of the earth in space is more than two hundred kilometers per second, but that for some unexplained reason the relative motion of the earth and the ether in the interferometer at Mount Wilson is reduced to ten kilometers per second."[2] The velocity of two hundred kilometers, or more, per second, is "towards an apex in the constellation Draco, near the pole of the ecliptic, which has a right ascension of 262° and a declination of + 65°." Thus far, Miller's results have not been confirmed. In fact, Rudolph Tomaschek[3] of Heidelberg performed two experiments, neither of which revealed any ether drift. In one experiment he used a charged electric condenser which, if moving through the ether, should produce a magnetic field, but none was observed, even when the test was made on the Jungfrau in the Alps. In the second experiment, one originally performed by F. T. Trouton (1863–1922) and H. R. Noble[4] of the University

[1] D. C. Miller, *Science*, Vol. 63, 1926, p. 437.
[2] D. C. Miller, *loc. cit.*, pp. 441, 442.
[3] R. Tomaschek, *Annal. d. Phys.*, 4. S., Vol. 78, 1925, pp. 743–756.
[4] F. T. Trouton and H. R. Noble, *Phil. Trans. Roy. Soc.*, London, A, Vol. 202, 1904, p. 165.

of London in 1903, a charged condenser was suspended by a wire. In case of an ether drift the condenser would turn so as to hang at right angles to the drift. No turning of the condenser could be observed. The theory of this experiment is still in doubt. Rowland's experiment of 1876,[1] which showed that a body carrying a charge of electricity and subjected to rapid rotation, exerts magnetic effects, after being exposed to searching criticism, was finally verified and accepted as correct. But the Trouton and Noble experiment and those of Tomaschek are sufficiently different to further complicate their theory. On ether drift, negative results were obtained also by Roy J. Kennedy[2] at the Mount Wilson Observatory with a modified form of the Michelson apparatus, completely enclosed in a sealed metal case containing helium gas, to prevent changes in pressure and temperature, by A. Piccard and E. Stahel at the summit of the Rigi in Switzerland, and by Carl T. Chase in Pasadena, California.

The assumed nul effect of the Michelson and Morley experiment of 1887 constituted the dominating stimulus which led Einstein to advance his special theory of relativity in 1905. The experiment seemed to show that the velocity of light was the same along and across the direction of the earth's motion through space. Hence Einstein assumed the principle of relativity. He postulated also that the velocity of light in a vacuum is the same under all conditions.

THE AURORA BOREALIS

This phenomenon has been the subject of speculation ever since the time of Benjamin Franklin, who attributed the phenomenon to electricity. That it is due to electric rays from the sun was suggested in 1872 by G. B. Donati of Florence. Eugen Goldstein of Berlin held that they were cathode rays from the sun. Kristian Birkeland (1867–1917) of

[1] Consult *Physical Papers of Henry Augustus Rowland*, Baltimore, 1902; with a commemorative address written by Thomas C. Mendenhall (1841–1924).

[2] R. J. Kennedy, *Proc. Nat. Acad.*, Vol. 12, Washington, 1926, p. 621.

Christiania, adopting this view, constructed a miniature artificial earth (terrela) and endeavored to reproduce the auroral phenomena in the laboratory. The terrela was placed in a vacuum tube and exposed to cathode rays. When it was magnetized then the illumination was concentrated upon a spiral path about the poles and a thin luminous ring about the equator. The mathematical theory of these phenomena was elaborated by Carl Störmer.

The spectrum of the northern light was readily recognized as that due to the gases in the atmosphere, except one prominent line $\lambda = 5577.35$Å in the green, which was not identified with any chemical element until J. C. McLennan and G. M. Shrum of Toronto, in 1925, found it in studying the effect of a large admixture of helium or of neon on the spectrum of oxygen.[1] It seems to belong to some previously unknown part of the spectrum of oxygen. By exciting mixtures of helium, oxygen and nitrogen, the above line was photographed on the same plate with the nitrogen band system, thus producing in the laboratory practically the entire auroral spectrum.

DIAMETERS OF STARS

The diameters of some of the planets were observed by astronomers as early as the eighteenth century. Thus James Bradley in 1733 wrote James Stirling that he had taken observations on the diameter of Jupiter by the use of a telescope having a Huygenian objective lens of 123 feet focal radius. The diameters of stars were too small to be observed by eighteenth or nineteenth century instruments. In 1890 A. A. Michelson explained an interference method of astronomical measurement. If the objective of a telescope is covered by a cap containing two apertures or slits, and the light from a star entering the telescope through those two slits, be observed, interference phenomena are obtained from the overlapping of the two images. As the distance between the slits

[1] J. C. McLennan and G. M. Shrum, *Proc. Roy. Soc.*, London, A, Vol. 108, 1925, pp. 501–512; *Nature*, Vol. 115, 1925, pp. 382, 607.

is gradually increased, the interference fringes become less and less distinct and at last vanish completely. It has been shown that if the wave length of the light from the star is divided by the distance between the slits, and the quotient multiplied by the constant 1.22, we obtain the angular diameter of the star expressed in radians.[1] In 1891 at the Lick Observatory, Michelson applied this method to the determination of the diameters of Jupiter's satellites, but the instruments of that time were not adapted to the successful application of this method to stellar diameters. The building of larger telescopes and interferometers made it possible in 1920 to apply the method to the brilliant star α Orionis which the Arabs called Betelgeuse, meaning "the giant's shoulder." The observations were taken, at Mount Wilson in California, by F. G. Pease. The distance between the two mirorrs of the interferometer, corresponding to our "slits," was nearly 3000 mm.; dividing the effective wave-length, 5750 Ångströms, or .000575 mm., by 3000 mm. and multiplying the quotient by 1.22 yielded a result amounting to .047 second of arc, which is the angular diameter of Betelgeuse.

It has been calculated that this angular diameter is nearly the same as that of a ball one inch in diameter, seen at a distance of 70 miles. To estimate the diameter of Betelgeuse in miles we must know its distance, which is about equal to the distance which light can travel in 175 years. This diameter is about 240 million miles or 300 times the diameter of our sun. Soon after this result was obtained it was found that the star Antares is even a bigger giant than Betelgeuse.

INFRA-RED SPECTRA

The researches of the nineteenth century on radiant heat and light in the infra-red part of the solar spectrum, due to William Herschel, M. Melloni, L. Nobili, S. P. Langley, and

[1] A. A. Michelson, *Phil. Mag.*, Vol. 30, 1890, p. 2; ''Light-Waves and their Uses,'' 1903, p. 135; *Science*, Vol. 57, 1923, p. 703.

others, were continued by F. Paschen [1] of Tübingen, who in 1894 extended Langley's studies from the lower limit of 5μ reached by Langley, to 9.3μ, and in 1897 with refinements in apparatus and methods, to 23μ. Accordingly, the spectroscopic method of research had at that time covered the range of wave-lengths in the spectrum from the ultra-violet 0.1μ to the infra-red 23μ, a range of nearly eight octaves.

Among the early workers in the emission spectra of elements in the infra-red were Paschen and Exum Percival Lewis (1863–1926) of the University of California. Lewis,[2] when experimenting at the Johns Hopkins University, aimed to continue Rowland's table of wave-lengths to the infra-red part of the spectrum, and, by using concave gratings, determined with great precision several infra-red lines of sodium, lithium, calcium, silver, and some other elements. Paschen used grating spectographs and reached results which, as we shall see, supported the combination principle of Ritz.

Using a fluorite spectrograph, Paschen and H. M. Randall measured, in 1910, the longest wave lengths of emission lines hitherto obtained. They lie somewhat beyond 9μ for sodium. For additional elements these researches were continued by Randall and E. F. Barker at the University of Michigan.

ULTRA-VIOLET SPECTRA

Glass being a strong absorber of ultra-violet rays, quartz, rock salt and fluor spar prisms came to be used. A. Cornu examined the solar ultra-violet spectrum as far as 2922Å, while A. Miethe and E. Lehmann in 1909 were able to proceed as far as 2912Å. As previously noted (p. 191) studies have been carried on in the ultra-violet spectra of metals. E. P. Lewis of the University of California determined the ultra-violet spectra of krypton and xenon, and discovered the continuous spectrum of hydrogen in the ultra-violet region.

[1] H. M. Randall, ''Infra-red Spectroscopy,'' *Science*, Vol. 65, 1927, p. 167; H. Rubens, in *Kultur der Gegenwart* (Physik), 1915, p. 196.
[2] E. P. Lewis, *Astrophys. Jour.*, Vol. 2, 1895, pp. 1, 106.

X-rays came to be recognized since the time of Laue and W. H. Bragg as light waves of very short wave-lengths. Their ability to liberate electrons from a surface on which they fall is found to be a great aid in the study of radiation, lying in the gap between X-rays and the previously observed ultra-violet rays reaching as far as, say, Theodore Lyman's rays of 1000Å, found in 1906. Millikan [1] and his collaborators have succeeded in improving the methods of ultra-violet spectroscopy, using concave gratings, so as to make possible the direct measurement of wave-lengths in this difficult region, and they have made some important determinations on optical spectra which can be emitted by the second ring or shell of electrons in the atoms of atomic number from 2 to 13 (helium to aluminum). J. J. Hopfield [2] photographed the spectra of hydrogen, nitrogen and oxygen in the extreme ultra-violet and showed thereby that these gases are not as opaque in that region as had been supposed.

Cosmic Rays

A wonderful disclosure of the existence of radiation involving rays of very much shorter wave-lengths than even X-rays was recently made by the successive observations of British, German, and American physicists. In 1903, E. Rutherford and J. C. McLennan noticed that the leakage of an electric charge from a well insulated electroscope could be reduced by placing it in a metal box with thick walls. This seemed to indicate the presence of highly penetrating rays, stopped by metal walls only in part. The German physicist Albert Gockel found in 1910 at Zurich and in 1911 at Bern that an electroscope in a balloon 13,000 feet high showed as intense "penetrating radiation" as on the earth's surface. The inference is that the rays in question are not due to radioactive material in the earth. Soon after, Victor F. Hess [3]

[1] *Proceed. Nat. Acad.*, Vol. 7, Washington, 1921, p. 289.
[2] *Phys. Rev.*, Vol. 20, 1922, p. 573.
[3] V. F. Hess, *Physik. Zeitschr.*, Vol. 12, 1911, p. 998,

and Werner Kolhörster[1] repeated the balloon measurements at a height of 5.6 miles and found the radiation eight times as great as at the earth's surface. In 1922 **R. A. Millikan** and I. S. Bowen, at Kelly Field in Texas, sent balloons to a height of ten miles and found the radiation increasing with the height, but only about one-fourth as rapidly as Hess and Kolhörster had stated. To remove the uncertainty relating to the origin of these rays, Millikan and his collaborators experimented on Pike's Peak, then at the very deep and snow fed Muir Lake and at Arrowhead Lake, in California, selected for their freedom from radioactive contamination. The electroscope readings kept decreasing down to a depth of forty-five feet below the surface of the water. Says Millikan:[2] "The atmosphere above the lake [Muir] was equivalent in absorbing power to 23 feet of water, so that we found rays, coming into the earth from outer space, so penetrating that they could pass through 45 plus 23, equalling 68 feet of water or the equivalent of 6 feet of lead, before being completely absorbed. This represents rays much harder (more penetrating) than any which had before even been imagined." Kolhörster's more recent experiments[3] in Switzerland seemed to indicate that these rays are most intense in the direction of the Milky Way and the constellations of Andromeda and Hercules, while Millikan had previously concluded that the rays came in equal quantities from all regions in space. Millikan found that the rays "are not homogeneous, but are distributed through a spectral region far up above X-ray frequencies—probably 1000 times the mean frequencies of X-rays; that these rays stimulate, upon striking matter, softer rays of about the frequency predicted by the theory of the Compton effect."[4] They extend over "a spectral region three octaves wide."

Some exceedingly fundamental questions are arising in the

[1] W. Kolhörster, *loc. cit.*, Vol. 14, 1913, p. 1066.
[2] R. A. Millikan, *Science*, Vol. 62, 1925, pp. 445–448.
[3] W. Kolhörster, *Science*, Vol. 64, 1926, Suppl. p. XII.
[4] For details and bibliography, see *Jour. Optical Soc. of Amer.*, Vol. 14, 1927, p. 112.

study of these rays. Millikan and G. H. Cameron have experimental evidence which, they believe, points to the conclusion that besides the tearing down process represented in the phenomena of radioactivity, there is going on in nature a building up process or a birth of chemical elements. The cosmic rays shooting through space are the announcements sent out through the ether of these new births.[1] These rays represent the precise amount of energy which, according to Einstein's equation showing the relation of mass to energy, will be emitted in the form of ether waves, when positive and negative electrons unite to create helium atoms or other light atoms such as oxygen, silicon, magnesium and iron. But one must be on guard against mere chance numerical coincidence.

Summary of Results on Spectra

Millikan summarizes the accomplishments in the study of spectra as follows: "The discovery of new experimental techniques for seeing invisible ether-waves . . . has completely bridged within the past two years the gap between artificial electromagnetic waves and heat waves, and in the short-wave region hot-spark vacuum spectrometry and β-rays methods of analysis have practically filled in completely the gap between the optical and the X-ray fields, while far above even the gamma rays of radium a new group of rays of well-nigh infinitely high frequency has been found. This continuous passage of frequencies from a thousand billion billion per second, over into the zero frequency, i.e., over into static electrical fields, all these waves possessing identical characteristics as to speed of propagation, as to polarization, and as to relations of electric and magnetic vectors, demands one and the same sort of transmitting mechanism or medium to take care of them all, by whatever name it may be called, whether a "world-ether" or "space" this last term meaning

[1] *Science*, Vol. 67, 1928, p. 401; Vol. 68, p. 279.

no longer emptiness, but emptiness endowed with definite properties."[1]

LIGHT QUANTA

An early application of the quantum theory to other phenomena than heat radiation was made by A. Einstein.[2] He applied it to light. Planck took his oscillators to be material bodies emitting radiation of frequency v and in quanta hv, and also absorbing radiation in separate quanta. If one body emits quanta and another body absorbs them, what transpires in the space between the two bodies? Einstein put forth the view that the energy passing between the two bodies was likwise composed of quanta (light quanta) flying with the velocity of light. Thus visible as well as invisible light rays are assumed to be made up of isolated parts flying through space independently of each other. This theory resembles Newton's emission theory, but in the quantum theory the indivisible parts are greater for the higher frequencies, while with Newton the red corpuscles were bigger than the violet. Einstein was led to his light quanta by his endeavor to escape conclusions at variance with observation which he drew from Maxwell's theory of electricity and the electron theory. His quanta proved to be of service in explaining fluorescence, phosphorescence, and photoelectric phenomena.

An experimental result supporting the hypothesis of light quanta is the "Compton effect," obtained by **A. H. Compton**,[3] then at the Washington University in St. Louis, and verified, after a critical examination, by Duane,[4] and Ross.[5] In Compton's experiment X-rays scattered from a solid were found to have a frequency less than that of the primary rays.

[1] R. A. Millikan, *Proceed. Am. Phil. Soc.*, Vol. 65, 1926, p. 74.

[2] A. Einstein, *Annal. d. Physik.*, Vol. 17, 1905, p. 132; Vol. 20, 1906, p. 199; Vol. 47, 1915, p. 879; *Zeitschr. f. Physik*, Vol. 31, 1925, p. 784.

[3] A. H. Compton, *Phys. Rev.*, Vol. 21, 1923, pp. 483–502; Vol. 22, pp. 409–413.

[4] W. Daune and collaborators. See *Proceed. Nat. Acad.*, Washington, Vol. 11, 1925, pp. 25–27.

[5] P. A. Ross, *Proceed. Nat. Acad.*, Vol. 9, 1923, p. 246; Vol. 10, 1924, p. 304.

His explanation in terms of the quantum theory assumes that a light quantum collides with a free electron whose mass was about ten times that of the quantum (an X-ray). The quantum recoiled and changed from a higher to a lower frequency, from blue toward red. That is, the quantum with energy $h\nu_0$ and impulse $h\nu_0/c$, in colliding with the free electron, surrendered part of its energy to the electron and recoiled as a new and smaller quantum $h\nu$. This experiment does not admit of explanation on the old wave theory of light and strongly favors the theory of quanta.

FOUCAULT'S EXPERIMENT AND MODERN VIEWS

In 1850 Foucault's *experimentum crucis* showing that the velocity of light is less in water than in air, led to the abandonment of Newton's emission theory. How is it possible in recent time to revive corpuscular theories? The answer is that for various reasons Foucault's experiment is no longer considered decisive. Alex. Wood [1] argues thus: "We interpreted the phenomenon of refraction wrongly. What really happens is that when the corpuscle reaches the surface of the water, or other medium, the component of its velocity parallel to the surface is diminished by action of a frictional kind. The component of its velocity perpendicular to the surface remains unchanged. The velocity in the water is therefore less than in the air. It is not our theory, but our application of it to this particular problem which was in error."

NATURE OF X-RAYS

From the very start the nature of X-rays was puzzling. Röntgen thought they were longitudinal waves, but C. G. Barkla's detection of partial polarization in 1905 disproved that guess. Stokes at Cambridge and Emil Wiechert at Königsberg in 1896 advanced the hypothesis that X-rays were

[1] Alex. Wood, *In Pursuit of Truth*, London, 1927, p. 47. For an explanation of Foucault's experiment on the theory of "Wave Mechanics" see Ludwig Flamm in *Die Naturwissenschaften*, Vol. 15, July 15, 1927.

pulses in the ether, while others considered them as flying particles. In 1912 **Max v. Laue**[1] in Munich made a brilliant experiment in which interference phenomena were obtained. Previously, the finest manufactured diffraction gratings had failed to indicate any bending of X-rays. Laue, using a crystal with its regularly spaced atoms as a natural grating, was able to obtain spectral results and to show that X-rays have wave-lengths ranging from 1 to $5 \cdot 10^{-9}$ cm. Thus X-rays seemed to be light waves of very short lengths.

Physicists, now, are in the anomalous position of treating light and X-rays sometimes as quanta and sometimes as waves. The strength of the wave theory lies in its easy ability to explain interference phenomena of light. That such phenomena can be explained only by the wave theory is not demonstrated. In fact, W. Duane[2] of Harvard University showed the possibility of explaining diffraction, colors of thin plates and crystal grating phenomena on the quantum theory. G. N. Lewis of the University of California, thoroughly revising our notions of time and of cause and effect, finds it possible without a luminiferous ether, to explain interference by the quantum theory.[3] But at present, these views are only clever suggestions.

PHOTOELECTRIC PHENOMENA AND THE QUANTUM THEORY

In 1887 H. Hertz observed that the ultra-violet light of an electric spark falling upon the negative electrode of a spark gap will facilitate an electric discharge. A year later Wilhelm Hallwachs (1859–1922) of Dresden discovered that under the influence of light, negative electricity is given off by bodies. P. Lenard found that swarms of electrons are emitted when ultra-violet light, and even X-rays, fall upon certain bodies, whether these bodies be in the open or in a

---

[1] W. Friedrich, P. Knipping und M. Laue, *Sitzber-Bayer. Akad., Math.-phys. Kl.* 1912, pp. 303–322, 363–373; *Jahrbuch für Radioaktivitat und Elektronik*, Vol. 11, 1914, p. 308.

[2] W. Duane, *Proceed. Nat. Acad.*, Vol. 9, 1923, p. 158.

[3] G. N. Lewis, *Anatomy of Science*, p. 119.

vacuum. The velocity of the ejected electrons depends not upon the intensity of the impinging light, but upon its wave-length—the greater the velocity the shorter the wave-length. For red or infra-red light no noticeable ejection resulted. On the wave theory of light no satisfactory explanation of these phenomena was found. Einstein pointed out an easy explanation on the quantum theory. The surface of a body absorbs the radiation by individual quanta. Each absorbed quantum $h\nu$ pulls out an electron, its energy being expended in two ways: one in the work of extracting the electron from the body, and the other in giving to that electron a kinetic energy $\frac{1}{2}mv^2$. Red and infra-red rays are too weak even to extract an electron from the body. We have the important equation, $\frac{1}{2}mv^2 = h\nu - P$, due to Einstein, which has been used experimentally for the determination of P for different metals and also of h. The verification of Einstein's equation engaged the attention of R. A. Millikan [1] in photo-electric experiments with light waves, also of F. C. Blake and W. Duane,[2] of M. de Broglie [3] and of C. D. Ellis [4] in experiments with X-rays and with γ-rays. According to Millikan this equation "ranks with the equations of Maxwell in its consequences" and "wrought havoc with existing theories and demanded a new formulation of ideas about relations of ether physics and matter physics." [5]

An interesting case arises when the change is in the opposite direction from $\frac{1}{2}mv^2$ to $h\nu$. When in a vacuum tube a shower of electrons (cathode rays) falls upon an anticathode, two kinds of X-rays are produced, the "characteristic radiation" and the "impulse radiation." These phenomena have been investigated by Ch. Barkla, W. H. Bragg, W. L. Bragg, G. Moseley, C. G. Darwin, M. Siegbahn, W. Duane, A. W. Hull and others. The "impulse radiation" forms a contin-

[1] R. A. Millikan, *The Electron*, chap. X.
[2] Daune, *Phys. Rev.*, Vol. 10, 1917, pp. 93, 624.
[3] Maurice de Broglie, *Third Solvay Congress*, 1921.
[4] C. D. Ellis, *Proceed. Royal Soc.*, A, Vol. 99, 1921, p. 261; Vol. 105, 1924, p. 60.
[5] *Proceed. Am. Phil. Soc.*, Vol. 65, 1926, p. 68.

uous spectrum which stops abruptly at a certain high frequency. On the quantum theory this means that in general the energy $\frac{1}{2}mv^2$ of the electron is in part converted into other forms of energy. In this process $h\nu$ may be smaller than $\frac{1}{2}mv^2$. But if $h\nu$ is greater, there is not enough energy present to produce X-ray radiation, and the spectrum comes to an abrupt end.[1] We pause a moment to remark that the "characteristic radiation" is really a short-wave line spectrum, arising presumably in the inmost part of the atoms of the anticathode and depending for its structure on the material of which the anticathode is composed, so that we have here an X-ray spectrum analysis for determining the presence in the anticathode of chemical elements much like the optical spectrum analysis of Bunsen and Kirchhoff. This "characteristic radiation" may be arranged in series, a short wave K series, a long wave L series, and a still longer wave M series.[2] We shall see later that these series are connected, as Moseley showed, by a definite law with the atomic number of the element in the periodic system. These "characteristic" X radiations possess continuous spectra, too, one at the short-wave extremity of each of the series K, L, M. The continuous band ends abruptly on its long-wave side, while the continuous spectrum of the "impulse radiation" has its abrupt end on its short-wave side. An explanation of the continuous bands adjoining each series has been outlined by Bohr with the aid of quantum relations.[3]

THE BALMER FORMULA AND THE RYDBERG CONSTANT

Over half a century ago the spectral lines of many luminous gases and vapors had been described, and tables of wavelengths prepared, for visible spectra, and for the near ultraviolet as well. But no law of the distribution of lines was discovered before 1884, when Balmer announced his well

[1] W. Duane and F. L. Hunt, *Phys. Rev.*, Vol. 6, 1915, p. 166; F. C. Blake and W. Duane, *Phys. Rev.*, Vol. 10, 1917, p. 624.

[2] F. Reiche, *Die Quantentheorie*, Berlin, 1921, pp. 140, 141, 142.

[3] A. Sommerfeld, *Atombau* etc., 4. Ed., 1924, p. 749.

known formula. **Johann Jakob Balmer** (1825–1898), a teacher in a girls' school and a privat-docent in Basel, presented to the scientific society at Basel, on June 25, 1884, his paper on spectral lines of hydrogen. This, his first research, was carried on when he was in his sixtieth year. Balmer[1] considered the wave-lengths of the four prominent lines in the spectrum of hydrogen and also a number of new lines in the violet and ultra-violet found in 1879 by H. C. Vogel (1841–1907) of Potsdam and certain lines in the spectra of certain white stars observed by Huggins. Balmer found that the ratios of the wave-lengths of the four principal lines could be expressed by surprisingly small numbers. And yet there seemed to be no analogy to the overtones in acoustics. By considering at first only the four principal hydrogen lines, Balmer gradually arrived at a formula having a basic number or factor 3645.6 mm/10^7. The wave-lengths of the four lines are found by multiplying this basic number by 9/5, 4/3, 25/21 and 9/8, respectively. If 4/3 be written 16/12, and 9/8 be written 36/32, then the four numerators are seen to be the squares of 3, 4, 5, 6, and the denominators are respectively less than the numerators by 4. Generalizing, Balmer wrote the formula $[m^2/(m^2 - n^2)]$, where m and n are integers. Taking $n = 2$ and $m = 3$, 4, 5, . . . he obtained a series of ratios which, when multiplied by the basic number, yielded with remarkable accuracy the nine spectral lines definitely assigned to hydrogen and also five additional lines found by Huggins in the spectra of white stars and attributed to hydrogen. The Balmer formula has served as a model for later spectral formulas and constitutes a rock foundation of the theory of spectral lines. In more recent literature the formula is expressed in somewhat different form.

Johannes Robert Rydberg[2] (1854–1919) of the University of Lund, in Sweden, gave in 1890, when he was docent at the

[1] J. J. Balmer, *Verhandl. d. Naturforsch. Gesellsch. in Basel,* Vol. 7, Basel, 1885, pp. 548–560. A second communication is on pages 750–752. See also *Annal. d. Physik,* Vol. 25, 1885, p. 80.
[2] *Phil. Mag.,* 5. S., Vol. 29, 1890, pp. 331–337.

university, the formula

$$n = n_0 - \frac{N_0}{(m + \mu)^2}$$

for a series of spectral lines, where the wave number $n = 10^8 \cdot \lambda^{-1}$, the wave-length λ being expressed in Ångström units, m being any positive integer, $N_0 = 109721.6$, a constant common to all series and to all elements, n_0 and μ constants peculiar to the series. N_0, or N_0 multiplied by the velocity of light c, is called the "Rydberg constant." Rydberg states that in doublets and triplets the difference of wave numbers is a constant for each element. At this time Rydberg had applied his formula to the first three groups of the elements then known in the periodical system. He and Balmer worked independently. In 1896 Balmer [1] gave a new formula which reproduced the series of spectral lines of lithium and thallium as determined observationally by **H. Kayser** and **C. Runge** at Hanover. Balmer reproduced also the different series of helium lines. Rydberg's research was brought to Balmer's attention at this time, and he remarked that his own new formula and Rydberg's were almost identical, except that one of Rydberg's constants was the same for all elements, while his own constants had special values for each element.

RITZ'S COMBINATION PRINCIPLE

Walther Ritz (1878–1909), a gifted Swiss physicist, died in the prime of life, yet was able to enrich mathematical physics and to open up new avenues in spectroscopy. He advanced a combination principle [2] in line spectra which had been recognized also by Rydberg: "By additive or subtractive combination, either of the series formulas themselves, or of the constants entering therein, new formulas are obtained which . . . enable one to compute newly discovered lines from

[1] J. J. Balmer, *Verhandl. d. Naturforsch. Gesellsch. in Basel,* Vol. 11, 1896, pp. 448–464.
[2] W. Ritz, *Gesammelte Werke, Oeuvres,* Paris, 1911, p. 62. Also, *Annal. d. Phys.,* Vol. 25, 1908, pp. 660–696.

those previously known.'' Or, more specifically in the later form: Each observed frequency ν may be conceived to be taken as the difference of two spectral terms ν' and ν'', so that $\nu = \nu' - \nu''$. This principal plays an important rôle in studying the different energy levels of an atom in the Bohr theory. In general, it has been found to be a unifying law applying to the entire spectral region from the infra-red to the ultra-violet even as far as the X-rays. Let us illustrate its application. If we write the Balmer formula in the present day form

$$\nu = R\left(\frac{1}{n^2} - \frac{1}{m^2}\right),$$

where $R = 109677.7$ cm^{-1}, $n = 2$, $m = 3, 4, 5, \ldots$ so that for the hydrogen line H_α one has

$$\nu' = R\left(\frac{1}{2^2} - \frac{1}{3^2}\right),$$

and for H_β,

$$\nu'' = R\left(\frac{1}{2^2} - \frac{1}{4^2}\right),$$

then Ritz's combination principle yields a new line

$$\nu'' - \nu' = R\left(\frac{1}{3^2} - \frac{1}{4^2}\right).$$

Similarly, using H_α and H_γ where for H_γ,

$$\nu'' = R\left(\frac{1}{2^2} - \frac{1}{5^2}\right),$$

then the principle yields

$$\nu'' - \nu' = R\left(\frac{1}{3^2} - \frac{1}{5^2}\right).$$

These theoretical results were verified experimentally by F. Paschen,[1] who found two strong hydrogen lines in the infra-red, which constitute a series of hydrogen lines. Further members of these were found experimentally by F. S. Brack-

[1] Paschen, *Annal. d. Phys.*, Vol. 27, 1908, p. 537.

ett,[1] who observed also the first two lines of the new series defined by $n = 4$, $m = 5, 6. \ldots$ If the frequency of line H_a be regarded as the difference of two spectral terms, one obtains by Ritz's principle the two frequencies involving $n = 1$, $m = 2$, and $n = 1$, $m = 3$. These suggest the series of lines for which $n = 1$, $m = 2, 3, 4, \ldots$ which were actually observed by Theodore Lyman[2] and R. A. Millikan[3] in the ultraviolet.

BAND SPECTRA

Between the continuous spectrum due to luminous solids and the line spectra of luminous gases lie the band spectra, so called because on small dispersion they appear continuous, though they are really made up of lines very close to each other having points of condensation. They came to be studied intensively in 1885 by Henri Alexandre Deslandres at Paris. At the time when Balmer set up his formula for line spectra, Deslandres, from a large amount of empirical data, obtained a formula[4] which served as a model of later developments. The band spectra are the characteristic spectra of molecules containing more than one atom, just as the line spectra are the characteristic spectra of single atoms.

The explanation of Deslandres' formulas on the quantum theory and of Bohr's theory was entered upon by N. Bjerrum at Copenhagen, **K. Schwarzschild**[5] in Potsdam, and T. Heurlinger[6] at Lund. Schwarzschild pictured band lines as corresponding to different states of rotation of absorbing gas molecules. The phenomenon is complex since it involves both vibrations and rotations. From the spectra, calculations have been made of the moments of inertia and the vibrational frequencies of molecules containing two atoms. Band spectra

---

[1] F. S. Brackett, *Astrophys. Jour.*, Vol. 56, 1922, p. 154.

[2] Th. Lyman, *Astrophys. Jour.*, Vol. 23, 1906, p. 181; Vol. 43, 1916, p. 89.

[3] R. A. Millikan, *loc. cit.*, Vol. 52, 1920, p. 47; Vol. 53, 1921, p. 150.

[4] See A. Sommerfeld, *Atombau u. Spektrallinien*, 4. Ed., 1924, p. 719.

[5] K. Schwarzschild, *Berlin Sitzungsber.*, April, 1916, p. 548.

[6] T. Heurlinger, *Dissertation*, Lund, 1918; *Phys. Zeitschr.*, Vol. 20, 1919, p. 188.

are divided into three classes: (1) bands in the extreme infra-red spectrum due only to the rotation of the molecules, (2) bands which are due both to vibrations and rotations, (3) bands involving molecular vibrations and rotations, together with motions of electrons. "The quantum theory as now applied to band spectra . . . interprets the three classes of bands as due to jumps between molecular stationary states accompanied respectively by changes in the rotational quantum numbers, rotational and vibrational quantum numbers and in the last class, rotational, vibrational and electronic quantum numbers." [1]

The fine structure of bands is explained as due in part to the dissimilarity among the molecules in isotopes. Thus HCl, with $Cl+$ of the atomic weights 35 or 37, yields corresponding band lines of HCl (35) and HCl (37) which have a slight difference in wave-lengths, so that by superposition of the two spectra, there is an apparent fine structure of the two lines. Centrifugal forces of molecular rotation may in some cases be sufficiently intense to cause disruption of the molecules, as was shown by R. S. Mulliken [2] of Harvard, in the case of Ca-Hydride. R. T. Birge,[3] J. C. Slater,[4] R. S. Mulliken,[5] R. Mecke [6] and F. Hund [7] have initiated a molecular theory by extending to molecules some of the concepts of the atomic theory relating to systems of electrons.[8] Thus, Birge arrived at the generalization that "the energy levels

[1] E. C. Kemble, *Bull. Nat. Research Council*, Vol. 11, No. 57, 1926, p. 12.

[2] R. S. Mulliken, *Phys. Rev.*, Vol. 25, 1925, p. 509. See also J. Franck and P. Jordan, *Anregung von Quantensprüngen durch Stösse*, 1926, p. 249.

[3] R. T. Birge, *Nature*, Vol. 116, 1925, pp. 170, 207, 783; Vol. 117, pp. 81, 229, 300.

[4] J. C. Slater, *Nature*, Vol. 117, p. 587.

[5] R. S. Mulliken, *Phys. Rev.*, Vol. 26, 1925, p. 561.

[6] R. Mecke, *Naturwissenschaften*, Vol. 13, 1925, p. 698, 755.

[7] F. Hund, *Zeitschr. f. Phys.*, Vol. 36, 1926, p. 657.

[8] For details consult the *Bulletin of the National Research Council*, Vol. 11, Part 3, 1926, No. 57. Report on molecular spectra in gases, by Edwin C. Kemble of Harvard Univ., R. T. Birge of the Univ. of California, W. F. Colby of the Univ. of Michigan, F. W. Loomis of New York Univ., and Leigh Page of Yale Univ.

associated with the valence electrons of molecules agree in all essential aspects with those associated with the valence electrons of atoms."[1]

Continuous Atomic Spectra

There are actually continuous spectra due to molecules, but, strange to say, there are also actually continuous spectra due to atoms. This fact was first brought to light by R. W. Wood[2] of the Johns Hopkins University in experiments on sodium vapor. Further observations were made by J. Holtsmark. It is seen that the sequence of the absorption lines of sodium continually increases in density to the end of the series, and upon attaining continuity reaches into the ultraviolet region.

J. Hartmann[3] of Göttingen has observed continuous emission and absorption bands in the stellar spectra of dissociated hydrogen, at the limit of the Balmer series. Continuous spectra are known also in the region of X-rays, as previously noted.

The theory[4] of these continuous spectra which lie adjacent to the limits of line series has been considered by Bohr, in 1922, in the light of the frequency condition $h\nu = E_2 - E_1$.

Magneto-optic and Electro-optic Phenomena

We have seen (p. 254) that Faraday in 1845 discovered the rotation of the plane of polarization of light in a magnetic field. Allied to this Faraday effect is a phenomenon observed over a quarter of a century later by **John Kerr**[5] (1824–1907) of Glasgow, namely, the rotation of the plane of polarization in a magnetic field during reflection of the light from the polished pole surface of a magnet. Kerr was able to announce this discovery in 1876 at the meeting of the British Association in

[1] R. T. Birge, *Nature*, Vol. 117, 1926, p. 301.
[2] R. W. Wood, *Phil. Mag.*, Vol. 18, 1909, p. 530.
[3] *Phys. Zeitschr.*, Vol. 18, 1917, p. 429.
[4] See A. Sommerfeld, *Atombau* etc., 4. Ed., 1924, p. 749.
[5] J. Kerr, *Phil. Mag.*, S. 5., Vol. 3, 1877, p. 321.

Glasgow. Under different directions of magnetization, different angles of incidence and different wave-lengths of the light, this very delicate phenomenon has been observed by many physicists. The dependence of the effect upon color has been examined especially by H. du Bois of Berlin in 1890, L. R. Ingersoll of Madison, Wis., in 1906, and Stanislaw Loria of Lemberg in 1912.

The theory of the Kerr effect has engaged the attention of many. W. Voigt (1850–1919) of Göttingen worked out a theory of the Kerr phenomenon from the modern electronic viewpoint.[1]

Frequently discussed in connection with the Kerr effect, though not optical in character, is the effect discovered by E. H. Hall[2] in the Rowland laboratory at the Johns Hopkins University, in 1879, indicating that in a thin sheet of metal a magnetic field perpendicular to the sheet will cause a bending of the electric lines of flow through the metal.

A very striking phenomenon is the magnetic breaking up of spectral lines (p. 173) observed in 1896, by Pieter Zeeman[3] of Amsterdam. It was found that spectral lines were resolved in a magnetic field into doublets and triplets.

Among the many physicists who wrestled with the theory of this phenomenon, are H. A. Lorentz and J. Larmor; from the standpoint of the quantum theory it received the attention of Debye, Sommerfeld, Bohr and others.[4]

In lines of complicated structure there occur the so-called anomalous effects in which a spectral line observed in a direction perpendicular to the magnetic lines is broken up into a larger number, into four, five, six, or more component lines.[5] R. W. Wood[6] was the first to observe the Zeeman effect in

[1] See L. R. Ingersoll's report in *Bulletin Nat. Research Council*, Washington, Vol. 3, Part 3, 1922, p. 260.

[2] E. H. Hall, *Am. Jour. of Science*, Vol. 20, 1880, p. 161.

[3] P. Zeeman, *Proceed. K. Akad. v. Wetensch*, Amsterd., Vol. 5, 1896, pp. 181, 242.

[4] See A. Landé, *Die neuere Entwicklung der Quantentheorie*, 1926, pp. 55–57.

[5] A. Landé, *op. cit.*, pp. 67–71.

[6] R. W. Wood, *Phil. Mag.*, Vol. 10, 1905, p. 408; Vol. 12, 1906, p. 329; Vol. 27, 1914, p. 1009.

band lines. No satisfactory explanation of the anomalous Zeeman effects has yet been given.

The electric analogue to the Zeeman effect was observed by Johannes Stark [1] at Aachen in 1913 by the use of canal rays. Hydrogen spectral lines in an electric field were resolved into a group of lines lying close to each other. This is called the "Stark effect." It resisted explanation by the classic theory but yielded readily to treatment by the quantum theory, as presented by Bohr,[2] Epstein,[3] and Schwarzschild.[4]

MECHANICS [5]

SPECIAL THEORY OF RELATIVITY

It has been stated that the outcome of the Michelson and Morley experiment of 1887 was interpreted as indicating the total absence of ether wind or ether drift at the place of experimentation. Disinclined to accept the conclusion that the ether moved with the earth, G. F. Fitzgerald in England and H. A. Lorentz in Holland, independently, sought another way out of the dilemma by suggesting, as we have already stated, that the experiment could be explained on the assumption that an object in motion contracts in the direction of its motion, the contraction increasing when the velocity increases. A. Einstein in 1905 went further and made the important generalization, known as the "special theory of relativity." The "Lorentz transformations" are valid in that theory. Disregarding the question of the existence or the non-existence of an ether, he proceeded to build up a theory resting upon as few postulates as possible. Two vital assumptions underlie this theory. One postulated that the velocity of light in a vacuum is a constant and is independent of the motion of the source. This independence was shown to exist by the Dutch

---

[1] J. Stark, *Sitzungsber. Berliner Akademie*, 1913, p. 932.

[2] N. Bohr, *On the Quantum Theory of Line Spectra*, Part I, II, 1918.

[3] P. Epstein, *Phys. Zeitschr.*, Vol. 17, 1916, p. 148.

[4] K. Schwarzschild, *Sitzungsber. Berliner Akademie*, May 11, 1916, p. 548.

[5] For an outline of nineteenth century events, consult Horace Lamb's lecture, *The Evolution of Mathematical Physics*, Cambridge, 1924.

astronomer, Willem de Sitter,[1] by considerations based on observations of double stars. The other assumption is the "principle of relativity" in the restricted sense, which asserts: If, relative to one coordinate system, a second is a uniformly moving coordinate system devoid of rotation, then natural phenomena run their course with respect to the second system according to the same general laws as with respect to the first system. Thus, if a yard stick in the second system appears to an observer in the first system to have the length $\sqrt{1 - (v^2/c^2)}$ (where v is the uniform velocity of the second system relative to the first, and c is the velocity of light in a vacuum), then to an observer in the second system a yard stick in the first system will appear to have the same length $\sqrt{1 - (v^2/c^2)}$.

A concomitant of the discussion of the relativity theory was a critical examination of the laws of motion of Galileo and Newton.[2] The first law (the "law of inertia") says that an isolated body at rest will remain at rest, if in motion it will continue in motion in a straight line with the same velocity. But it was explained that we do not know of any body in nature which is at absolute rest, not on the earth nor on the sun or stars. There is rest only with respect to some system of coordinates. Einstein gave a critical examination of what he called a "Galilean system of coordinates," a system in which the law of inertia holds relative to it, and in which no gravitational field exists, which is therefore not rigidly attached to the earth. "The visible fixed stars are bodies for which the law of inertia certainly holds to a high degree of approximation. . . . The laws of the Mechanics of Galileo-Newton can be regarded valid only for a Galilean system of coordinates." Einstein gave a new interpretation of Fizeau's experiment on the velocity of light in water flowing through a pipe (p. 159). Fizeau had concluded that the ether was carried along by the water, but with a velocity less than that

[1] W. de Sitter, *Physik. Zeitschr.*, Vol. 14, 1913, p. 429, 1267.
[2] See, for example, E. Freundlich, *Grundlagen der Einsteinschen Gravitations theorie*, Berlin, 1920, pp. 29–42.

of the water. Einstein,[1] disregarding the ether and assuming that the velocity of light in water is the same with respect to the liquid whether or not the water is in motion in the pipe, explained the experiment as an immediate and accurate consequence of the "Lorentz transformations" applied to the problem: Given the velocity of light in water and the velocity of the water in the pipe, to find the velocity of light relative to the pipe.

GENERAL THEORY OF RELATIVITY

The Einstein theory of 1905 was restricted to uniform motion. In 1915 he generalized the theory into a theory of the relativity of all motion. The general theory of relativity is based upon three postulates: *First,* The "general principle of relativity," according to which all systems of coordinates are equivalent for the description of physical phenomena; *Second,* The "principle of equivalence," according to which inertial mass is equal to gravitational mass, a principle based upon the fact that all bodies have the same acceleration; *Third,* "Mach's principle," according to which, in a gravitational field, the properties of space are determined by the masses of bodies. The general theory of relativity thus presents a theory of gravitation and in effect reduces gravitation to a property of space-time. The gravitational field of force is replaced by a curvature of the space-time continuum. Gravitational phenomena are conditioned by the geometrical properties of a non-Euclidean space-time continuum which are determined by matter.

This extremely subtle theory attracted attention throughout the world. Trained mathematicians devoted themselves to its fuller exposition or to still further generalization. H. Weyl[2] at Zurich and **A. S. Eddington**[3] at Cambridge, England,

[1] A. Einstein, *Relativity the Special and general theory,* transl. by R. W. Lawson, New York, 1921, p. 46.

[2] H. Weyl, *Space, Time, Matter,* transl. by H. L. Brose, New York, 1921.

[3] A. S. Eddington, *Space, Time, and Gravitation,* Cambridge, 1920; *Report on the Relativity Theory of Gravitation,* London, 1920,

gave expositions including electrical phenomena in the general relativity theory. Other novel viewpoints were taken by R. C. Tolman [1] at Berkeley, California, E. Cartan [2] at Paris, and G. D. Birkhoff [3] at Cambridge, Massachusetts. The number of workers in this field grew to enormous proportions. A critical attitude was maintained. Nevertheless, comparatively few writers stood out in firm opposition to the theory. Among the latter are C. L. Poor, [4] T. J. J. See, [5] Ph. Lenard, [6] and P. Painlevé. A number of observational astronomers and experimental physicists devoted their labors to testing the general theory of relativity. Thus far, no experimental physicist has shown experiments in contradiction with it.

Proceeding to tests which have been applied to the theory, we note that according to the general theory of relativity a slight variation from the motion of a planet by Newton's law of gravitation should take place; for example, the major axis of the elliptical orbit of Mercury should rotate around the sun 43 seconds of arc in a century. Leverrier in 1859 and S. Newcomb in 1895 had actually found a perihelion movement of the orbit of Mercury of about 43 seconds per century, which they could not explain on Newtonian mechanics. Thus relativity seemed to explain a phenomenon which the Newtonian mechanics had found inexplicable. In a later computation Newcomb obtained 41 seconds. But the close agreement between relativity theory and observation has been disturbed still further by the astronomer Ernst Grossmann [7] who critically examined Newcomb's work and by a somewhat different selection and treatment of the great mass of observational data arrived at a perihelion movement per century of $+ 29''$ by

[1] R. C. Tolman, *The Theory of Relativity of Motion*, Berkeley, 1917; *General Electric Review*, Vol. 23, 1920, p. 486.
[2] E. Cartan, *Journal de mathématiques*, 9. S., Vol. 1, 1922, p. 141.
[3] G. D. Birkhoff, *Relativity and Modern Physics*, Cambridge, 1923.
[4] C. L. Poor, *Gravitation versus Relativity*, 1922.
[5] T. J. J. See, *Electrodynamic Wave-theory of Physical Forces*, Vol. II. *New Theory of the Aether*, Kiel, 1923; *Astronomische Nachrichten*, Feb., 1926.
[6] Ph. Lenard, *Jahrb. d. Radioakt. u. Electr.*, Vol. 15, 1918; p. 117; Vol. 17, 1920, p. 307.
[7] E. Grossmann, *Zeitschr. f. Phys.*, Vol. 5, 1921, p. 280.

one set of data, and $+ 38''$ by another set of data. According to Grossmann the discrepancy between Einstein's theoretical figures and his own is $14''$ and $5''$. This motion of the perihelion is, according to the theory of relativity, greater for elliptical orbits of high eccentricity, like that of Mercury. For other planets which have much smaller eccentricity, the perihelion motion predicted by relativity is so small as to escape detection.[1]

According to the general theory of relativity a ray of light will be deflected from its rectilinear path when passing through a gravitational field. During an eclipse of the sun, stars near the sun become visible and can be photographed. If such stellar photographs are compared with those taken of the same stars in night time, apparent relative positions of stars during the eclipse can be compared with their positions at other times. A bending of the light rays would change the apparent location of the stars. The Royal Astronomical Society and the Royal Society of London, in 1919, sent an expedition to Sobral in Brazil and to the island of Principe in West Africa, and obtained data which confirmed the theoretical results fairly well. A closer confirmation was afforded by the photographs taken by W. W. Campbell,[2] director of the Lick Observatory, and R. Trumpler, when on the W. H. Crocker eclipse expedition to Wallal, Western Australia, to observe the total solar eclipse of Sept. 21, 1922. Campbell found the angular displacement of the star images 1.72 seconds of arc, as against Einstein's predicted value of 1.74 seconds.

Another test of the general theory of relativity is afforded by its prediction of a displacement toward the red of spectral lines produced at the surface of stars, when compared with the spectral lines of the same element produced at the surface of the earth. In the case of the sun, the effect is so small that measurement is very difficult. Before 1919, German observers

---

[1] A. Einstein, *Relativity, The Special and General Theory*, New York, 1921, pp. 150–152.

[2] W. W. Campbell and R. Trumpler, *Lick Observatory Bulletins*, Vol. 11, 1923–1924, p. 41.

on cyanogen bands claimed to have detected a shift, while other observers, particularly C. E. St. John of Mount Wilson, obtained negative results.[1] In 1923 St. John[2] succeeded in measuring a shift for sunlight, in case of 331 iron lines. He concluded that the apparently discordant shift was not due to relativity alone, but also to the Doppler effect and to differential scattering of light passing through the solar atmosphere. He showed that it is possible to disentangle the three effects. In 1925 W. S. Adams[3] of Mount Wilson observed a spectral shift toward the red of light from a heavy star. Startling is the application of special relativity in atomic theory to the explanation of the fine structure of spectral lines.

Strange to say, this very abstract theory of relativity received wide popular attention. Men everywhere were attracted or repelled by the apparent paradoxes to which it led. Humorists found in it material for the exercise of their art.

Philosophic Aspects of Relativity

"One of the characteristics of the recent progress of theoretical physics," says V. F. Lenzen,[4] "is that, in general, new concepts and principles do not require the abandonment of the older theories. The earlier theories occur in the later as limiting cases. This may be illustrated by numerous examples, but I shall confine myself to the theory of relativity. Thus Newton's theory is a limiting case of the special theory, the special theory is a limiting case of the general theory. This aspect of the development of physical thought seems to me to be best described by the Hegelian principle that the truth of the lower stages is preserved in that of the later stages of development." In the words of Einstein:[5] "No one must

[1] E. Freundlich, *Die Naturwissenschaften*, 1919, p. 520.

[2] C. E. St. John, *Proceed. Nat. Acad. of Sciences*, Washington, Vol. 12, 1926, p. 65.

[3] *Science*, Vol. 61, 1925, p. X.

[4] V. F. Lenzen, *Univ. of California Publications in Philosophy*, Vol. 4, 1923, p. 158.

[5] A. Einstein in the *London Times*, reprinted in Slosson's *Easy Lessons in Einstein*, 1921.

think that Newton's great creation can be overcome in any real sense by this or by any other theory. His clear and wide ideas will forever retain their significance as the foundation on which our modern conceptions of physics have been built.''

EQUIVALENCE OF ENERGY AND MASS. SOLAR RADIATION

The view of Einstein,[1] that energy like matter possesses inertia leads to novel conclusions. If oxygen and hydrogen, taken in proper amounts for forming water, be weighed and the mixture of the two exploded, and allowed to cool, the doctrine that energy possesses inertia demands that the water weigh less than the gases from which it was formed, by an amount equivalent to the heat energy radiated. According to theory 9×10^{20} ergs (that is, c^2 ergs, c being the velocity of light) of energy are equivalent to one gram of mass. This heat energy radiated is too small to be measured by present day measurements.

This theory plays a leading part in recent cosmological speculation. By the transformation of mass into energy, says J. H. Jeans,[2] ''the long standing puzzle of the source of the sun's radiation appears at last to have been solved. . . . The source of the sun's radiation is the sun's mass; the sun keeps up its radiation by transforming its mass into energy. . . . The rate of radiation is about 250 million tons a minute, and this represents a real decrease of the sun's mass.''

In the nineteenth century, an answer to the puzzle of the sun's energy had been ventured by Robert Mayer and William Thomson (Lord Kelvin), by the fall of meteors into the sun and the conversion of their mechanical energy into heat. Later, Helmholtz and William Thomson advanced the solar contraction theory and the accompanying change of potential energy into heat. This theory played a prominent rôle in the controversy between physicists who would not allow the sun and the earth an age of more than 60 or 100 million years, and

[1] A. Einstein, *Annal. d. Phys.*, Vol. 20, 1906, pp. 627–633; P. R. Heyl, *Fundamental Concepts of Physics*, 1926, p. 71.
[2] J. H. Jeans, *Atomicity and Quanta,* Cambridge, 1926, p. 12.

the geologists who insisted that so short a period made it impossible to explain the evolution of geologic formations and of life on the earth. This controversy came to an abrupt end by the discovery of radium, when the physicists became willing to let geologists assume as great an age for the sun and earth as they thought they needed. But more careful calculation has convinced some recent physicists that even radioactivity could not explain solar energy, because of the short, "half-life period" of radium; if the quantity of radium is halved every 1730 years, the radiation therefrom would have to vary correspondingly, and this is contrary to observation.[1] More promising is the present intra-atomic theory alluded to above. It is advocated by Jeans and Eddington. Mass is changed into energy. Jeans, moreover, postulates the existence of radioactive substances in the sun that are of greater atomic weight than uranium.

A NEW QUANTUM MECHANICS

The early formulations of the quantum theory, even as they were extended in 1915 and 1916, have been found in some respects inadequate and in need of revision. For example, the old theory has not been able to account satisfactorily for the anomalies in the Zeeman effect. As regards the difficulties of classical mechanics, Dirac[2] stated: "It has long been thought that the way out of this difficulty lies in the fact that there is one basic assumption of the classical theory which is false, and that if this assumption were removed and replaced by something more general, the whole atomic theory would follow quite naturally."

Initiatory steps in the effort to lay the foundation for a systematic theory of quantum mechanics were taken by W. Heisenberg[3] at Göttingen. Parts of his formulation have been simplified and parts generalized by M. Born, P. Jordan, W.

[1] D. H. Menzel, *Science*, Vol. 65, 1927, p. 433.
[2] P. Dirac, *Proc. Roy. Soc.*, London, S. A, Vol. 110, 1926, p. 561.
[3] W. Heisenberg, *Zeitschr. f. Phys.*, Vol. 33, 192, p. 879.

Pauli and P. Dirac. A more recent formulation of quantum mechanics has been made by E. Schrödinger [1] in Zurich. Inspired by the writings of Louis de Broglie [2] in Paris, he presents an undulatory theory of mechanics which is transformable into the systems of Born and Heisenberg. The Bohr orbits are superseded by a structure represented by vibrational types of a character which, as E. B. Wilson [3] remarked, resembles in some points the ideas put forward in 1903 by J. J. Thomson [4] who for many years has been proposing and testing out theories of Faraday tubes of force and light corpuscles. De Broglie's and Schrödinger's theories will be noted more fully at the close of the history of atomic models.

BROWNIAN MOVEMENTS

An English botanist, Robert Brown [5] (1773–1858) observed in 1827, under the microscope, an extremely lively and haphazard movement of very small particles in water. Each particle rises and sinks, rises again, independently of other particles, without rest. The smaller the grain the more active it is. These are the so-called "Brownian movements." They take place in other fluids. **Jean Perrin** of the Sorbonne observed them even with minute spheres of water supported by the "black spots" on soap bubbles. He described the movements as "eternal and spontaneous." [6] No satisfactory explanation of them was offered until 1876 when W. Ramsay advanced the hypothesis that they are due to impact of the particles with moving molecules. Afterwards Joseph Delsaulx (1828–1891) and Ignace J. J. Carbonnelle (1829–1889) explained that "in the case of large surfaces, molecular impacts, which cause pressure, will produce no displacement of

---

[1] E. Schrödinger, *Annal. d. Phys.*, Vol. 79, 1926, pp. 361, 489, 734; Vol. 80, 1926, p. 437; Vol. 81, 1926, p. 109.

[2] L. de Broglie, *Ann. de physique*, Vol. 3, 1925, pp. 22–128.

[3] E. B. Wilson, *Science*, Vol. 65, 1927, pp. 265–271.

[4] R. Brown, *Edinburgh New Phil. Journal*, Vol. 5, 1828, p. 358.

[5] J. J. Thomson, Silliman's Lectures, Yale Univ., published in *Electricity and Matter*, 1904, p. 62; *Phil. Mag.*, Vol. 48, 1924, p. 737; Vol. 50, 1925, p. 1181.

[6] J. Perrin, *Atoms*, trans. by D. L. Hammick, London, 1923, p. 85.

the suspended body, because taken altogether they tend to urge the body in all directions at once. But, if the surface is smaller than the area necessary to ensure that all irregular motions will be compensated, we must expect pressures that are unequal and continually shifting from point to point. These pressures will not be made uniform by the law of aggregates. Their resultant being no longer zero, they will vary continuously in intensity and direction.'' Similar conclusions were reached by **Léon Georges Gouy** [1] of Lyon (1888), **Henry F. W. Siedentopf** [2] (1900) and A. Einstein [3] (1905). These explanations illustrate in an interesting manner how chance or probability enters modern theories in physics. If, by chance, at a certain moment, the molecules should all or nearly all, press against a large surface in the same direction, that surface might be made to move. Say Perrin: [4] ''If we were no bigger than bacteria, we should be able at such moments (when a particle rises) to fix the dust particle at the level reached in this way, without going to the trouble of lifting it and to build a house, for instance, without having to pay for the raising of the materials. But the bulkier the particle to be raised, the smaller is the chance that molecular agitation will raise it to a given height. Imagine a brick weighing a kilogramme suspended in the air by a rope. It must have a Brownian movement, though it will certainly be very feeble. As a matter of fact . . . the time we would have to wait before we had an even chance of seeing the brick rise to a second level by virtue of its Brownian movement . . . will be found to be such that by comparison the duration of geological epochs and perhaps of our universe itself will be quite negligible'' Thus the law that in a medium in thermal equilibrium no contrivance can exist capable of transforming heat energy (molecular motion) of the medium into work appears only as a statistical law, but for bodies of ordinary size, its violation

[1] *Journal d. Phys.*, Vol. 7, 1888, p. 188.
[2] *Forsch. d. Röntgenst.*, Vol. 1, 1898.
[3] *Annal. d. Physik.*, Vol. 17, 1905, p. 549.
[4] J. Perrin, *Atoms,* 1923, p. 87.

is so extremely improbable that it would be foolish to take it into practical consideration. The above hypothesis explaining the Brownian movements though seductive, needs experimental verification, such as was given it in 1908 by Jean Perrin through the preparation of suitable emulsions, and measurement of the distribution of grains in a column between certain limits of height. While Perrin in Paris experimented on Brownian movements in liquids, R. A. Millikan [1] and Harvey Fletcher at the University of Chicago, in 1911, experimented on these movements in gases.

LANGLEY ON AËRODYNAMICS

Some scientific men of the latter part of the nineteenth century seriously doubted the possibility of constructing a successful flying machine of metal and wood which would rise and fly without the aid of gases lighter than air. Hiram S. Maxim's experiment of 1894 in England rather tended to sustain that view. These doubts were dispelled by the researches of Samuel Pierpont Langley, secretary of the Smithsonian Institution in Washington. For many years he experimented on supporting surfaces which he described in his *Experiments in Aërodynamics* (1891) and the *Internal Work of the Wind* (1893). He showed that if a thin, plane surface, upwardly inclined to its direction of motion, is moved at high speed against still air, the reaction of the air results in a lifting force. Quantitative data were obtained. He found that under certain definite conditions, the power required in aerial navigation would in theory diminish indefinitely as the speed increased, and that it would actually diminish in practice up to a certain limit. This is known as ''Langley's law,'' which has been justified in practice, although its application is further limited by the demands of safety during an increase in speed and decrease in power. On May 6, 1896, Langley launched one of his aerodromes (''air runners'') upon its first flight from a house boat on

[1] *Phys. Review,* Vol. 33, 1911, p. 81; N. S., Vol. 1, 1913, p. 218.

the Potomac, about thirty miles below Washington, at a private trial, Alexander Graham Bell (1847–1922) being the only witness. In Bell's contemporary statement[1] we read: "The absolute weight of the aerodrome, including that of the steam engine and all appurtenances, was, as I was told, about 25 pounds, and the distance from tip to tip of the supporting surfaces was, as I observed, about 12 or 14 feet. . . . The aerodrome . . . started from a platform about 20 feet above the water and rose at first directly in the face of the wind, moving all the time with remarkable steadiness and subsequently swinging around in large curves of perhaps a hundred yards in diameter, and continually ascending until its steam was exhausted, when, at a lapse of about a minute and a half and at a height which I judged to be between 80 and 100 feet in the air, the wheels ceased turning, and the machine, deprived of the aid of its propellers, to my surprise did not fall, but settled down so softly and gently that it touched the water without the least shock, and was in fact immediately ready for another trial." Bell took a photograph with a pocket camera, from which enlarged pictures have been taken.[2] Langley[3] in 1897 estimated his work thus: "I have thus far had only a purely scientific interest in the results of these labors. Perhaps if it could have been foreseen at the outset how much labor there was to be, how much of life would be given to it, and how much care, I might have hesitated to enter upon it at all. And now reward must be looked for, if reward there be, in the knowledge that I have done the best I could in a difficult task, with results which it may be hoped will be useful to others. I have brought to a close the portion of the work which seemed to be especially mine— the demonstration of the practicability of mechanical flight— and for the next stage, which is the commercial and practical

[1] A. G. Bell, *Nature*, Vol. 54, 1896, May 28, p. 80. See also S. P. Langley, *McClure's Magazine*, June, 1897; *Smithsonian Report for 1897*, pp. 169–181.
[2] *Smithsonian Report for 1900*, p. 216, Plate VI.
[3] S. P. Langley, *Smithsonian Report for 1900*, p. 216.

development of the idea, it is probable that the world may look to others.''

The success of the aerodrome led to the thought of a man-carrying machine. Langley hesitated, but encouraged by President McKinley, he went to work. He received in 1898 an appropriation of $50,000. The internal combustion engine was just coming into notice; a contract was let for a 12 horse-power engine to weigh not more than 100 pounds, but the engine builder was unable to meet the specifications. A mechanical engineer, Charles M. Manly, agreed to cooperate with Langley and to make an engine. Manly worked with enthusiasm and devotion. After some experiments, a 52.4 horsepower engine was built, weighing 187 pounds, with a speed of 950 revolutions per minute. In 1903 the machine was launched with Manly in the aviator's chair, but he experienced difficulty in steering and the machine crashed into the Potomac. A second trial was unsuccessful, the rudder becoming entangled with the launching track. Langley was severely criticized by Congressmen and by the press. Private capital refused aid for further trials, unless arrangements were made for commercialization.[1] Langley died in 1906.

In 1914 a number of successful flights were made with Langley's machine, supplied with a new motor; the soundness of Langley's principles of airplane construction was thus shown experimentally.

With the opening of the present century experimentation on air navigation was pursued with zest. Soon after the death of Langley, its theoretical aspects were taken up by F. W. Lanchester in England and L. Prandtl in Göttingen. The first wind tunnel of importance, constructed for experimentation on aviation, was that of A. G. Eiffel in Paris. In Europe the dirigible balloon was developed. In America, Orville Wright with his brother Wilbur, of Dayton, Ohio, was the first to fly successfully with a heavier-than-air machine, in 1903. The brothers invented a system of control since used

[1] H. Leffmann, *Smithsonian Report*, 1918, pp. 157–167.

in flying machines. European and American inventors came to display great activity in aeroplane design. The most successful types before the Great War were the monoplanes of Louis Blériot, Morane, and Nieuport, the biplanes of the Voisin brothers, Henry Farman, Glenn Curtis and the Wright brothers.

THE CONSTITUTION OF MATTER

BODIES SMALLER THAN ATOMS

The initial experimental steps in this movement were taken by Joseph John Thomson, at the Cavendish physical laboratory at Cambridge, when he entered upon the study of the nature of X-rays and of electric discharges through rarefied gases. We have given accounts of earlier researches of this gifted experimenter. Born near Manchester in 1856, educated at Owens College and at Trinity College in Cambridge, he became second wrangler and second Smith's prizeman in 1880. The first fruits of his intense training in mathematical physics were treatises on the Motion of Vortex Rings and on the Application of Dynamics to Physics and Chemistry. As Cavendish professor of experimental physics at Cambridge during 1884–1918, he trained many distinguished physicists. Since 1918 he holds the honorary professorship. In 1896, when considering electric discharges through gases he paid particular attention to rays which Goldstein (1876) had named "cathode rays" and which had commanded the attention also of Julius Plücker (1801–1868), Crookes, Hertz, Lenard and others. J. J. Thomson studied the deflection of "cathode rays" in magnetic and electric fields and arrived at the conclusion, in 1897, that these "rays" were not ether waves, but were particles of matter. He asked himself, "what are these particles? Are they atoms or molecules, or matter in a still finer state of equilibrium?"[1] He made the determination of the ratio m/e where m is the mass of each particle, and e is the charge of negative electricity carried by

[1] J. J. Thomson, *Phil. Mag.*, 5. S., Vol. 44, Oct. 1897, p. 302.

each. He found that this ratio is "independent of the nature of the gas and that its value 10^{-7} is very small compared with 10^{-4}, which is the smallest value of this quantity previously known, and which is the value for the hydrogen ion in electrolysis." [1] He continues: "The smallness of m/e may be due to the smallness of m or the largeness of e, or to the combination of these two. . . . The explanation which seems to me to account in the most simple and straightforward manner for the facts is founded on a view of the constitution of the chemical elements which has been favorably entertained by many chemists: this view is that the atoms of the different chemical elements are different aggregations of atoms of the same kind. In the form in which this hypothesis was enunciated by Prout,[2] the atoms of the different elements were hydrogen atoms; in this precise form the hypothesis is not tenable, but if we substitute for hydrogen some unknown primordial substance X, there is nothing known which is inconsistent with this hypothesis, which is one that has been recently supported by Sir Norman Lockyer for reasons derived from the study of the stellar spectra. . . . Thus on this view we have in cathode rays matter in a new state, . . . a state in which all matter—that is, matter derived from different sources such as hydrogen, oxygen, etc.—is of one and the same kind; this matter being the substance from which all the chemical elements are built up." Here then, we have the earliest conclusion drawn carefully from strict experimental evidence, that there exist particles smaller than atoms. Before this time the atom had been generally assumed to be indivisible. The very word "atom," as used by the Greeks, signified a not, $temn\bar{o}$ cut. Thomson's experiments indicating that the atom was made up of parts marked a new epoch in science. Prout's hypothesis, which for eighty years had been buried by orthodox chemists, because the atomic weights were found to be non-integral

[1] *Loc. cit.*, pp. 310, 311.

[2] William Prout (1785–1850), an English physician who in 1815 published an anonymous paper in which he advanced the hypothesis that the atoms of all other elements were really aggregates of hydrogen atoms.

numbers, was resuscitated and brought to full life after the discovery of isotopes.

THE NAME ELECTRON

At this time J. J. Thomson called these particles "corpuscles." The name "electron" was introduced [1] by G. Johnstone Stoney (1826–1911), in 1891, not of course as the name of these particles, but as the name of the fundamental unit of electricity, namely, the electric charge on a hydrogen ion in electrolysis which charge he had proposed in 1874 (first published in 1881) as a natural unit upon which together with the velocity of light and the coefficient of gravitation, a natural absolute system of measure could be based [2] in place of the purely arbitrary C G S-system. These ideas were in conformity with Faraday's experiments on electrolysis which had indicated that electricity, like matter, was atomic in character, as was clearly set forth also by H. Helmholtz in his Faraday Lecture in 1881.[3] Later the word "electron" came to be applied to J. J. Thomson's "corpuscles."

J. J. THOMSON AND RUTHERFORD

Ernest Rutherford was experimenting in the Cavendish laboratory at Cambridge, as a pupil of Thomson. It is of interest, therefore, to have Rutherford's account of this memorable period. "The proof in 1897 of the independent existence of the electron as a mobile electrified unit, of mass minute compared with that of the lightest atom, was of extraordinary importance. It was soon seen that the electron must be a constituent of all the atoms of matter, and that optical spectra had their origin in their vibrations. The discovery of the electron and the proof of its liberation by a variety of methods from all the atoms of matter was of the utmost

[1] G. J. Stoney, *Scientific Trans. of the Roy. Dublin Soc.*, 11. S., Vol. 4, 1891, p. 563.
[2] G. J. Stoney, *Proceed. Dublin Roy. Soc.*, Vol. 3, 1881, p. 51; *Phil. Mag.*, 5. S., Vol. 11, 1881.
[3] Helmholtz, *Wissenschaftliche Abhandlungen*, Vol. 3, p. 69.

signification, for it strengthened the view that the electron was probably the common unit in the structure of atoms which the periodic variation of the chemical properties had indicated. It gave for the first time some hope of the success of an attack on that most fundamental of all problems—the detailed structure of the atom. In the early development of this subject science owes much to the work of Sir J. J. Thomson, both for the boldness of his ideas and for his ingenuity in developing methods of estimating the number of electrons in the atom, and, of probing its structure. He early took the view that the atom must be an electrical structure, held together by electrical forces, and showed in a general way lines of possible explanation of the variation of physical and chemical properties of the elements, exemplified in the periodic law."[1]

As will be seen, Rutherford himself became extremely active and successful in research on the constitution of matter. Born in 1871 at Nelson in New Zealand, he attended colleges of his native country. In 1894, he entered Trinity College, Cambridge, and later prosecuted research in the Cavendish laboratory. During 1898–1907 he was professor of Physics at McGill University in Canada, and during 1907–1919 he was professor at the University of Manchester. In 1919 he became professor of experimental physics at Cambridge and succeeded J. J. Thomson as director of the Cavendish laboratory.

OVERTHROW OF THE PRINCIPLE OF THE CONSERVATION OF MASS

In 1901 **W. Kaufmann**[2] announced a most important experimental result, namely that the mass of an electron increased rapidly as its speed neared the velocity of light. This afforded an experimental basis for the electromagnetic theory of the origin of mass as worked out by J. J. Thomson,[3] in 1881, and by **Oliver Heaviside**[4] (1850–1925) in 1889. According to this experiment mass was truly a variable; and

---

[1] E. Rutherford, *Science*, Vol. 58, 1923, p. 211.
[2] W. Kaufmann, *Göttinger Nachrichten*, Nov. 8, 1901.
[3] J. J. Thomson, *Phil. Mag.*, Vol. 11, 1881, pp. 229, 1230.
[4] O. Heaviside, *Collected Papers*, Vol. 2, p. 514.

thus the great principle of the conservation of mass was over-thrown, as a general law. This principle had been advanced on speculative grounds by the French physician Jean Rey [1] as early as 1630, and near the close of the eighteenth century had been adopted by A. L. Lavoisier (1743–1794) as embody-ing the experience of chemists engaged in careful weighing of substances undergoing chemical changes in the laboratory. Under those conditions no deviations from this law could be noticed. Only bodies having velocities approaching that of light experience an appreciable increase in mass due to their motion.

KELVIN'S MODEL OF AN ATOM

In 1901 Lord Kelvin, who thirty-four years previously had brought forth the "vortex atom," suggested a new atomic model, to fit the new facts of observation. He wrote an ar-ticle entitled "Aepinus atomized." [2] Aepinus of St. Peters-burg was an admirer of B. Franklin and adopted his one-fluid theory of electricity. Kelvin assumed that this fluid consists of minute, equal and similar bodies (electrions), much smaller than the atoms of ponderable matter. In 1902, he remarked [3] that "atoms of electricity (electrions) now almost universally accepted, had been thought of by Faraday, Clerk Maxwell and definitely proposed by Helmholtz," that "they were much smaller than the atoms of matter, and permeated freely through the spaces occupied by them" and that "an atom of electricity in the interior of an atom of matter experienced electric force towards the center of the atom"; "every kind of matter has electricity in it. . . . If the electrions or atoms of electricity, succeeded in getting out of the atoms of mat-ter, they proceed with velocities which might exceed the velocity of light, and the body was radio-active." In short, Kelvin considered an atom of matter to consist of a uniform

[1] Jean Rey, *The Increase in Weight of Tin and Lead on Calcination, 1630,* Alembic Club Reprints, No. 11, 1895.
[2] Lord Kelvin, *Phil. Mag.,* Vol. 3, 1902, p. 257; Vol. 8, 1904, p. 528; Vol. 10, 1905, p. 695.
[3] Lord Kelvin, *Nature,* Vol. 67, 1902, pp. 45, 103.

sphere of positive electrification, throughout which negative electricity was distributed in the form of discrete electrons.

That radioactivity is an atomic property, each atom acting as a constant source of emission of energy, had been the guiding principle of P. Curie and Mme. Curie, in their researches, according to their statement of 1902.[1]

J. J. Thomson's Model of an Atom

The Kelvin atom was developed by J. J. Thomson. He[2] advanced the view that "if the mass of the atom of radium were due to the presence in it of a large number of corpuscles, each carrying a charge . . . of negative electricity . . . associated with an equal charge of positive, so as to make the atom electrically neutral, then . . . the intrinsic energy possessed by the atom would be so great" as to be able to maintain the radiation from radium for 30,000 years. In 1904 he[3] assumed a sphere of positive electrification with electrons moving about in the sphere. He assumed the properties of the atom to depend upon the number of electrons, upon their distribution in their orbits on concentric shells and upon the stability of the system.

Rutherford's Model of an Atom

Rutherford[4] when at the University of Manchester found that the Kelvin and J. J. Thomson model of an atom would not readily lend itself to the explanation of the amount of scattering of the α particles passing through different kinds of matter, for instance through a thin sheet of gold. Accordingly, Rutherford modified that model by turning it inside out, so that the positive charges were concentrated at the center in a nucleus only about .0001 of the diameter of the atom ("like a fly in a cathedral"), this nucleus being surrounded by electrons distributed so as to make an atom electri-

---

[1] *Comptes Rendus,* Vol. 134, 1902, p. 85.
[2] J. J. Thompson, *Nature,* Vol. 67, 1903, pp. 601, 602.
[3] J. J. Thomson, *Phil. Mag.,* Vol. 7, 1904, p. 237.
[4] Rutherford, *Phil. Mag.,* Vol. 21, 1911, p. 669.

cally neutral. It became necessary to assume also that the greater part of the mass of the atom was in the positve charge. This model of an atom, resembling somewhat the "dynamids"[1] designed by Lenard in 1903, is a planetary system in miniature. If a positively charged α particle passed close to the center of the gold atom, it would describe a hyperbolic orbit. The deflection of the α particle was greater, the nearer it passed the nucleus of the gold atom. Thus the scattering of α particles, as determined experimentally by Rutherford and Effie Gwend Marsden was made to throw light on the structure of the atom.

Atomic Number

In the theory of the atom the "atomic number" plays an important rôle. The number of electrons in an atom is an atomic number, that is, the ordinal number of the element in Mendeleeff's table, thus: Hydrogen 1, helium 2, lithium, 3, beryllium 4, and so on. Experiments on the light elements, made in 1911, by **C. G. Barkla**[2] (then at the University of London, since 1913 professor of physics at the University of Edinburgh) indicated that the number of electrons in atoms of light elements may be counted by measuring the scattering power per atom. This subject was taken up by **Henry Gwyn Jeffrey Moseley**[3] (1884–1915), a demonstrator in physics at the University of Manchester and at Oxford, who later fell in action in the Great War at the Dardanelles. He developed the science of X-ray spectroscopy. He[4] showed in 1914 that from the spectrum of X-rays, which one obtains when a chemical element is placed at the anticathode, one can obtain the ordinal number for that element. He first examined spectra of elements of atomic weight between calcium and zinc, and found that a similar spectrum consisting of two strong lines was emitted by each of these elements. He showed

[1] A. Sommerfeld, *Atombau* etc., 4. Ed., 1924, p. 14.
[2] C. C. Barkla, *Phil. Mag.*, Vol. 21, 1911, p. 648.
[3] We are using a sketch of Moseley by Rutherford in *Nature,* Vol. 96, 1915, p. 33.
[4] Moseley, *Phil. Mag.*, Vol. 26, 1913, p. 1024; Vol. 27, 1914, p. 703.

that the frequency of a given line in the spectra varies very nearly as the square of a number, $(N - b)$, where b is a constant, and N is a whole number which varies by unity in passing from one element to the next. Moseley identified the integers N with the atomic numbers of the elements when arranged in increasing order of atomic weight. Similar results were obtained for the great majority of solid elements. He concluded that the atomic number N expresses the number of units of positive electric charge in the nucleus. Since in the cases examined the frequency of a given line increased by definite amounts in going from one element up to the next, he was able to predict that there were three and only three missing elements between aluminum and gold. He predicted their atomic number and also their spectra. For uranium he obtained the atomic number 92 and he concluded that there could not be more than 92 elements up to uranium (inclusive). Georges Urbain went from Paris to England to utilize Moseley's new method, in the determination of the much debated question of the number of rare earth elements. Moseley's proof that the properties of an element are fixed by its atomic number is of great theoretical and practical importance.

ISOTOPES

Strong suspicion of the existence of isotopes developed as early as 1912 in the study of radioactivity by F. Soddy, A. S. Russell and K. Fajans. **T. W. Richards** (1868–1928) of Harvard University pointed out that there exist well marked differences between the atomic weights of lead from different sources.[1] Thus he found the atomic weight of common lead to be 207.19, of uraniolead 206.08, of Australian mixture 206.34. Richards[2] asks: "Shall we call these substances different elements, or the same? The best answer is that pro-

[1] T. W. Richards, *Smithsonian Report for 1918*, pp. 205–219; *Science*, N. S., Vol. 49, 1919, pp. 1–11.
[2] T. W. Richards, *Smiths. Rep.*, 1918, p. 217.

posed by Professor Soddy who invented a new name,[1] and called them 'isotopes' of the same element." The word "isotope" signifies "equally placed" in the periodic table of the chemical elements. It was found that two isotopes can not be distinguished from each other by any chemical test. They differ in atomic weights. Usually two isotopes have also equal spectra, but W. D. Harkins[2] and L. Aronberg of Chicago found that in the case of the line $\lambda = 4058$Å for lead, the wave-length was a bit greater for radiolead than for ordinary lead. Before 1919 the only isotopes known belonged to the heaviest elements of the radioactive type. But in 1919 it was ascertained definitely that isotopes exist also among some of the light and non-radioactive elements. As early as 1913 a partial separation of the gas neon, by the method of diffusion, into two fractions, differing somewhat in their atomic weights, was accomplished by J. J. Thomson. F. W. Aston, working in the Cavendish Laboratory at Cambridge, perfected a method which had been used by J. J. Thomson, for the analysis of positive rays by electric and magnetic fields,[3] and developed a positive ray spectrography.[4] By means of his new spectrograph he was able to separate particles of different mass and bring together those of equal mass. Aston showed[5] conclusively that the gas neon consisted of two isotopes of masses 20 and 22, respectively, "with the faint possibility of a third mass 21." Since the atomic weight of neon, determined chemically, is 20.200, it was concluded that the two isotopes are mixed in a constant ratio. In the case of chlorine, the chemically determined atomic weight was 35.46, not an integer, but Aston found that it had two isotopes with weights 35 and 37, in the constant ratio 3 to 1. No isotopes were found for hydrogen, carbon, nitrogen and oxygen. By December, 1920, Aston had found isotopes for nine chemical

[1] F. Soddy, *Chemistry of the Radio-Elements, Part II*, London, 1914, p. 5.
[2] *Astrophys. Jour.*, Vol. 47, 1918, p. 96.
[3] J. J. Thomson, *Rays of Positive Electricity*, p. 7 ff.
[4] F. W. Aston, *Phil. Mag.*, Vol. 38, 1919, p. 707.
[5] F. W. Aston, *Phil. Mag.*, Vol. 39, 1920, pp. 449, 611.

elements.[1] All the elements examined by Aston were in the gaseous state. By a somewhat different method A. J. Dempster [2] at the University of Chicago examined a number of metals, including magnesium, zinc, and calcium. He found that magnesium had three isotopes of atomic weight 24, 25 and 26; the chemically determined atomic weight being 24.32. By the discovery of isotopes the atomic weight has lost some of its former dominating position in chemistry. There are two isotopes of lead differing from each other in atomic weight by as much as 8 units, yet they behave chemically exactly alike. On the other hand, elements RaD and Po have the same atomic weight 210, yet possess different chemical properties.[3] According to modern views, the atomic weights of primitive constituents are integral numbers.

THE BOHR ATOM [4]

It has long been evident that a theory of the atom must explain the phenomena of spectroscopy. Spectral lines seemed to be due to radiations resulting from the motions of electrons. But the perplexing experimental data of radiation of heat had given rise to the quantum theory. The problem arose to frame a theory of the structure and dynamics of the atom that would explain the experimental facts on which the quantum theory rests. First of all, an atomic model should explain how an atom can emit sharp homogeneous spectral lines. This the Rutherford model could not do, for if an electron revolving around its nucleus with a frequency v sends out a radiation frequency v, the electron loses energy by this radiation and must revolve with a steadily decreasing frequency. It is at this stage that **Niel Bohr** took up the problem. He first published on this subject in 1913.[5] Building upon the gen-

[1] *Smithsonian Report for 1920*, p. 239.
[2] A. J. Dempster, *Phys. Rev.*, Vol. 11, 1918, p. 316; Vol. 17, 1921, p. 427.
[3] A. Sommerfeld, *Atombau* etc., 4. Ed., 1924, p. 162.
[4] For details see A. Sommerfeld, *Atombau und Spekrallinien*, 1924.
[5] N. Bohr, *Phil. Mag.*, Vol. 26, 1913, pp. 1, 476, 857.

eral theory of the Rutherford model and applying the quantum theory, he introduced three postulates:

I. An electron can revolve about its nucleus only in certain special circular orbits for which, according to the quantum theory, the moment of momentum of the electron is an integral multiple of $h/2\pi$, where h is Planck's constant. Thus, while the Newtonian classical dynamics would make possible any number of orbits of any dimension, the new theory allows only certain stable orbits differing from each other by definite steps.

II. The ordinary electron revolves about its nucleus in an invariable orbit, without radiating or absorbing energy. This again is in striking contrast to classical views.

III. Radiation takes place when and only when the electron falls from an orbit of greater energy to one of less energy, nearer the nucleus. Moreover, when the electron falls from an orbit in which the energy is E_2 into another orbit of energy E_1, the energy expressed by $E_2 - E_1$ is of the amount $h\nu$ and constitutes homogeneous, monochromatic radiation. The formula $E_2 - E_1 = h\nu$ is called Bohr's "frequency condition."

The theory was first applied to the hydrogen atom which has only one electron revolving around the positive nucleus, but has an indefinite number of allowable orbits that were mechanically possible. By allowing, in each of a group of hydrogen atoms, the electron to jump from the 3d, 4th, 5th, . . . or nth allowable orbit ("energy-level") into the 2d orbit, the individual lines of the Balmer series are emitted. More than this, if in each of a group of atoms, the electron jumps from the 2d, 3d, . . . or nth allowable orbit into the first orbit, Lyman's ultra-violet series is obtained, and if the jump is from the 4th, 5th, . . . or nth into the 3d orbit, Bergmann's infra-red series results. This was a great victory for the Bohr theory. The most extraordinary numerical agreement of theory and observation, in the case of the hydrogen atom, forced physicists to direct their attention to the theory. Moreover, the Bohr theory permitted the nucleus to move, for in reality the nucleus is not stationary. In the hydrogen atom, the nucleus and electron move around a common center of gravity.

Even in his early studies Bohr endeavored to construct models for atoms of higher elements (lithium, barium, boron, carbon), with several circular orbits, each occupied by several electrons, the number of electrons in the outermost orbit being equal to the valency of the element in question. These and similar studies carried on by W. Kossel, L. Vegard, A. Sommerfeld, R. Ladenburg and others must be taken as only preliminary skirmishes in a long campaign to conquer a most difficult field.

To be sure, the simply ionized helium atom, with one electron and a doubly charged positive nucleus, yielded readily to treatment on Bohr's theory. For this case, the equation differs from the one for the Balmer series only by a constant and produces certain series of helium lines which before this had been falsely ascribed to hydrogen.[1] R. A. Millikan and I. S. Bowen of the California Institute of Technology have succeeded in stripping in succession, one, two, three, four, five, and six outer electrons from certain atoms and in studying the effects, experimentally.[2]

While the helium atom with only one electron easily yielded to treatment, the neutral helium atom with its two electrons offers difficulties which Bohr, E. C. Kemble, J. H. Van Vleck and others have been endeavoring to overcome.[3]

ELLIPTICAL ORBITS

As we have already seen, the quantum theory was extended in 1915 to systems of several degrees of freedom. Sommerfeld applied this generalization to the theory of the Bohr atom. In the case of two degrees of freedom, two conditions arise which must be satisfied in the determination of the permissible

---

[1] F. Reïche, *The Quantum Theory*, transl. by H. S. Hatfield and H. L. Brose, 2. Ed., London, 1924, p. 90.
[2] R. A. Millikan, *Science*, Vol. 69, 1924, p. 475.
[3] *Phil. Mag.*, Vol. 42, 1921, p. 123; Vol. 44, 1922, p. 842.

paths for the electrons. Bohr had used circular orbits to which only one quantum condition could be applied. Sommerfeld introduced elliptical orbits (which may be circles in special cases) in which each point of the path is determined by two variables (the distances from a focus and an angle) and was able thereby to impose two quantum conditions. The theory was generalized still further so as to apply to systems of higher degrees of freedom. In these developments, W. Wilson, K. Schwarzschild and P. S. Epstein participated.

THE THEORY OF RELATIVITY APPLIED TO THE ATOM

We have referred to the motion of the perihelion of a planetary orbit (that of Mercury in particular) due to the relativity theory. A corresponding effect should occur in elliptical electron orbits. In 1915 Sommerfeld investigated this matter and arrived at extremely beautiful results; it led to the explanation of the fine structure of spectral lines. In this penetrating mathematical formulation, P. Epstein was also active. By the motion of the perihelion the orbit loses its closed character; moreover, the velocity of the electron in its elliptical orbit, varies and results in changes of mass of the electron. In consequence, the jump of an electron from one orbit to another no longer produces exactly the same spectral line, but produces slightly different lines very close together. For example,[1] the hydrogen line H should consist of five components arranged in a group of two lines and a group of three. The mean distance between the two groups should be, according to theory, 0.126Å; by observation, Paschen and Meissner found 0.124Å. Millikan says:[2] "Seldom in the history of physics have purely theoretical formulæ had such amazing success in the field of precise prediction as have Sommerfeld's relativity—doublet formulæ and Epstein's extension of the same sort of orbit considerations to the prediction of the number and character of multiplicity of lines found

[1] F. Reiche, op. cit., p. 96.
[2] R. A. Millikan, Proc. Am. Philos. Soc., Vol. 65, 1926, p. 74.

in the Stark effect. The whole interpretation of spectroscopic fine structure through changes in so-called azimuthal and inner quantum numbers is one of the great achievements of all time resulting from the interplay between penetrating theoretical analysis and skillful and refined experimental technique.''

BOHR'S LATER RESULTS

In 1918 Bohr advanced what is known as his ''principle of correspondence'' between quantum and classical theory, which reaches farther than a ''principle of selection'' previously advanced by A. Rubinovicz. According to this principle of correspondence, for very high quantum numbers, the quantum theory of electron orbits passes over into the theory of classical mechanics. The difference in the frequency, calculated by quantum theory and by the classical theory, expressed mathematically, is the difference between a difference-quotient and a differential-quotient (derivative). For high quantum numbers indicating high energy levels, the difference-quotient approaches the other as a limiting value. In case of such approach, the previous achievements of classical optics become available in the new theory. Questions relating to the intensity of the emitted wave and of polarization, which are successfully treated by the classical theory, become available in the new theory for large quantum numbers, and by extrapolation have been applied boldly to all quantum numbers. Further developments of the ''correspondence principle'' were made by Bohr, H. A. Kramers and J. C. Slater, in a joint study,[1] in 1924.

THE STATIC ATOM

While physicists and mathematicians were busy elaborating the dynamics of the Bohr atom, another atomic model was invented by certain chemists, which was a ''static'' atom, in contrast to the ''kinetic'' atom of the physicists. When the details of the real structure of the atom come to be known, the

[1] *Phil. Mag.*, 6. S., Vol. 47, 1924, p. 785.

physicists and chemists, must of course agree in their pictures of it. At present neither scientific group can claim very close approach to actual reality. One group approaches the problem mainly from spectroscopy, the other group mainly from localized valency. A form of static atom was described in 1916 by Gilbert Newton Lewis [1] of the University of California and developed further by Irving Langmuir [2] of the General Electric Company in Schenectady. This atom had the positive electricity concentrated in a very small massive nucleus and the electrons are distributed around it in space. Each electron occupies a certain "cell," in which it may be at rest so far as the needs of chemical statics are concerned. The possibility of electronic motions in these cells had been suggested as a compromise between chemists and physicists. The demands of chemical statics were well satisfied by the static atom. Temporarily it rendered good service to the chemist. But since about 1923 comparatively little attention has been paid to the static atom.

Exact Measurement of e

As early as 1899, it was shown by John S. Townsend [3] of Oxford that, as had been surmised by Stoney, the positive or negative charge carried by an ion in gases was equal to the charge carried by the hydrogen ion in electrolysis of water. Of the various methods devised since J. J. Thomson's pioneer work, to measure this fundamental unit, that of Robert Andrews Millikan, of the University of Chicago and since 1921 of the California Institute of Technology, is the most accurate. He made an oil droplet rise and fall between two horizontal plates and noticed the changes in velocity due to its capture of one or more ions.[4] He showed conclusively that

[1] G. N. Lewis, *Jour. Amer. Chem. Soc.*, Vol. 38, 1916, p. 726.
[2] Langmuir, *Jour. Am. Chem. Soc.*, Vol. 41, 1919, p. 868. For details on static atom see *General Physics for Colleges* by D. L. Webster, H. W. Farwell, E. R. Drew, New York, 1923.
[3] Townsend, *Phil. Trans. Roy. Soc.* A, Vol. 193, 1899, p. 129.
[4] Millikan, *Phys. Rev.*, Vol. 2, 1913, p. 136; *Phil. Mag.*, Vol. 34, 1917, p. 1. R. A. Millikan, *The Electron*, Chicago, 1917, Chap. V.

electricity consists of equal units, that the electric charge of each single ion is always the same, that this unit of charge is not merely a statistical mean, as the atomic weights have been shown to be, since the discovery of isotopes. From his measurements he demonstrated what had been previously surmised by Benjamin Franklin and by recent physicists, namely, that electricity has really atomic structure. Says A. Gullstrand: "His (Millikan's) exact evaluation of the unit has done physics an inestimable service, as it enables us to calculate with a higher degree of exactitude a large number of the most important physical constants." [1]

Collisions of Electrons and Atoms

We have already referred to experiments in which the impact of α-rays with atoms led Rutherford to the discovery of nuclei of atoms, and in which the impact of α-rays with atoms led C. T. R. Wilson to the number and distribution of electrons that were set free. While these rapid particles seemed to collide according to the laws of classical mechanics, the slower moving electrons, in their collision with atoms and molecules, were found by James Franck [2] and Gustav Hertz, experimenting at Berlin, to behave quite contrary to the classical mechanics and to confirm the quantum theory. In a vacuum tube containing traces of vapor of mercury, the mercury atoms are bombarded by electrons given off at the electrodes. A spectroscope reveals a certain spectral line of mercury whenever a sufficient voltage is applied to the electrodes which cause the electrons to fly at a speed above a certain minimum. At a lower voltage the electrons do not acquire sufficient energy to supply the required $h\nu$, and the spectral line does not appear. A slow electron when impinging upon an atom rebounds elastically without change in the internal energy of the atom in all cases when the energy

[1] *Science*, Vol. 59, 1924, p. 326.
[2] J. Franck und G. Hertz, *Verhandl. d. Deutsch. Phys. Gesellsch.*, Vol. 15, 1913, p. 34; Vol. 16, 1914, p. 457; *Phys. Zeitschr.*, Vol. 17, 1916, pp. 409, 430; Vol. 20, 1919, p. 132.

$\frac{1}{2}mv^2$ of the electron is less than hv, where v relates to the frequency of the spectral lines due to electrons inside the atom. But when this $\frac{1}{2}mv^2$ exceeds hv, the colliding electron may transmit part of its energy to the atom, the colliding electron losing energy, and the atom gaining energy and becoming "excited."

On the subject of "excited" atoms, which by impact have thus been thrown into a quantum state of higher energy than the normal, a remarkable theoretical deduction was drawn by two young physicists in Copenhagen, O. Klein [1] and S. Rosseland. They concluded that for the case of thermal equilibrium, if the second law of thermodynamics be assumed to hold true, there must be some hitherto unrecognized mechanism by which an "excited" atom is able to return to its normal state without radiating energy at all. It may impart its surplus energy to an electron by a "collision of the second kind" so-called, to distinguish it from "collision of the first kind" which produces the "excited atom." This conclusion received support from experiments on spectral lines carried on by S. Loria,[2] G. Cario,[3] K. Donat [4] and others. This discovery promises to clear up obscure points relating to the interaction of ether waves and matter. Experiments showing directly the gain of kinetic energy by electrons in collision with atoms and ions have been carried on by I. Langmuir [5] of the General Electric Co., in Schenectady.

CRYSTAL STRUCTURE

The great variety of crystal forms have long been classified, but only recently have methods been devised for the study of the grouping of atoms in crystals. This has been done largely through the experiments of W. H. Bragg and his son, W. L. Bragg. It is found that, through the definite ordering of the

---

[1] O. Klein und S. Rosseland, *Zeitschr. f. Physik*, Vol. 4, 1921, p. 46.
[2] S. Loria, *Phys. Rev.*, Vol. 26, 1925, p. 573.
[3] Günther Cario, *Zeitschr. f. Physik*, Vol. 10, 1922, p. 185.
[4] K. Donat, *loc. cit.*, Vol. 29, 1924, p. 345.
[5] I. Langmuir, *Phys. Rev.*, Vol. 26, 1925, p. 585; J. Franck und P. Jordan, *Anregung von Quantensprüngen durch Stösse*, Berlin, 1926, p. 215.

atoms in a crystal, the crystal acts like an optical grating—a grating ten thousand times more finely ruled than one made with a dividing engine. In 1912, Max v. Laue and his collaborators discovered that X-rays are regularly diffracted by crystals acting as gratings. W. H. Bragg[1] was able to observe the reflection of X-rays from the surface of a crystal and he showed that the diffraction of X-rays furnished a simple method of finding the wave-length of the bright lines in an X-ray spectrum. By the study of the positions and intensities of the spectra in different orders thrown by the crystal, it became possible to examine the structure of the crystal, and to deduce the distance between successive planes of atoms in it. The results indicate that the atom and not the molecule is the unit of the crystal structure. Researches on crystal structure by X-rays were carried on also by Charles Galton Darwin and A. H. Compton. Otto Lehmann has brought to light the unexpected existence of crystalline arrangement in some liquids. They are best shown in certain complex organic substances at a temperature slightly above their melting point. When polarized light passes through them, patterns and colors are produced. Abram T. Joffé of Leningrad has investigated the physical deformation of crystals. Of great practical importance is Joffé's discussion of the breakdown of potentials in insulators and their relation to the cohesive and chemical forces in solid materials. His results point to a new and improved method of installation of insulators and condensers.[2]

DYNAMICS OF THE ATOM

That the theory of the Bohr atom, with its arbitrary assumptions, will be superseded by new developments, is to be expected. A first endeavor along this line is the new treatment of the dynamics of the atom which was initiated at Göttingen by Werner Heisenberg in 1925 and by Max Born[3] and P.

---

[1] W. H. Bragg in *Science*, Vol. 60, 1924, p. 139.
[2] A. T. Joffé in *Physikalische Zeitschrift*, Vol. 28, 1927, pp. 911–916.
[3] M. Born, *Probleme der Atom dynamic*, 1926.

Jordan. It deals with the frequency and intensity of spectral lines, but, instead of starting with orbital motions of electrons around a nucleus, as in the Bohr atom, it begins directly with the frequencies and intensities themselves. The endeavor is to introduce greater clarity of principles. Similar studies have been made by P. Dirac at Cambridge in England. Among the first successes of the new theory are the explanations of the Zeeman effect and the A. H. Compton effect (the change of wave-length and direction produced when X-rays and γ-rays are scattered by impact).

WAVE MECHANICS

An abstract theory, under the name of "wave mechanics," has been advanced by Louis de Broglie [1] of Paris and is being extended by E. Schrödinger, formerly in Zurich, later in Berlin. The theory covers somewhat the same ground as does that of the Bohr atom, and claims to do it better. Applying the theory of relativity to the quantum theory, de Broglie measures the energy of a unit particle m at rest by mc^2 units, where c is the velocity of light, and also by $h\nu$, where h is Planck's constant, and ν is the frequency of a periodic change. That is, $mc^2 = h\nu$. De Broglie raises here the question, what form will this equation take when the particle is in motion? According to relativity, motion increases the mass, and apparently slows down the frequency; mc^2 increases, $h\nu$ decreases under motion. Hence the above equation is invalid. Here de Broglie introduced the new assumption that the mass-particle or electron is enveloped in a group of waves travelling with a particle as sort of body guard the individual waves travelling more rapidly than the particle by dying out a little way ahead of it, while new waves spring up behind it. By this device, de Broglie increases ν and restores the balance in his equation. The device is not new to physics. It bears some resemblance to Newton's theory of "fits". De Broglie applied

---

[1] Louis de Broglie, *Thèses*, Paris, 1924; *Ondes et mouvements*, Paris, 1926. See P. R. Heyl in *Scientific Monthly*, January, 1928.

these ideas to the electron travelling in its atomic orbit, and met with success in explaining Bohr's whole-number condition of permissible orbits, but also encountered some new difficulties. We pause to state that de Broglie's wave mechanics is in harmony with some remarkable experiments [1] made by C. Davisson and L. H. Germer at the Bell Telephone laboratories, exhibiting a selective reflection of electrons by crystals of nickel. It was found that for a certain uniform speed of electrons there are beams of electrons leaving the crystal in perfectly sharp directions, satisfying the equation.

De Broglie's wave mechanics was made the starting point of new theoretical developments by Schrödinger [2] who raised the question, what need is there in a group of waves of the mass-particle? Why not drop it and let the group-wave take its place? Thus arose the theory of the "wave-atom." It is a mathematical theory starting from "Hamilton's principle" in mechanics. This "wave atom" contains no revolving electrons. It does all the Bohr atom does, and more. It explains the relative intensity of the lines of the spectrum which the Bohr atom did not explain. Remarkable is the ease with which the Schrödinger atom lines up with classical requirements. It promises conciliation between the corpuscular or quantum theory of light and the undulatory theory. Heretofore the two have been "like a shark and a tiger, each supreme in its own element and helpless in that of the other." The wave mechanics promises to be an amphibian creature, equally powerful on land and water. And yet, no one expects the new theory to be final. "Physical theories are useful," says Duane, "if they explain a large number of facts in simple ways, and if they furnish definitions of terms and a nomenclature to be used in describing phenomena. Physical theories are tools and not creeds."

[1] *Physical Review*, Vol. 29, 1927, p. 908. See W. Duane in *Science*, Vol. 66, 1927, p. 639.
[2] E. Schrödinger, *Annal. d. Phys.*, Vol. 79, 1926, pp. 361, 489, 734; Vol. 80, 1926, p. 487; Vol. 81, 1926, p. 109.

ELECTRICITY AND MAGNETISM

ELECTROMAGNETIC THEORY

Maxwell's electromagnetic theory of light (pp. 256–258) received further development during the last century by H. Hertz and O. Heaviside. At one time Maxwell's equations were given a mechanical interpretation.[1] H. A. Lorentz says:[2] "The fundamental equations of electromagnetism can be given a form corresponding to certain general theorems of mechanics and one can invent mechanical 'models' in which phenomena pass off parallel to the electromagnetic ones. But one encounters in this procedure the difficulty that the models, unless they are supposed to be valid only for a limited number of events, become so complicated . . . as not to be satisfactory."

Maxwell's theory restricted itself mainly to the general laws of the electromagnetic field and did not concern itself with what transpires within matter. But the advent of the electron theory made it desirable to reconstruct the electromagnetic theory to fit the atomistic conception of electricity. In this field the work of H. A. Lorentz [3] of Leyden was dominating. The electron theory assumes that electromagnetic processes considered as transpiring in matter rather than in the ether, are due to the location and motion of electrons. The conductivity of metals is explained by the motion of "free" electrons. When an electric force moves electrons from a nonconductor, that body becomes polarized. Magnetization is conceived as a more or less circular motion of electrons. The fundamental equations of Maxwell hold in the new presentation. In the electron theory of electrical conductivity, different views were held on the number of free electrons in a metal and the lengths of their free paths. A satisfactory electron theory of metals has only recently been rendered possible

---

[1] O. Lodge, *Modern Views of Electricity*, 1892.

[2] *Kultur der Gegenwart, Physik*, 1915, p. 323.

[3] H. A. Lorentz, *Versuch einer Theorie der elektrischen und optischen Erscheinungen in bewegten Körpern*, Leiden, 1895. Also *Kultur der Gegenwart, Physik*, 1915, p. 324.

through the application by Sommerfeld [1] of a new theory of statistics due to E. Fermi of Rome. The electron theory also predicts that for high current densities there would be a departure from Ohm's law, and this was first shown experimentally by P. W. Bridgman [2] of Harvard University to be true for gold and silver. There was an increase in resistance, greater for the thick than for the thin gold, and greater for gold than for the same thickness of silver.

An interesting application of the electron theory arose in the Fitzgerald-Lorentz contraction. The elder **Lord Rayleigh** pointed out that an ordinary transparent body, when shrunk, ought to be doubly refracting for light rays passing in certain directions. But no trace of double refraction was found either by him, or by De Witt Bristol Brace [3] (1859–1905) of the University of Nebraska, who repeated the experiment with apparatus so sensitive that one-fiftieth part of the predicted effect would have been detected. According to Lorentz these experiments did not prove that there is no contraction, their nul result being exactly what would be expected on his own theory that the electrons would contract in just the same ratio as the transparent body. Thus the experiments were interpreted as really confirming Lorentz's electron theory. After the advent of Einstein's theory of relativity, H. Weyl generalized that theory so that it accounts not only for gravitational phenomena, but also for electromagnetic phenomena and arrived at equations which are identical with the electromagnetic equations of Maxwell. These equations have proved themselves capable of interpretation under various different conditions and therefore possess qualities almost magical. Well may we quote again the words of Goethe's Faust, "War es ein Gott der diese Zeichen schrieb?"

[1] A. Sommerfeld, *Die Naturwissenschaften*, Vol. 15, 1927, p. 825.
[2] *Phys. Rev.*, 2. S., Vol. 19, 1922, p. 387.
[3] D, B. Brace, *Phil. Mag.*, Vol. 7, 1904, p. 317.

MAGNETON

Modern views of magnetism connect with Ampère's conception of magnetism as due to electric currents. In explanations of the ferromagnetic, paramagnetic and diamagnetic properties of bodies, the electrons moving in circular and elliptic orbits receive fundamental consideration. Theories of magnetism involving some form of atomic model have been developed since 1903 by J. J. Thomson, W. Voigt, P. Langevin, P. Weiss and E. T. Whittaker. It is to Weiss that we owe the word "magneton," to represent an elementary magnet, the analogue of the electron. Magnetomechanical experiments have been undertaken by several physicists. The magnetization of large steel rods by mere rotation about its axis was first shown experimentally by S. J. Barnett[1] and Mrs. L. J. H. Barnett at the Ohio State University, and were communicated to the American Physical Society, in December, 1914. Before that, the only known method of magnetizing a body was by placing it in a magnetic field. In rotation, "the magneton, if it has angular momentum, will change in orientation so as to make its direction of rotation coincide more nearly with the direction of impressed rotation." "The body whose magnetons originally pointed in all directions equally, becomes magnetized along the axis of impressed rotation." Barnett obtained better determinations of the ratio between the speed of rotation and the resulting magnetic intensity, during 1915, and he made similar determinations for nickel, cobalt, soft iron and Heusler's alloy.

The Barnett effect is the converse of the effect predicted by O. W. Richardson,[2] namely the production of rotation by magnetization. In 1915 and 1916 A. Einstein and W. J. de Haas[3]

[1] S. J. Barnett, *Phys. Rev.*, Vol. 6, 1915, p. 239; *Bulletin National Research Council*, Washington, Vol. 3, 1922, Report on Theories of Magnetism by A. P. Wills of Columbia Univ., S. J. Barnett of the Carnegie Institution, J. Kuntz of the Univ. of Illinois, S. L. Quimby of Columbia Univ., E. M. Terry of the Univ. of Wisconsin, and S. R. Williams of Oberlin College.

[2] O. W. Richardson, *Phys. Rev.*, Vol. 26, 1908, p. 248.

[3] A. Einstein and W. J. de Haas, *Verhandl. d. deutsch. phys. Gesellsch.*, Vol. 17, 1915, p. 152.

experimented on this converse effect for which later J. Q. Stewart,[1] W. Sucksmith and L. F. Bates [2] by more thorough investigation, obtained data simlar to Barnett's data of 1914 and 1915, and equal to only one-half the value obtained by Einstein and de Haas. These later results are half of what is demanded by theory. There is here an anomaly simliar to that observed in the Zeeman effect, which has not yet been satisfactorily explained.[3]

Direct evidence of the existence cf a magneton is afforded by experiments of Otto Stern and Walter Gerlach [4] who volatilized silver and allowed the silver atoms to escape through a slit in the wall of the furnace, to traverse a non-uniform magnetic field, to be finally deposited upon a glass plate. The atoms were deposited in two narrow bands, nearly symmetrically situated to the undisplaced band in the absence of a magnetic field. Evidently, half the silver atoms were attracted toward the pole piece and the other half repelled. The magnetic moment of the normal atom of silver in the gaseous state was found to be that of one Bohr magneton. In Bohr's atomic theory a magneton is a certain quantum unit of magnetic moment due to electrons moving in their atomic orbits.

We proceed to the presentation of a few of the important practical developments of the electromagnetic theory.

THE PUPIN COIL

This coil is a basic invention for long distance telephony due to Michael Pupin of Columbia University. The invention was accomplished by mathematical analysis and verified by experiment. Before Pupin it was recognized by some that, just as heavy incompressible bodies like metals have far greater

---

[1] J. Q. Stewart, *Phys. Rev.*, Vol. 11, 1918, p. 100.

[2] W. Sucksmith and L. F. Bates, *Proc. Roy. Soc.*, S. A, Vol. 104, 1923, p. 499.

[3] S. J. Barnett and L. J. H. Barnett, *Proc. Am. Acad. Arts and Sciences,* Vol. 60, 1925, p. 128; A. Sommerfeld, *Atombau*, etc., 4. Ed., 1924, p. 635.

[4] Stern and Gerlach, *Zeitschr. f. Phys.*, Vol. 9, 1922, p. 349.

kinetic and elastic reactions than air, and transmit sound much better, so vibratory motion of electricity will be sent through a conducting wire much more readily the higher the kinetic and elastic reaction, that is, the higher the inductance and the lower the capacity of the moving electricity. The rôle of inductance in the mathematical theory of telephonic transmission was studied in France by Aimé Vaschy, and in England by Oliver Heaviside. A coil of wire wound around an iron core suggests inductance. Placing coils in a telephone line was tried by Vaschy and others, but without success. Pupin succeeded, because he was guided, as he expressed it, "by the mathematical solution of the generalized Lagrangian problem," which said, "place your inductance coils into your telephone-line at such distances apart that for all vibratory motions of electricity which it is desirable to transmit, there shall be several coils per wave-length . . . one coil every four or five miles on overhead wires, and one coil in about every one to two miles in a telephone cable."[1] Pupin tells us[2] how he pondered over the generalized Lagrangian problem one day in 1894, while climbing up the Furka pass in Switzerland, and that it was there that the intimate analogy between a vibrating string and electric oscillations in a wire flashed through his mind. Pupin gave out the mathematical theory of this subject in March, 1899 and applied for a patent somewhat later.

WIRELESS TELEGRAPHY AND TELEPHONY

As in the case of the electric telegraph, telephone, electric lamp and other inventions widely used in modern life, the invention of the "thermionic valve" had rival claimants and gave rise to litigation.[3] It serves as a detector or receiver of

[1] Michael Pupin, *From Immigrant to Inventor,* New York, 1925, pp. 335, 336.

[2] *Loc. cit.,* pp. 331, 332, 336.

[3] J. A. Fleming, *The Thermionic Valve,* London, 1919, Chaps. I, II and the Appendix. On pages 5–7 and 46 Fleming describes the "Edison effect," a thermionic effect observed by Edison in 1883 in the incandescent lamp. It was examined soon after by Fleming, but the theory of such phenomena was not sufficiently advanced for this effect to be understood and utilized at that time.

feeble electric oscillations in the ether, those electromagnetic waves in Maxwell's electromagnetic theory whose actual existence was shown in the memorable experiments of H. Hertz. We should premise that, before the invention of the thermionic valve, several other detectors of waves had been invented. Of these the following three are perhaps the most noted: (1) The coherer (p. 260), as developed by E. Branly, O. Lodge, and G. Marconi, depending for its action upon imperfect contact. The Marconi coherer, with its nickel-silver filings, was used about five years during the development of radiotelegraphy. (2) The magnetic detector due originally to E. Rutherford, E. Wilson and G. Marconi. Marconi's magnetic detector was based upon the fact that electric oscillations hasten magnetic changes (reduce hysteresis) in iron. This device caused the use of the coherer to decline. (3) The crystal detectors developed from observations made by H. H. C. Dunwoody of the United States army, G. W. Pickard of Boston, and G. W. Pierce of Harvard university, on the contact of certain crystals with metals. These detectors made their appearance in 1906. They act as rectifiers of the oscillation trains into gushes of electricity travelling in the same direction and able to affect a telephone receiver. These crystal detectors have been widely used by amateurs in radiotelegraphy.

The "thermionic valve" was a radical improvement upon the various detectors in previous use. Its invention became possible by the many years of research in theoretical physics carried on by J. J. Thomson and others. In its various forms the instrument affords an emission, from an incandescent cathode, of ions of some sort, which O. W. Richardson, a pupil of J. J. Thomson, has called "thermions" and which are for the most part electrons. In 1904 J. A. Fleming of London made use of thermionic emission from an incandescent cathode of metal or carbon within a vacuum bulb having for an anode a cold metal plate. This device, called the Fleming valve, enabled him to "rectify," high frequency alternating currents, that is, to convert electric oscillations of high frequency into gushes of unidirectional currents which could be detected by a galvanometer or telephone. A somewhat similar tube was developed in Germany by J. Elster and H. Geitel.

The use of the Fleming valve was steadily growing in practice until some years after the modifications introduced in the United States by Lee de Forest who began experimenting before 1904 and at first developed a valve which is virtually that which had been invented by Fleming somewhat earlier. In 1906 and later he patented devices for amplifying feeble electric currents. He introduced into the two-anode valve a second cold electrode in the form of a grid placed between the hot and cold electrode. This grid was a perforated plate or a wire zig-zag. The new instrument was called "audion." It enabled him not only to rectify electric oscillations, but also to relay and repeat them on a magnified scale. Since then this instrument as well as other parts in wireless telegraphy and radio equipment have been very highly and efficiently developed.

SOUND

The theory of sound has received no radically new advances since the time of Helmholtz and the elder Lord Rayleigh. Photographic methods have been developed for recording wave motion producing sound. If a sound wave in air is instantaneously illuminated by an electric spark, the light from the spark will be refracted by the sound wave acting as a lens, and the wave will be registered on the photographic plate.[1] In 1912 D. C. Miller published an account of an apparatus for the demonstration of photography of sound curves. The apparatus can be arranged with a film moving in a special camera, or it can be arranged with a rotating mirror and screen for exhibiting the curves in lecture demonstration.

Photographs of compression waves of sound have been applied by Wallace C. Sabine [2] (1868–1919) of Harvard Uni-

[1] D. C. Miller, *The Science of Musical Sounds*, New York, 1916, p. 89.
[2] W. C. Sabine, *American Architect*, Vol. 68, 1900 (several pages); Vol. 104, 1913, pp. 252–279; *Proceed. Am. Acad. of Arts and Sciences*, Vol. 42, 1906, pp. 51–84.

versity to the study of auditorium acoustics. As early as 1900 Sabine entered upon the development of scientific methods of determining the acoustic properties of auditoriums. He made a detailed study of the design of halls and of the defects of halls due to reverberations, echoes, etc. Reverberations have been reduced by the proper use of thick absorbing felt placed on the side of walls and ceiling. In Austria Gustav Jäger [1] investigated architectural acoustics and gave formulas for the growth and decay of sound which are of the type of the growth and decay of an electric current in an inductive circuit. His law of decay is in agreement with the result reached by Sabine in 1900. Among later researches are those of F. R. Watson [2] at the University of Illinois, and Ernst Petzold and F. Trendelenburg in Germany.

RETROSPECT

Experimental physics made its first great onward stride in the seventeenth century when, breaking away from the medieval habit of appeal to reason without considering observable facts, the leaders of thought assumed the seemingly less intellectual attitude, by subjecting themselves to the reign of brute fact. We behold in this century "a recoil from the inflexible rationality of medieval thought." [3] Chief among the seventeenth century leaders were Galileo, Kepler, Huygens and Newton. In that century there occurred a great generalization in science, the establishment of the law of universal gravitation, by which the force of gravity known to mankind ever since the dawn of observation and reason as acting upon bodies on the earth's surface, was extended to apply to all bodies of the solar system. This generalization called for

[1] J. Jäger, *Sitzber, Akad. Wiss.*, Wien, Vol. 120, 1911, 2a, pp. 613–634.

[2] F. R. Watson, *Bulletin No. 73, Engineering Exp. Sta.*, Univ. of Illinois, 1914; *Science*, Vol. 67, 1928, p. 335.

[3] A. N. Whitehead, *Science and the Modern Work*, New York, 1926, p. 12.

orderly thought, for intellectual power of the highest order, but a power subjected to a mode of procedure which in medieval times was normally unknown, namely, the reign of stubborn facts.

The more detailed application of the law of gravitation to celestial mechanics, made during the eighteenth century, constituted a careful study of quantitative relations. But in other departments of science, in chemistry and physics, quantitative relations were frequently neglected. The eighteenth century has been called materialistic. Heat, light, electricity, magnetism, and the agent active in oxidation, were looked upon by most scientists as different forms of matter, some forms being imponderable. The words "caloric" and "phlogiston" serve as reminders of that age. "Phlogiston" was sometimes assumed as ponderable—having weight. The ash residue of burning wood weighed less than the wood itself, because phlogiston had been driven out. We have here crude quantitative considerations. But when iron or lead were burned, the expulsion of phlogiston from iron and lead left a residue heavier than the original metal. Here quantitative relations were ignored, until the close of the century when Lavoisier began to pay due homage to the balance, and rejected "phlogiston" as going contrary to the evidence supplied by that instrument.

In the case of "caloric" quantitative relations were even slower to receive general attention, otherwise Count Rumford's heat experiments in the boring of cannon would have been promptly accepted as conclusive evidence against the existence of that form of matter.

The nineteenth century brought with it law and order in many respects. It was a century of correlation.[1] The many isolated distinct forms of matter of the previous century were reduced to two: matter and the new concept of energy. The corpuscular theory of light passed away and the wave theory was developed to a perfection reached, perhaps, by no other

[1] Paul R. Heyl, *Fundamental Concepts of Physics in the Light of Modern Discovery*, Baltimore, 1926, Chap. II.

scientific theory. In the latter part of the nineteenth century Lord Kelvin saw only two clouds in the scientific firmament. But these two clouds were destined to bring great cyclonic disturbances.

The nineteenth century physicist was like the explorer who, reaching Niagara Falls, contemplated with intellectual satisfaction the grand display of natural phenomena before him. The twentieth century physicist is like the explorer who, going further, arrived at Yellowstone Park and was perplexed by the endeavor to reconcile the fact that in that region not only does water *fall*, but also *rises* and shoots on high, not steadily, but in intermittent streams. A Russian physicist [1] states that while the past third or half century has added greatly to our knowledge of physical facts, our harmonious coordination of these facts is very imperfect, as compared with the coordination, half a century ago, of the facts then known. In this respect we have retrograded, he claims. We are now having incomprehensible hypotheses, i.e., hypotheses which are in conflict with supposedly well established physical laws. We introduce mathematical formulas involving quantities playing a wide rôle in many diversified phenomena but whose physical significance is not clear. In the electromagnetic theory of light we have the electric force E and the magnetic force H, and vibratory phenomena. Once it was thought that these forces and vibrations could be explained by the properties of the ether, but now no one is able to postulate non-contradictory mechanical properties of the ether to explain all known phenomena In fact some scientists deny the very existence of an ether. Planck introduced the constant h, but what is h? To be sure by using $h\nu$ explanations of photoelectric and some other phenomena were given, but how shall we explain interference of light, polarization, refraction and dispersion? Why are only certain electronic orbits possible, within the atom, which satisfy an apparently arbitrary equation, when, according to Newtonian mechanics, there is no limit to the number

[1] O. D. Chwolson, *Die Evolution des Geistes der Physik.*, 1925, pp. 184–197.

of possible orbits? Why does an electron in an atom not radiate energy while moving in its orbit? These assumptions explain observed phenomena. But it must be admitted that the physicist has been in a position of the physician who finds that certain recipes accomplish marvelous cures, but has no clear idea in what manner these cures are effected.

There is much force in the argument relating to incomprehensible hypotheses. But had the older physics no hypotheses of that kind? What is the mechanism by which the earth attracts an apple? It was not known. We have become accustomed to that mystery and are not concerned about it. But the new mysteries shock us. If at the present time we have a more imposing number of incomprehensible hypotheses, this fact indicates that, at this still primitive period of advancement in science, the larger the sphere of knowledge grows, the greater becomes its contact with the unknown. We like to believe that, some time in the future, a maximum number of incomprehensible hypotheses will be reached and passed, and that eventually we shall be led to harmonious coordination, to the old Pythagorean ideal of the "harmony of the spheres."

THE EVOLUTION OF PHYSICAL LABORATORIES

The Earliest Laboratories for Research

It would be useless to search Antiquity or the Middle Ages for laboratories devoted to physical investigation. Before the time of Galileo and of Gilbert of Colchester the necessity of experimentation was usually overlooked. Hard thinking was frequently regarded as the sole requisite for scientific discovery. It was not until the time when Gilbert constructed a sphere out of loadstone and showed that our earth behaves magnetically much like his miniature representation of it, that the experimental method secured a firm foothold among physical philosophers; it was not until the young Galileo ascended the leaning tower of Pisa and dropped iron balls of different weights to show that a light ball will fall with the same acceleration as a heavy ball, that the Aristotelian idea concerning physical research was abandoned. The simultaneous clang of those two weights, as they struck the ground, "sounded the death-knell of the old system of philosophy and heralded the birth of the new."

It is amusing to observe that in those days many people reputed for wisdom looked upon experiments as dangerous to intellectual and moral life. In a history of the Royal Society, written in 1667,[1] the author deems it necessary in all seriousness to defend experimentation, arguing that "experiments will not injure education," that "experiments [are] not dangerous to the universities." The arguments were necessary indeed, for the Oxford pulpit declared that Robert Boyle's researches were destroying religion and his experiments were undermining the universities.[2]

The advent of the experimentalist marks the origin of laboratories. We do not mean laboratories of the modern type. Previous to the nineteenth century all of them, with hardly any exception, were private laboratories owned by individual investigators or their patrons.

CHEMICAL RESEARCH LABORATORIES ANTEDATE THE PHYSICAL

For chemistry and astronomy, laboratory facilities were established much earlier than for physics. To the present day the word "Laboratorium" carries in Germany the meaning "chemical" laboratory.[3] The Middle Ages had its laboratories for alchemy and astrology. The search for the elixir of life and the key to the transmutation of metals stimulated activity. These were studies congenial to the avarice of the

[1] Tho. Sprat, *The History of the Royal Society of London*, 1667, pp. 323, 328. Consult also Robert Boyle, *The Usefulness of Experimental Philosophy; by Way of Exhortation of the Study of it*, in three parts, Oxford, 1663, 1671. He argues that experimental science does not lead to atheism.

[2] A. D. White, Vol. I., p. 405.

[3] See articles "Laboratorium" in Brockhaus's or Meyer's *Konversations-Lexikon*.

human heart. In the gallery of the Louvre in Paris is a painting by the Flemish artist Teniers, the elder (?). It represents a chemical laboratory of the sixteenth century.[1] The artist portrays a large basement room with forge-furnaces. The floor is covered with alembics, crucibles, and retorts. A group of enthusiasts are seated round one of the tables. Allowing somewhat for the imagination of the artist, this painting probably pictures to us the more luxurious quarters enjoyed by alchemists who commanded the purse and protection of some powerful patron. The majority of alchemists experimented in secret retreats far from luxurious. Even after the complete victory of the inductive method, experimental research was usually carried on in rooms intended for domestic or commercial purposes. As late as the beginning of the nineteenth century, the laboratory of the most distinguished chemist of his day, Berzelius, was his kitchen, in which chemistry and cooking went on together. When, through the influence of Gilbert, Galileo, and their successors, physics began to be an experimental science, it was generally pursued in the same apartments as its sister science, chemistry. Formerly specialization was less marked than at present and it was no uncommon thing for a scholar to be a master in several branches of science.

EARLY PRIVATE PHYSICAL LABORATORIES FOR RESEARCH

The earliest physical experiments were made in private laboratories. The investigator usually turned part of his house or room into a scientific workshop. When Robert Boyle at Oxford worked on the elasticity of gases, proving the law which bears his name, he employed a tube of such length, that he "could not conveniently make use of it in a chamber," and he was "fain to use it on a pair of stairs." Newton performed his classic experiments on the dispersion of white light into its component colors at his lodgings in Cambridge.

[1] See a reproduction of the picture in *Johnson's Universal Cyclopædia*, article, "Laboratories."

Benjamin Franklin, after experimenting with the kite, put up an insulated iron rod at his house in Philadelphia, in order that he might lose no opportunity to make tests whenever the air was heavily charged with electricity.

LABORATORIES FOR EDUCATIONAL PURPOSES

Previous to the nineteenth century, scientific laboratories existed simply for original investigation; they seldom played a part in elementary or in higher *education*. Doubtless, the error of this practice was felt by many teachers and scientists, and chief among such men was the Moravian educational reformer, **Johann Amos Comenius** (1592–1671), who said: "Men must be instructed in wisdom so far as possible, not from books, but from the heavens, the earth, the oaks and the beeches; that is, they must learn and investigate the things themselves, and not merely the observations and testimonies of other persons concerning the things." "Who is there," he cries, "who teaches physics by observation and experiment, instead of by reading an Aristotelian or other textbook?"[1]

Near the close of the eighteenth century, Joseph Priestley, the discoverer of oxygen, expressed himself as follows: "I am sorry to have occasion to observe that natural science is very little, if at all, the object of *education* in this country. . . . I would observe that, if we wish to lay a good foundation for a philosophical taste, and philosophical pursuits, persons should be accustomed to the sight of experiments and processes in *early life*. They should, more especially, be early initiated in the theory and practice of *investigation,* by which many of the old discoveries may be made to be really *their own;* on which account they will be much more valued by them."[2]

In this passage Priestley advances an idea which is finding its practical realization at the present time, since it is only in comparatively recent years that there have been established

[1] W. H. Welch, "The Evolution of Modern Scientific Laboratories," *Electrician* (London), Vol. 37, 1896, p. 172.

[2] J. Priestley, *On Air*, Birmingham, 1790, Vol. I., p. xxix.

laboratories for pupils of high-school grade, in which the young students themselves practise physical manipulation.

We have seen that experimental research was in vogue earlier in chemistry than in physics. Chemistry again takes the lead in the establishment of laboratories connected with educational institutions and planned for the use of students. Why this lagging behind on the part of physics? There appear to be two reasons. In the first place, chemistry appealed more directly to the needs of practical life. A knowledge of chemistry was indispensable for metallurgy. On the other hand, the age of steam had not yet arrived; electricity and magnetism were sciences still in their infancy. The second reason for the priority of chemical laboratories is that they are less expensive. Earthen vessels, bottles, test-tubes, a stock of ordinary chemicals, are not expensive, yet go a long way towards equipping a chemical laboratory. Physical apparatus, on the other hand, is very costly. Three hundred years ago an air-pump, thermometer, and telescope were expensive luxuries; they are expensive now. One hundred and sixty years ago Priestley wrote, "Natural Philosophy is a science which more especially requires the aid of wealth." [1]

Great educational movements usually begin on top. The laboratory method of instruction was first introduced into the universities and thence descended to the more elementary schools. Lord Kelvin [2] claims that the first chemical laboratory for the instruction of students was established at the University of Glasgow, prior to the year 1831, but the first laboratory of the type existing to-day was apparently established by Liebig, who, in 1824, became extraordinary professor of chemistry at the University of Giessen. [3] Certainly the new movement in the teaching of chemistry was started in Germany with much greater momentum and with more far-

[1] Joseph Priestley, *History of Electricity*, 4th ed., London, 1775, p. xv.

[2] "Scientific Laboratories," *Nature*, Vol. 31, 1885, pp. 409–413.

[3] T. C. Mendenhall, "The Evolution and Influence of Experimental Physics," in the *Quarterly Calendar of the University of Chicago*, Vol. III., August, 1894, p. 10,

reaching influence than in Scotland. Students from all parts of the civilized world flocked to the little university in the small town of Giessen.[1] Chemical laboratories were soon built in Tübingen, Bonn, Berlin, and other places.

The earliest American institutions in which students were sent regularly to the chemical laboratory to make their own experiments were the Rensselaer Polytechnic Institute at Troy, New York, and the Massachusetts Institute of Technology in Boston. At the former, laboratory work was required of students prior to 1831,[2] probably from its very foundation in 1824. The movement was independent of that at Giessen. At the Massachusetts Institute of Technology perhaps more systematic courses were given. The laboratory method was in vogue there from the time of the school's foundation at the close of the Civil War.[3]

The transition from private laboratories to those belonging to universities was a gradual one. Usually it took effect in this wise. A few ·teachers permitted the most enthusiastic and promising of their students to enter their private laboratories. Thus, **Heinrich Gustav Magnus** (1802–1870) in Berlin threw open a few rooms in his residence for physical experimentation. Like Liebig, Magnus, while himself a student, had drawn his inspiration for experimental research from Berzelius and Gay-Lussac. The influence which Magnus exerted in Germany was very great. "He loved youth, and knew how to make himself beloved while imparting a taste for that science to which he had consecrated his life."[4] He began his work at the University of Berlin in 1834 as extraordinary professor of physics and in 1845 was advanced to the position of ordinary professor. Some idea of the work in his private laboratory may be obtained from his students. Says one of his American pupils: "While I was engaged there

[1] Ira Remsen, "On Chemical Laboratories," *Nature,* Vol. 49, 1894, p. 531.

[2] *Science,* Vol. 20, 1892, p. 53; N. S., Vol. 8, 1898, p. 205.

[3] *Science,* Vol. 19, 1892, p. 351.

[4] "Life and Labours of Henry Gustavus Magnus," *Smithsonian Report,* 1870, pp. 223–230.

three other students were present, one occupied by an investigation of acoustics, another in polarized light, and a third in the measurement of crystals of recently discovered chemical compounds."[1]   Among the greatest of his pupils who experimented under him were G. H. Wiedemann, Helmholtz, and Tyndall.   As the number of students increased, the private laboratory became more and more inadequate; the university began to give financial aid and the private establishment grew into a regular university institution.   By this process the private laboratory of Magnus evolved into the physical laboratory of the University of Berlin, which was opened in 1863.   A similar mode of evolution can be traced in case of Liebig's chemical laboratory at Giessen and Purkinje's physiological laboratory at Breslau.[2]

Physical Laboratories for Students

Physical laboratories for students were gradually established in connection with other German universities.   Thus, at Heidelberg one was opened by **Philipp Gustav Jolly** (1810–1884) in 1846.   It consisted of two rooms in what was originally a private dwelling.[3]   In 1850 the apparatus was moved to somewhat more commodious quarters, in which later Kirchhoff and Bunsen instituted their wonderful researches in spectrum analysis.   Referring to these new quarters, Quincke says: "However modest this institute may appear to the present generation, it contained the only physical laboratory in which a German student at that time could do practical work."   If Quincke means to exclude private laboratories, then this statement may be true, but students were drawn to Berlin to work in the private laboratory of Magnus long before this.   Helmholtz was there in 1847.

The University of Glasgow in Scotland, which was men-

[1] A. R. Leeds, "A Laboratory of Experimental Research," *Jour. Franklin Inst.* (3), Vol. 59, 1870, p. 210.

[2] *Science,* Vol. 3, 1884, p. 173.

[3] G. Quincke, *Geschichte d. physik. Instituts d. Univ. Heidelberg,* Heidelberg, 1885.

tioned as laying claim to the earliest student's laboratory
in chemistry, is also a candidate for the honor of having
first given laboratory instruction in physics. In 1845 Lord
Kelvin (William Thomson) became professor of natural
philosophy at Glasgow. He invited some of his students to
aid him in his original researches; others volunteered for
service.[1] "The physical laboratory for many years was a
disused wine-cellar in the old university buildings."[2] Thus
old Bacchus was superseded by the modern goddess Scientia.
Experimental research was carried on for nearly a quarter
of a century in this room and in another one, added later.
Finally, in 1870, the university was moved into new and pa-
latial buildings. The students' laboratory work under Kelvin
was mostly original investigation. "Their interest was excited,
was kept alive by their constant intercourse with the guiding
spirit of the place, and their zeal was such that . . . the laboratory corps, as it used to be called, has been known to divide
itself into two squads—one which worked during the day, the
other during the night, for weeks together, so that the work
never paused."[3] Neither at Glasgow nor at Berlin were the
laboratory courses in physics regular prescribed branches, constituting an integral part of the curriculum; entrance into the
laboratory was purely optional. The earliest institution in
which laboratory physics was pursued according to a systematic plan for its educational value, and was a required part
of the work necessary for a degree, is, we believe, the Massachusetts Institute of Technology in Boston. The institution
competing with it for that honor is King's College in London.
New England and Old England took the new departure about

[1] Says Kelvin: "Three-fourths of my volunteer experimentalists used
to be students who entered the theological classes immediately after the
completion of the philosophical curriculum. I well remember the surprise of a great German professor when he heard of this rule and usage:
'What! do the theologians learn physics?' I said, 'Yes, they all do;
and many of them have made capital experiments.' "—*Nature*, Vol. 31,
1885, p. 411.

[2] *Nature*, Vol. 55, 1897, p. 487.

[3] *Ibidem*, p. 487. Consult also Kelvin's evidence given before the
Royal Commission on Scientific Instruction, *Minutes of Evidence*, 1870,
p. 332.

the same time. Says W. G. Adams: "Professors of physics at different universities have usually selected their best students to assist them in their private laboratories, to the mutual advantage of professor and student, but I believe that Professor Clifton was the first to propose, more than three years ago, that a course of training in a physical laboratory should form a part of the regular work of every student of physics. This system was adopted and at once put in action at King's College, on a very considerable scale for a college with no endowment whatever, and has been working now for nearly three years. Two large rooms adjoining the museum of physical apparatus were fitted up for a physical laboratory, and a third room was built for a store and battery room."[1]

Robert Bellamy Clifton's name is indeed closely identified with instruction in experimental physics in England. He was the first occupant of the chair of natural philosophy at Owens College, Manchester. After his removal to Oxford, he planned the first laboratory in England "which was specially built and designed for the study of experimental physics. It has served as a type. Clerk Maxwell visited it while planning the Cavendish Laboratory (at Cambridge), and traces of Professor Clifton's designs can be detected in several of our university colleges."[2] Maxwell took charge of the department of physics at Cambridge University in 1871, and his laboratory was built in 1874.[3]

Both at Cambridge and Oxford laboratory practice was optional, and the number of students undertaking experimental work was small.[4] But out of this small number rose some of England's physicists of later time.

In the early part of the nineteenth century France was the great centre for experimental research. And yet, as Professor

[1] *Nature*, Vol. 3, 1871, p. 323.
[2] A. W. Rücker, *Nature*, Vol. 50, 1894, p. 344.
[3] See *A History of the Cavendish Laboratory, 1871–1910*, London, 1910; R. T. Glazebrook, *James Clerk Maxwell and Modern Physics*, New York, 1896, p. 73.
[4] Glazebrook, *op. cit.*, p. 76; *Minutes of Evidence taken before the Royal Commission on Scientific Instruction and the Advancement of Science*, 1870, pp. 387, 388, 28.

Welch says, "France was long in supplying her scientific men with adequate laboratory facilities." "Bernard, that prince of experimenters, worked in a damp, small cellar, one of those wretched Parisian substitutes for a laboratory which he has called 'the tombs of scientific investigators.'" Gay-Lussac's laboratory was on the ground floor and, to protect himself from the dampness, he wore wooden shoes. But in spite of this, French scientists investigated and taught with enthusiasm. Says Liebig in his autobiography:[1] "The lectures of Gay-Lussac, Thenard, Dulong, etc., in the Sorbonne, had for me an indescribable charm. . . . French exposition has, through the genius of the language, a logical clearness in the treatment of scientific subjects very difficult of attainment in other languages, whereby Thenard and Gay-Lussac acquired a mastery in experimental demonstration. The lecture consisted of a judiciously arranged succession of phenomena,—that is to say, of experiments, whose connection was completed by oral explanations. The experiments were a real delight to me, for they spoke to me in a language I understood."

Gay-Lussac invited Liebig to work in his "private laboratory." As elsewhere, there were in Paris no public laboratories for students. Original workers were dependent upon their own financial resources. Says Arago: "At the end of the eighteenth century and the beginning of the nineteenth, no one was a real physicist unless possessing a valuable collection of instruments well polished, well varnished, and arranged in glass cases." When, in 1806, Gay-Lussac, who owned only a few instruments of research, was a candidate for the Academy of Sciences, he had much trouble in overcoming these prejudices. We know that Dulong expended nearly all his wealth on apparatus. Fresnel conducted his immortal experiments privately, and defrayed from his own resources the heavy expense for apparatus. Foucault carried on most of his experiments at his own residence. On one occasion savants flocked to the humble abode of Ampère in the Rue

[1] *Smithsonian Report*, 1891, p. 263.
[2] Arago, "Eulogy of Gay-Lussac," *Smithsonian Report*, 1876, p. 152.

Fossés Saint Victor to see a platinum wire, as soon as it was traversed by an electric current, set itself across the meridian.[1]

For many years French scientists complained of meagre laboratory equipment and lack of room, until, at last, Duruy, the minister of public instruction (1864–1869), undertook to meet the requirements. At the beginning of the nineteenth century, Germany took lessons from France; at this new period the process was reversed. Says Professor Welch: "No more unbiassed recognition of the value and significance of the German laboratory system can be found than in the reports of Lorain, in 1868, and of Wurtz, in 1870, based upon personal study of the construction and organization of German laboratories."

Two decrees of July 31, 1868, affirm the necessity of supplementing the lectures on science with practical exercises or manipulations. The same decrees provide that besides the laboratories for students there shall be established special laboratories for original research for the use of professors and other savants. The result was the establishment of a large number of laboratories for physics and for other sciences.[2] Referring to these changes, Darboux wrote, in 1892: "You know what profound transformations have been accomplished in these establishments [the faculty of sciences] within 20 years. Everywhere the buildings have been reconstructed and enlarged; they have been supplied with large laboratories for the experimental sciences. In some places these are still too small,—the remedy is easy. . . . A barracks on a site not far distant is sufficient. Certainly, we professors of the faculties of Paris will never forget the services rendered to superior instruction by the barracks and halls of Gerson." [3]

A physical laboratory was founded in the old Sorbonne in 1868. J. Jamin was director of it until his death in 1886.

[1] Heller, II., p. 609.

[2] *Circular of Information*, Bureau of Education, Washington, D. C. No. 4, 1881, p. 119.

[3] *Report of the Commissioner of Education*, Washington, D. C., 1892–1893, Vol. 1, p. 234.

In 1894 it was transferred to the new Faculty of Sciences
and was reconstructed. It became celebrated through the researches of its director, G. Lippmann.[1]

PHYSICAL LABORATORIES IN THE UNITED STATES

In the United States the growth of laboratories during the
last 50 years has been surprising. As already noted, the
Massachusetts Institute of Technology took the initiative in
physics. The idea of giving regular laboratory courses in
this subject to large classes was strongly advocated by **William Barton Rogers,** the first president of the Institute. In
drawing up the scope and plans of the new school, in 1864,
he stated some of the leading objects of such a laboratory.[2]

Edward C. Pickering was put in charge of the department.
In April, 1869, J. D. Runkle, then acting president of the
Institute, wrote as follows: ''Pickering has drawn, in quite
full detail, a plan for the physical laboratory, which I will
send you before long. . . . Pickering is very anxious to be
ready by October next to instruct the third year's class by
laboratory work; and if an experience of one year shall be
favorable, as I feel it must be, we can then gradually enlarge
our facilities and take in the lower classes. I am convinced
that in time we shall revolutionize the instruction in physics
just as has been done in chemistry.''[3]

After a trial of a little over one year Pickering made the
following statement: ''The great difficulty is to enable 20 or
30 students to perform the same experiment without duplicat-
ing the apparatus, and to avoid the danger of injury to delicate apparatus. Our plan is this: Two large rooms (one
nearly 100 feet in length) are fitted up with tables, supplied
with gas and water. . . . On each is placed the apparatus
prepared for a single experiment, which always remains in

[1] A. Berget, in *La Nature*, Vol. 26, 1898, p. 225; *Nature*, Vol. 58,
p. 12.
[2] *Life and Letters of William Barton Rogers*, Boston and New York,
1896, Vol. II., p. 303.
[3] *Op. cit.*, Vol. II., p. 287,

this place, thus avoiding the danger of breaking it in moving. A full written description is also given of each experiment." [1] Several other institutions, Cornell for instance, were quick to follow suit. In the article just quoted Pickering says: "There are now (1871) in America at least four similar laboratories in operation or preparation, and the chances are that in a few years this number will be greatly increased."

Notwithstanding Pickering's prediction, the vast majority of our colleges and universities failed to make provision for physical laboratories for students until much later. In this matter, the technical schools were in the lead. University instruction, as distinguished from technical, is of more recent date. In 1871 Harvard College had no instruments for electrical measurements, and Professor Trowbridge had to borrow from Professor Cooke's private collection in order to make some tests on his new cosine galvanometer. [2] Most of the large physical laboratories in this country have been erected and equipped within the last 50 years. In 1892 we had "some half-dozen that will compare with any university laboratories in Europe," [3] with the exception, perhaps, of a few like the one in Zürich, devoted to physics and electrotechnics, which was built and equipped at an expense of 3,000,000 francs.

The difficulty of arranging laboratory work in physics for large classes, which Pickering endeavored to overcome, cannot be said to have been removed satisfactorily. Some of our large universities devote a whole building to the purpose of a physical laboratory and yet teach the elementary college physics by text-book and illustrated lectures, without giving the pupils an opportunity to experiment for themselves. The teaching force and laboratory facilities are inadequate for classes of, perhaps, several hundred members. Experimental work is done only by the few students who elect more advanced

[1] *Nature*, Vol. 3, 1871, p. 241.
[2] *Science*, N. S., Vol. VIII, 1898, p. 204. For comparison of dimensions of several American, English, and German physical laboratories, see *Nature*, Vol. 58, 1898, pp. 621, 622.
[3] A. G. Webster, "A National Physical Laboratory," *The Pedagogical Seminary*, Vol. II., 1892, p. 91.

physics, or by those who are pursuing technical courses. If there is any truth in the statement that even Faraday never could understand any scientific experiment thoroughly until he had not only seen it performed by others, but had performed it himself, then it is clear that the above method is far from ideal.

There are two distinct methods of conducting large laboratory classes in physics. One is to let all the pupils perform the same experiment (measurement) simultaneously, each student being supplied with all the apparatus necessary for the experiment. The second method is to let each student perform a different experiment, so that, at one time, there are as many different experiments in progress as there are students.

The first method has the great advantage of permitting teachers to discuss, once for all, the theory of the experiment with the class as a whole, instead of repeating it with each student individually. Moreover, it is easier to superintend a large class when all are working at the same thing than when each is performing a separate task. The great disadvantage of this mode of procedure is that few institutions, if any, have the resources to furnish each student of a large class with the same instrument of precision. Wherever this course has been followed, the apparatus has necessarily been of cheap quality and frequently the experimental work has lacked the desired degree of accuracy.

The strong point of the second method is that it necessitates no duplication or multiplication of apparatus, thus making it easier to equip the laboratory with instruments of high quality. Each student is at a different task. The members of the class rotate from one experiment to another on successive days. There is less opportunity for students to compare results, each pupil being thrown more upon his own resources. It is an individual method, calling for a great deal of "elbow instruction." A teacher cannot at one time take care of as many pupils by this method as by the first. Again, the order in which the experiments are taken up is different for each student, making it impossible, as a rule, to take the experiments in a logical succession.

So far as we know, there are few colleges and universities in which either of the two methods has been carried out in its purity with all students. Usually, in large classes, a combination of the two has been found more in harmony with existing conditions.

Since about 1885 laboratory courses were developed and strengthened, not only in our higher institutions of learning, but also in our high schools. Many high schools to-day are better equipped than were some of the prominent colleges forty years ago.

Laboratory instruction in physics in secondary schools was at the close of the nineteenth century, perhaps, more fully developed in the United States than in France and Germany. Darboux, dean of the Paris faculty of sciences, reported in 1892 as follows: "There exists indeed in every lycée a physical cabinet, but the instruments to be put into the hands of the students for the manipulations in physics, chemistry, and natural history are wanting."[1] In Germany the desirability of letting the pupil handle apparatus and see it in action, was abundantly discussed, and laboratories were conducted accordingly.[2]

The departure in the direction of individual laboratory work, including measurements, for secondary schools took definite shape in the United States when, in 1886, Harvard College changed its entrance requirements in physics. "It was now decided to establish a requirement of laboratory work to be recommended by the College in place of the text-book work, although the latter, considerably increased, remained as an alternative for those who could not command laboratory

[1] *Report of the Commissioner of Education*, Washington, 1892, 1893, Vol. 1, p. 233.
[2] Consult E. J. Goodwin, "Some Characteristics of Prussian Schools," *Educational Review*, December, 1896; also a critical review of this article in *Poske's Zeitschrift für den Physikalischen und Chemischen Unterricht*, X. Jahrgang, 1897, pp. 161, 162.

facilities. It was soon evident, in view of the inexperience of teachers and the very different standards and methods likely to be adopted by them, that a special course of experiments, carefully thought out, . . . was needed to make the new plan a success." A pamphlet was issued by Harvard in 1887, afterward somewhat revised, under the title, *Descriptive List of Elementary Physical Experiments.*

NATIONAL LABORATORIES FOR RESEARCH

In recent years there has been a growing demand for the establishment of national laboratories for experimentation which is beyond the resources of laboratories connected with educational institutions. England, Germany, and France have long had institutions which wholly or in part fulfilled these demands. England has the Royal Institution with the new Davy-Faraday Research Laboratory; Germany has its Imperial Physico-Technical Institute in Charlottenburg; France for 100 years has had its Conservatoire des Arts et Métiers and, for some years past, also an electrical testing laboratory in Paris.[1]

THE ROYAL INSTITUTION

Of the famous laboratories of the Royal institution in London an English writer said in 1870: "Probably a greater part than to the universities is to be ascribed in the spread and development of modern science to the Royal Institution, which has been the scene of the teaching and labors of the three by far greatest philosophers of our century, of Young, of Davy, and of Faraday."[2] The Briton of to-day speaks of it as the "Pantheon of Science" The theatre, model-room, and workshops of the Royal Institution were erected in 1800. The aim of the Institution, according to its founder, Count Rumford, was the promotion of applied science. It originally

[1] A. G. Webster, *Pedagogical Seminary,* Vol. II., 1892, p. 101.
[2] C. K. Akin in *Minutes of Evidence . . . on Scientific Instruction,* 1870, p. 20.

contained a workshop for blacksmiths with forge and bellows. All sorts of models of machinery were brought together. After 1802, when Rumford left England, the industrial element declined, and original research in pure science predominated. When the physical laboratory of the Royal Institution was erected, there was nothing equal to it in England. Nevertheless it was very unpretentious. It became memorable for the brilliant researches of Sir Humphry Davy, Faraday, and Tyndall. For 70 years it remained unaltered, and at the end of that time it was very inferior to the new laboratories in Oxford, Cambridge, Manchester, and Glasgow.[1] When the reconstruction of the laboratories at the Royal Institution came under consideration, the plan was at first opposed by Tyndall. He almost prayed that the place where Davy and Faraday had made their discoveries might be preserved.[2] But improvements were necessary and were made about 1871.

Through the generosity of **Dr. Ludwig Mond**, the laboratories of the Royal Institution were recently enlarged, and a new laboratory, liberally endowed and equipped with modern apparatus, was erected immediately adjoining the Royal Institution. This new scientific workshop, called the "Davy-Faraday Research Laboratory," was opened December 22, 1896, and it was placed under the directorship of Lord Rayleigh and Professor J. Dewar. It was "the only public laboratory in the world solely devoted to research in pure science" and "open to men and women of all schools and of all views on scientific questions."[3]

For many years, in the latter part of the last century, considerable attention was given to the standardizing of apparatus at the *Kew Observatory*, England. Meteorological instruments, compasses, photographic lenses were tested and verified. Important researches were also carried on there on terrestrial magnetism.[4] In this work the government helped

[1] *Nature,* Vol. 7, 1872–1873, p. 264.
[2] *Ibidem,* p. 264.
[3] *Nature,* Vol. 55, 1896, p. 209.
[4] *Nature,* Vol. 55, 1897, p. 368.

but little. It furnished the site and the use of an old building; all other expenses were defrayed through private benefaction.

THE REICHSANSTALT

Germany became the envy of other nations because of her magnificent new Imperial Physico-Technical Institute in Charlottenburg, commonly called the *Reichsanstalt,* toward the foundation of which **Werner Siemens**, in 1884, donated about $125,000. The Reichstag voted the necessary additions to this sum. New buildings were provided, and in 1888 **Helmholtz** was made president. His successors in the presidency, with their dates of service, ar as follows: **Friedrich Kohlrausch** (1895–1905), **Emil Warburg** (1905–1922), **Walter Nernst** (1922–1924), **Friedrich Paschen** (1924–   ). The Reichsanstalt has not only departments equipped for purely theoretical research, but also others devoted to the study of problems useful to industry.

LABORATORIES IN FRANCE

France, for 100 years, has had its Conservatoire des Arts et Métiers. It was founded in the old priory of St. Martin des Champs in 1794, as a public repository for machines, models, tools, plans, descriptions. From time to time free courses of lectures on applied science were given to workingmen and artisans. In the physical line a beginning was made by the purchase of the "Cabinet de Physique" owned by Charles, and by the establishment of the chair of physics in 1829.

Through the participation of 18 nations, an International Committee of Weights and Measures was organized in 1875. A fine laboratory was erected in the Pavillon de Breteuil, in the Park of St. Cloud, near Paris, for the purpose of constructing international standards of the metric system.[1]

[1] A. G. Webster, *op. cit.,* p. 94.

NATIONAL PHYSICAL LABORATORY OF GREAT BRITAIN

In the closing years of the nineteenth century, an important new movement was started in Great Britain; the *National Physical Laboratory* was established, with **Richard T. Glazebrook** as director.[1] He served in that capacity from 1899 to 1919, and was succeeded by Joseph Petavel, formerly professor of engineering in Manchester. The ultimate scientific control of the Laboratory rests with the president and council of the Royal Society of London. Its object, as expressed by Glazebrook, is "to make the forces of science available to the nation." For the first two years the work of the Laboratory was carried on at the Kew Observatory, where Glazebrook started with three assistants. In 1900 Bushy House and grounds, at Teddington, about 12 miles from London, was selected as the permanent site. The Laboratory enjoyed a rapid growth. In 1918, there were eight departments with a staff of 532 persons. In 1911, there was opened a national experimental tank for testing models of ships. One building is given to aerodynamics.

THE BUREAU OF STANDARDS IN THE UNITED STATES

The United States *Bureau of Standards* was created by act of Congress on March 3, 1901. It took over the duties of the old division of weights and measures of the Coast and Geodetic Survey. This division had been established in 1830, with Ferdinand Rudolph Hassler in charge. From 1832 until 1901 the superintendent of the United States Coast Survey was also director of the work on weights and measures. The Bureau of Standards was originally housed in temporary quarters near the Capitol in Washington. Its permanent location is some distance from the heart of the city, at the corner of Van Ness street and Connecticut avenue, where on a large site, it occupies more than a dozen buildings, and has

[1] *Nature,* Vol. 63, 1901, p. 300; Vol. 64, 1901, p. 290; Vol. 104, 1919, p. 8; Vol. 116, 1925, p. 63.

a large staff of scientific workers. It serves as a national physical laboratory and carries on measurments and investigations in the wide field of theoretical and practical physics and chemistry. **S. W. Stratton** was director of the Bureau during its first twenty-two years of existence. His successor is **George Kimball Burgess.**

INDEX

CATALOGUE OF DOVER BOOKS

PHYSICS

General physics

FOUNDATIONS OF PHYSICS, R. B. Lindsay & H. Margenau. Excellent bridge between semi-popular works & technical treatises. A discussion ot methods of physical description, construction of theory; valuable tor physicist with elementary calculus who is interested in ideas that give meaning to data, tools of modern physics. Contents include symbolism, mathematical equations; space & time foundations of mechanics; probability; physics & continua; electron theory; special & general relativity; quantum mechanics; causality. "Thorough and yet not overdetailed. Unreservedly recommended," NATURE (London). Unabridged, corrected edition. List of recommended readings. 35 illustrations. xi + 537pp. 5⅜ x 8.
S377 Paperbound **$2.75**

FUNDAMENTAL FORMULAS OF PHYSICS, ed. by D. H. Menzel. Highly useful, fully inexpensive reference and study text, ranging trom simple to highly sophisticated operations. Mathematics integrated into text—each cnapter stands as short textbook ot field represented. Vol. 1: Statistics, Physical Constants, Special Theory of Relativity, Hydrodynamics, Aerodynamics, Boundary Value Problems in Math. Physics; Viscosity, Electromagnetic Theory, etc. Vol. 2: Sound, Acoustics, Geometrical Optics, Electron Optics, High-Energy Phenomena, Magnetism, Biophysics, much more. Index. Total of 800pp. 5⅜ x 8. Vol. 1 S595 Paperbound **$2.00**
Vol. 2 S596 Paperbound **$2.00**

MATHEMATICAL PHYSICS, D. H. Menzel. Thorough one-volume treatment of the mathematical techniques vital for classic mechanics, electromagnetic theory, quantum theory, and relativity. Written by the Harvard Professor of Astrophysics for junior, senior, and graduate courses, it gives clear explanations of all those aspects of function theory, vectors, matrices, dyadics, tensors, partial differential equations, etc., necessary tor the understanding of the various physical theories. Electron theory, relativity, and other topics seldom presented appear here in considerable detail. Scores of definitions, conversion factors, dimensional constants, etc. "More detailed than normal for an advanced text . . . excellent set of sections on Dyadics, Matrices, and Tensors," JOURNAL OF THE FRANKLIN INSTITUTE. Index. 193 problems, with answers. x + 412pp. 5⅜ x 8. S56 Paperbound **$2.00**

THE SCIENTIFIC PAPERS OF J. WILLARD GIBBS. All the published papers of America's outstanding theoretical scientist (except for "Statistical Mechanics" and "Vector Analysis"). Vol I (thermodynamics) contains one of the most brilliant of all 19th-century scientific papers—the 300-page "On the Equilibrium of Heterogeneous Substances," which tounded the science of physical chemistry, and clearly stated a number of highly important natural laws for the first time; 8 other papers complete the first volume. Vol II includes 2 papers on dynamics, 8 on vector analysis and multiple algebra, 5 on the electromagnetic theory of light, and 6 miscellaneous papers. Biographical sketch by H. A. Bumstead. Total of xxxvi + 718pp. 5⅝ x 8⅜.
S721 Vol I Paperbound **$2.50**
S722 Vol II Paperbound **$2.00**
The set **$4.50**

BASIC THEORIES OF PHYSICS, Peter Gabriel Bergmann. Two-volume set which presents a critical examination of important topics in the major subdivisions of classical and modern physics. The first volume is concerned with classical mechanics and electrodynamics: mechanics of mass points, analytical mechanics, matter in bulk, electrostatics and magnetostatics, electromagnetic interaction, the field waves, special relativity, and waves. The second volume (Heat and Quanta) contains discussions of the kinetic hypothesis, physics and statistics, stationary ensembles, laws of thermodynamics, early quantum theories, atomic spectra, probability waves, quantization in wave mechanics, approximation methods, and abstract quantum theory. A valuable supplement to any thorough course or text.
Heat and Quanta: Index. 8 figures. x + 300pp. 5⅜ x 8½. S968 Paperbound **$2.00**
Mechanics and Electrodynamics: Index. 14 figures. vii + 280pp. 5⅜ x 8½.
S969 Paperbound **$1.75**

THEORETICAL PHYSICS, A. S. Kompaneyets. One of the very few thorough studies of the subject in this price range. Provides advanced students with a comprehensive theoretical background. Especially strong on recent experimentation and developments in quantum theory. Contents: Mechanics (Generalized Coordinates, Lagrange's Equation, Collision of Particles, etc.), Electrodynamics (Vector Analysis, Maxwell's equations, Transmission of Signals, Theory of Relativity, etc.), Quantum Mechanics (the Inadequacy of Classical Mechanics, the Wave Equation, Motion in a Central Field, Quantum Theory of Radiation, Quantum Theories of Dispersion and Scattering, etc.), and Statistical Physics (Equilibrium Distribution of Molecules in an Ideal Gas, Boltzmann statistics, Bose and Fermi Distribution, Thermodynamic Quantities, etc.). Revised to 1961. Translated by George Yankovsky, authorized by Kompaneyets. 137 exercises. 56 figures. 529pp. 5⅜ x 8½. S972 Paperbound **$2.50**

ANALYTICAL AND CANONICAL FORMALISM IN PHYSICS, André Mercier. A survey, in one volume, of the variational principles (the key principles—in mathematical form—from which the basic laws of any one branch of physics can be derived) of the several branches of physical theory, together with an examination of the relationships among them. Contents: the Lagrangian Formalism, Lagrangian Densities, Canonical Formalism, Canonical Form of Electrodynamics, Hamiltonian Densities, Transformations, and Canonical Form with Vanishing Jacobian Determinant. Numerous examples and exercises. For advanced students, teachers, etc. 6 figures. Index. viii + 222pp. 5⅜ x 8½. S1077 Paperbound **$1.75**

Acoustics, optics, electricity and magnetism, electromagnetics, magnetohydrodynamics

THE THEORY OF SOUND, Lord Rayleigh. Most vibrating systems likely to be encountered in practice can be tackled successfully by the methods set forth by the great Nobel laureate, Lord Rayleigh. Complete coverage of experimental, mathematical aspects of sound theory. Partial contents: Harmonic motions, vibrating systems in general, lateral vibrations of bars, curved plates or shells, applications of Laplace's functions to acoustical problems, fluid friction, plane vortex-sheet, vibrations of solid bodies, etc. This is the first inexpensive edition of this great reference and study work. Bibliography. Historical introduction by R. B. Lindsay. Total of 1040pp. 97 figures. 5⅜ x 8.
S292, S293, Two volume set, paperbound, **$4.70**

THE DYNAMICAL THEORY OF SOUND, H. Lamb. Comprehensive mathematical treatment of the physical aspects of sound, covering the theory of vibrations, the general theory of sound, and the equations of motion of strings, bars, membranes, pipes, and resonators. Includes chapters on plane, spherical, and simple harmonic waves, and the Helmholtz Theory of Audition. Complete and self-contained development for student and specialist; all fundamental differential equations solved completely. Specific mathematical details for such important phenomena as harmonics, normal modes, forced vibrations of strings, theory of reed pipes, etc. Index. Bibliography. 86 diagrams. viii + 307pp. 5⅜ x 8.
S655 Paperbound **$1.50**

WAVE PROPAGATION IN PERIODIC STRUCTURES, L. Brillouin. A general method and application to different problems: pure physics, such as scattering of X-rays of crystals, thermal vibration in crystal lattices, electronic motion in metals; and also problems of electrical engineering. Partial contents: elastic waves in 1-dimensional lattices of point masses. Propagation of waves along 1-dimensional lattices. Energy flow. 2 dimensional, 3 dimensional lattices. Mathieu's equation. Matrices and propagation of waves along an electric line. Continuous electric lines. 131 illustrations. Bibliography. Index. xii + 253pp. 5⅜ x 8.
S34 Paperbound **$2.00**

THEORY OF VIBRATIONS, N. W. McLachlan. Based on an exceptionally successful graduate course given at Brown University, this discusses linear systems having 1 degree of freedom, forced vibrations of simple linear systems, vibration of flexible strings, transverse vibrations of bars and tubes, transverse vibration of circular plate, sound waves of finite amplitude, etc. Index. 99 diagrams. 160pp. 5⅜ x 8.
S190 Paperbound **$1.35**

LIGHT: PRINCIPLES AND EXPERIMENTS, George S. Monk. Covers theory, experimentation, and research. Intended for students with some background in general physics and elementary calculus. Three main divisions: 1) Eight chapters on geometrical optics—fundamental concepts (the ray and its optical length, Fermat's principle, etc.), laws of image formation, apertures in optical systems, photometry, optical instruments etc.; 2) 9 chapters on physical optics—interference, diffraction, polarization, spectra, the Rayleigh refractometer, the wave theory of light, etc.; 3) 23 instructive experiments based directly on the theoretical text. "Probably the best intermediate textbook on light in the English language. Certainly, it is the best book which includes both geometrical and physical optics," J. Rud Nielson, PHYSICS FORUM. Revised edition. 102 problems and answers. 12 appendices. 6 tables. Index. 270 illustrations. xi +489pp. 5⅜ x 8½.
S341 Paperbound **$2.50**

PHOTOMETRY, John W. T. Walsh. The best treatment of both "bench" and "illumination" photometry in English by one of Britain's foremost experts in the field (President of the International Commission on Illumination). Limited to those matters, theoretical and practical, which affect the measurement of light flux, candlepower, illumination, etc., and excludes treatment of the use to which such measurements may be put after they have been made. Chapters on Radiation, The Eye and Vision, Photo-Electric Cells, The Principles of Photometry, The Measurement of Luminous Intensity, Colorimetry, Spectrophotometry, Stellar Photometry, The Photometric Laboratory, etc. Third revised (1958) edition. 281 illustrations. 10 appendices. xxiv + 544pp. 5½ x 9¼.
S319 Clothbound **$10.00**

EXPERIMENTAL SPECTROSCOPY, R. A. Sawyer. Clear discussion of prism and grating spectrographs and the techniques of their use in research, with emphasis on those principles and techniques that are fundamental to practically all uses of spectroscopic equipment. Beginning with a brief history of spectroscopy, the author covers such topics as light sources, spectroscopic apparatus, prism spectroscopes and graphs, diffraction grating, the photographic process, determination of wave length, spectral intensity, infrared spectroscopy, spectrochemical analysis, etc. This revised edition contains new material on the production of replica gratings, solar spectroscopy from rockets, new standard of wave length, etc. Index. Bibliography. 111 illustrations. x + 358pp. 5⅜ x 8½.
S1045 Paperbound **$2.25**

FUNDAMENTALS OF ELECTRICITY AND MAGNETISM, L. B. Loeb. For students of physics, chemistry, or engineering who want an introduction to electricity and magnetism on a higher level and in more detail than general elementary physics texts provide. Only elementary differential and integral calculus is assumed. Physical laws developed logically, from magnetism to electric currents, Ohm's law, electrolysis, and on to static electricity, induction, etc. Covers an unusual amount of material; one third of book on modern material: solution of wave equation, photoelectric and thermionic effects, etc. Complete statement of the various electrical systems of units and interrelations. 2 Indexes. 75 pages of problems with answers stated. Over 300 figures and diagrams. xix +669pp. 5⅜ x 8.
S745 Paperbound **$2.75**

MATHEMATICAL ANALYSIS OF ELECTRICAL AND OPTICAL WAVE-MOTION, Harry Bateman. Written by one of this century's most distinguished mathematical physicists, this is a practical introduction to those developments of Maxwell's electromagnetic theory which are directly connected with the solution of the partial differential equation of wave motion. Methods of solving wave-equation, polar-cylindrical coordinates, diffraction, transformation of coordinates, homogeneous solutions, electromagnetic fields with moving singularities, etc. Index. 168pp. 5⅜ x 8. S14 Paperbound **$1.75**

PRINCIPLES OF PHYSICAL OPTICS, Ernst Mach. This classical examination of the propagation of light, color, polarization, etc. offers an historical and philosophical treatment that has never been surpassed for breadth and easy readability. Contents: Rectilinear propagation of light. Reflection, refraction. Early knowledge of vision. Dioptrics. Composition of light. Theory of color and dispersion. Periodicity. Theory of interference. Polarization. Mathematical representation of properties of light. Propagation of waves, etc. 279 illustrations, 10 portraits. Appendix. Indexes. 324pp. 5⅜ x 8. S178 Paperbound **$2.00**

THE THEORY OF OPTICS, Paul Drude. One of finest fundamental texts in physical optics, classic offers thorough coverage, complete mathematical treatment of basic ideas. Includes fullest treatment of application of thermodynamics to optics; sine law in formation of images, transparent crystals, magnetically active substances, velocity of light, apertures, effects depending upon them, polarization, optical instruments, etc. Introduction by A. A. Michelson. Index. 110 illus. 567pp. 5⅜ x 8. S532 Paperbound **$2.45**

ELECTRICAL THEORY ON THE GIORGI SYSTEM, P. Cornelius. A new clarification of the fundamental concepts of electricity and magnetism, advocating the convenient m.k.s. system of units that is steadily gaining followers in the sciences. Illustrating the use and effectiveness of his terminology with numerous applications to concrete technical problems, the author here expounds the famous Giorgi system of electrical physics. His lucid presentation and well-reasoned, cogent argument for the universal adoption of this system form one of the finest pieces of scientific exposition in recent years. 28 figures. Index. Conversion tables for translating earlier data into modern units. Translated from 3rd Dutch edition by L. J. Jolley. x + 187pp. 5½ x 8¾. S909 Clothbound **$6.00**

ELECTRIC WAVES: BEING RESEARCHES ON THE PROPAGATION OF ELECTRIC ACTION WITH FINITE VELOCITY THROUGH SPACE, Heinrich Hertz. This classic work brings together the original papers in which Hertz—Helmholtz's protegé and one of the most brilliant figures in 19th-century research—probed the existence of electromagnetic waves and showed experimentally that their velocity equalled that of light, research that helped lay the groundwork for the development of radio, television, telephone, telegraph, and other modern technological marvels. Unabridged republication of original edition. Authorized translation by D. E. Jones. Preface by Lord Kelvin. Index of names. 40 illustrations. xvii + 278pp. 5⅜ x 8½. S57 Paperbound **$1.75**

PIEZOELECTRICITY: AN INTRODUCTION TO THE THEORY AND APPLICATIONS OF ELECTRO-MECHANICAL PHENOMENA IN CRYSTALS, Walter G. Cady. This is the most complete and systematic coverage of this important field in print—now regarded as something of scientific classic. This republication, revised and corrected by Prof. Cady—one of the foremost contributors in this area—contains a sketch of recent progress and new material on Ferro-electrics. Time Standards, etc. The first 7 chapters deal with fundamental theory of crystal electricity. 5 important chapters cover basic concepts of piezoelectricity, including comparisons of various competing theories in the field. Also discussed: piezoelectric resonators (theory, methods of manufacture, influences of air-gaps, etc.); the piezo oscillator; the properties, history, and observations relating to Rochelle salt; ferroelectric crystals; miscellaneous applications of piezoelectricity; pyroelectricity; etc. "A great work," W. A. Wooster, NATURE. Revised (1963) and corrected edition. New preface by Prof. Cady. 2 Appendices. Indices. Illustrations. 62 tables. Bibliography. Problems. Total of 1 + 822pp. 5⅜ x 8½. S1094 Vol. I Paperbound **$2.50** S1095 Vol. II Paperbound **$2.50** Two volume set Paperbound **$5.00**

MAGNETISM AND VERY LOW TEMPERATURES, H. B. G. Casimir. A basic work in the literature of low temperature physics. Presents a concise survey of fundamental theoretical principles, and also points out promising lines of investigation. Contents: Classical Theory and Experimental Methods, Quantum Theory of Paramagnetism, Experiments on Adiabatic Demagnetization. Theoretical Discussion of Paramagnetism at Very Low Temperatures, Some Experimental Results, Relaxation Phenomena. Index. 89-item bibliography. ix + 95pp. 5⅜ x 8. S943 Paperbound **$1.25**

SELECTED PAPERS ON NEW TECHNIQUES FOR ENERGY CONVERSION: THERMOELECTRIC METHODS; THERMIONIC; PHOTOVOLTAIC AND ELECTRICAL EFFECTS; FUSION, Edited by Sumner N. Levine. Brings together in one volume the most important papers (1954-1961) in modern energy technology. Included among the 37 papers are general and qualitative descriptions of the field as a whole, indicating promising lines of research. Also: 15 papers on thermoelectric methods, 7 on thermionic, 5 on photovoltaic, 4 on electrochemical effect, and 2 on controlled fusion research. Among the contributors are: Joffe, Maria Telkes, Herold, Herring, Douglas, Jaumot, Post, Austin, Wilson, Pfann, Rappaport, Morehouse, Domenicali, Moss, Bowers, Harman, Von Doenhoef. Preface and introduction by the editor. Bibliographies. xxviii + 451pp. 6⅛ x 9¼. S37 Paperbound **$3.00**

SUPERFLUIDS: MACROSCOPIC THEORY OF SUPERCONDUCTIVITY, Vol. I, Fritz London. The major work by one of the founders and great theoreticians of modern quantum physics. Consolidates the researches that led to the present understanding of the nature of superconductivity. Prof. London here reveals that quantum mechanics is operative on the macroscopic plane as well as the submolecular level. Contents: Properties of Superconductors and Their Thermodynamical Correlation; Electrodynamics of the Pure Superconducting State; Relation between Current and Field; Measurements of the Penetration Depth; Non-Viscous Flow vs. Superconductivity; Micro-waves in Superconductors; Reality of the Domain Structure; and many other related topics. A new epilogue by M. J. Buckingham discusses developments in the field up to 1960. Corrected and expanded edition. An appreciation of the author's life and work by L. W. Nordheim. Biography by Edith London. Bibliography of his publications. 45 figures. 2 Indices. xviii + 173pp. 5⅝ x 8⅜. S44 Paperbound **$1.45**

SELECTED PAPERS ON PHYSICAL PROCESSES IN IONIZED PLASMAS, Edited by Donald H. Menzel, Director, Harvard College Observatory. 30 important papers relating to the study of highly ionized gases or plasmas selected by a foremost contributor in the field, with the assistance of Dr. L. H. Aller. The essays include 18 on the physical processes in gaseous nebulae, covering problems of radiation and radiative transfer, the Balmer decrement, electron temperatures, spectrophotometry, etc. 10 papers deal with the interpretation of nebular spectra, by Bohm, Van Vleck, Aller, Minkowski, etc. There is also a discussion of the intensities of "forbidden" spectral lines by George Shortley and a paper concerning the theory of hydrogenic spectra by Menzel and Pekeris. Other contributors: Goldberg, Hebb, Baker, Bowen, Ufford, Liller, etc. viii + 374pp. 6⅛ x 9¼. S60 Paperbound **$2.95**

THE ELECTROMAGNETIC FIELD, Max Mason & Warren Weaver. Used constantly by graduate engineers. Vector methods exclusively: detailed treatment of electrostatics, expansion methods, with tables converting any quantity into absolute electromagnetic, absolute electrostatic, practical units. Discrete charges, ponderable bodies, Maxwell field equations, etc. Introduction. Indexes. 416pp. 5⅜ x 8. S185 Paperbound **$2.00**

THEORY OF ELECTRONS AND ITS APPLICATION TO THE PHENOMENA OF LIGHT AND RADIANT HEAT, H. Lorentz. Lectures delivered at Columbia University by Nobel laureate Lorentz. Unabridged, they form a historical coverage of the theory of free electrons, motion, absorption of heat, Zeeman effect, propagation of light in molecular bodies, inverse Zeeman effect, optical phenomena in moving bodies, etc. 109 pages of notes explain the more advanced sections. Index. 9 figures. 352pp. 5⅜ x 8. S173 Paperbound **$1.85**

FUNDAMENTAL ELECTROMAGNETIC THEORY, Ronald P. King, Professor Applied Physics, Harvard University. Original and valuable introduction to electromagnetic theory and to circuit theory from the standpoint of electromagnetic theory. Contents: Mathematical Description of Matter—stationary and nonstationary states; Mathematical Description of Space and of Simple Media—Field Equations, Integral Forms of Field Equations, Electromagnetic Force, etc.; Transformation of Field and Force Equations; Electromagnetic Waves in Unbounded Regions; Skin Effect and Internal Impedance—in a solid cylindrical conductor, etc.; and Electrical Circuits—Analytical Foundations, Near-zone and quasi-near zone circuits, Balanced two-wire and four-wire transmission lines. Revised and enlarged version. New preface by the author. 5 appendices (Differential operators: Vector Formulas and Identities, etc.). Problems. Indexes. Bibliography. xvi + 580pp. 5⅜ x 8½. S1023 Paperbound **$2.75**

Hydrodynamics

A TREATISE ON HYDRODYNAMICS, A. B. Basset. Favorite text on hydrodynamics for 2 generations of physicists, hydrodynamical engineers, oceanographers, ship designers, etc. Clear enough for the beginning student, and thorough source for graduate students and engineers on the work of d'Alembert, Euler, Laplace, Lagrange, Poisson, Green, Clebsch, Stokes, Cauchy, Helmholtz, J. J. Thomson, Love, Hicks, Greenhill, Besant, Lamb, etc. Great amount of documentation on entire theory of classical hydrodynamics. Vol I: theory of motion of frictionless liquids, vortex, and cyclic irrotational motion, etc. 132 exercises. Bibliography. 3 Appendixes. xii + 264pp. Vol II: motion in viscous liquids, harmonic analysis, theory of tides, etc. 112 exercises, Bibliography. 4 Appendixes. xv + 328pp. Two volume set. 5⅜ x 8.
S724 Vol I Paperbound **$1.75**
S725 Vol II Paperbound **$1.75**
The set **$3.50**

HYDRODYNAMICS, Horace Lamb. Internationally famous complete coverage of standard reference work on dynamics of liquids & gases. Fundamental theorems, equations, methods, solutions, background, for classical hydrodynamics. Chapters include Equations of Motion, Integration of Equations in Special Gases, Irrotational Motion, Motion of Liquid in 2 Dimensions, Motion of Solids through Liquid-Dynamical Theory, Vortex Motion, Tidal Waves, Surface Waves, Waves of Expansion, Viscosity, Rotating Masses of liquids. Excellently planned, arranged; clear, lucid presentation. 6th enlarged, revised edition. Index. Over 900 footnotes, mostly bibliographical. 119 figures. xv + 738pp. 6⅛ x 9¼. S256 Paperbound **$3.75**

HYDRODYNAMICS, H. Dryden, F. Murnaghan, Harry Bateman. Published by the National Research Council in 1932 this enormous volume offers a complete coverage of classical hydrodynamics. Encyclopedic in quality. Partial contents: physics of fluids, motion, turbulent flow, compressible fluids, motion in 1, 2, 3 dimensions; viscous fluids rotating, laminar motion, resistance of motion through viscous fluid, eddy viscosity, hydraulic flow in channels of various shapes, discharge of gases, flow past obstacles, etc. Bibliography of over 2,900 items. Indexes. 23 figures. 634pp. 5⅜ x 8.   S303 Paperbound **$2.75**

Mechanics, dynamics, thermodynamics, elasticity

MECHANICS, J. P. Den Hartog. Already a classic among introductory texts, the M.I.T. professor's lively and discursive presentation is equally valuable as a beginner's text, an engineering student's refresher, or a practicing engineer's reference. Emphasis in this highly readable text is on illuminating fundamental principles and showing how they are embodied in a great number of real engineering and design problems: trusses, loaded cables, beams, jacks, hoists, etc. Provides advanced material on relative motion and gyroscopes not usual in introductory texts. "Very thoroughly recommended to all those anxious to improve their real understanding of the principles of mechanics." MECHANICAL WORLD. Index. List of equations. 334 problems, all with answers. Over 550 diagrams and drawings. ix + 462pp. 5⅜ x 8.
                                                                    S754 Paperbound **$2.00**

THEORETICAL MECHANICS: AN INTRODUCTION TO MATHEMATICAL PHYSICS, J. S. Ames, F. D. Murnaghan. A mathematically rigorous development of theoretical mechanics for the advanced student, with constant practical applications. Used in hundreds of advanced courses. An unusually thorough coverage of gyroscopic and baryscopic material, detailed analyses of the Coriolis acceleration, applications of Lagrange's equations, motion of the double pendulum, Hamilton-Jacobi partial differential equations, group velocity and dispersion, etc. Special relativity is also included. 159 problems. 44 figures. ix + 462pp. 5⅜ x 8.
                                                                    S461 Paperbound **$2.25**

THEORETICAL MECHANICS: STATICS AND THE DYNAMICS OF A PARTICLE, W. D. MacMillan. Used for over 3 decades as a self-contained and extremely comprehensive advanced undergraduate text in mathematical physics, physics, astronomy, and deeper foundations of engineering. Early sections require only a knowledge of geometry; later, a working knowledge of calculus. Hundreds of basic problems, including projectiles to the moon, escape velocity, harmonic motion, ballistics, falling bodies, transmission of power, stress and strain, elasticity, astronomical problems. 340 practice problems plus many fully worked out examples make it possible to test and extend principles developed in the text. 200 figures. xvii + 430pp. 5⅜ x 8.   S467 Paperbound **$2.00**

THEORETICAL MECHANICS: THE THEORY OF THE POTENTIAL, W. D. MacMillan. A comprehensive, well balanced presentation of potential theory, serving both as an introduction and a reference work with regard to specific problems, for physicists and mathematicians. No prior knowledge of integral relations is assumed, and all mathematical material is developed as it becomes necessary. Includes: Attraction of Finite Bodies; Newtonian Potential Function; Vector Fields, Green and Gauss Theorems; Attractions of Surfaces and Lines; Surface Distribution of Matter; Two-Layer Surfaces; Spherical Harmonics; Ellipsoidal Harmonics; etc. "The great number of particular cases . . . should make the book valuable to geophysicists and others actively engaged in practical applications of the potential theory," Review of Scientific Instruments. Index. Bibliography. xiii + 469pp. 5⅜ x 8.   S486 Paperbound **$2.50**

THEORETICAL MECHANICS: DYNAMICS OF RIGID BODIES, W. D. MacMillan. Theory of dynamics of a rigid body is developed, using both the geometrical and analytical methods of instruction. Begins with exposition of algebra of vectors, it goes through momentum principles, motion in space, use of differential equations and infinite series to solve more sophisticated dynamics problems. Partial contents: moments of inertia, systems of free particles, motion parallel to a fixed plane, rolling motion, method of periodic solutions, much more. 82 figs. 199 problems. Bibliography. Indexes. xii + 476pp. 5⅜ x 8.   S641 Paperbound **$2.50**

MATHEMATICAL FOUNDATIONS OF STATISTICAL MECHANICS, A. I. Khinchin. Offering a precise and rigorous formulation of problems, this book supplies a thorough and up-to-date exposition. It provides analytical tools needed to replace cumbersome concepts, and furnishes for the first time a logical step-by-step introduction to the subject. Partial contents: geometry & kinematics of the phase space, ergodic problem, reduction to theory of probability, application of central limit problem, ideal monatomic gas, foundation of thermo-dynamics, dispersion and distribution of sum functions. Key to notations. Index. viii + 179pp. 5⅜ x 8.
                                                                    S147 Paperbound **$1.50**

ELEMENTARY PRINCIPLES IN STATISTICAL MECHANICS, J. W. Gibbs. Last work of the great Yale mathematical physicist, still one of the most fundamental treatments available for advanced students and workers in the field. Covers the basic principle of conservation of probability of phase, theory of errors in the calculated phases of a system, the contributions of Clausius, Maxwell, Boltzmann, and Gibbs himself, and much more. Includes valuable comparison of statistical mechanics with thermodynamics: Carnot's cycle, mechanical definitions of entropy, etc. xvi + 208pp. 5⅜ x 8.   S707 Paperbound **$1.45**

Technological, historical

A DIDEROT PICTORIAL ENCYCLOPEDIA OF TRADES AND INDUSTRY, Manufacturing and the Technical Arts in Plates Selected from "L'Encyclopédie ou Dictionnaire Raisonné des Sciences, des Arts, et des Métiers" of Denis Diderot. Edited with text by C. Gillispie. This first modern selection of plates from the high point of 18th century French engraving is a storehouse of valuable technological information to the historian of arts and science. Over 2000 illustrations on 485 full-page plates, most of them original size, show the trades and industries of a fascinating era in such great detail that the processes and shops might very well be reconstructed from them. The plates teem with life, with men, women, and children performing all of the thousands of operations necessary to the trades before and during the early stages of the industrial revolution. Plates are in sequence, and show general operations, closeups of difficult operations, and details of complex machinery. Such important and interesting trades and industries are illustrated as sowing, harvesting, bee-keeping, cheesemaking, operating windmills, milling flour, charcoal burning, tobacco processing, indigo, fishing, arts of war, salt extraction, mining, smelting, casting iron, steel, extracting mercury, zinc, sulphur, copper, etc., slating, tinning, silverplating, gilding, making gunpowder, cannons, bells, shoeing horses, tanning, papermaking, printing, dyeing, and more than 40 other categories. Professor Gillispie, of Princeton, supplies a full commentary on all the plates, identifying operations, tools, processes, etc. This material, presented in a lively and lucid fashion, is of great interest to the reader interested in history of science and technology. Heavy library cloth. 920pp. 9 x 12. T421 Two volume set **$18.50**

CHARLES BABBAGE AND HIS CALCULATING ENGINES, edited by P. Morrison and E. Morrison. Babbage, leading 19th century pioneer in mathematical machines and herald of modern operational research, was the true father of Harvard's relay computer Mark I. His Difference Engine and Analytical Engine were the first machines in the field. This volume contains a valuable introduction on his life and work; major excerpts from his autobiography, revealing his eccentric and unusual personality; and extensive selections from "Babbage's Calculating Engines," a compilation of hard-to-find journal articles by Babbage, the Countess of Lovelace, L. F. Menabrea, and Dionysius Lardner. 8 illustrations, Appendix of miscellaneous papers. Index. Bibliography. xxxviii + 400pp. 5⅜ x 8. T12 Paperbound **$2.00**

HISTORY OF HYDRAULICS, Hunter Rouse and Simon Ince. First history of hydraulics and hydrodynamics available in English. Presented in readable, non-mathematical form, the text is made especially easy to follow by the many supplementary photographs, diagrams, drawings, etc. Covers the great discoveries and developments from Archimedes and Galileo to modern giants— von Mises, Prandtl, von Karman, etc. Interesting browsing for the specialist; excellent introduction for teachers and students. Discusses such milestones as the two-piston pump of Ctesibius, the aqueducts of Frontius, the anticipations of da Vinci, Stevin and the first book on hydrodynamics, experimental hydraulics of the 18th century, the 19th-century expansion of practical hydraulics and classical and applied hydrodynamics, the rise of fluid mechanics in our time, etc. 200 illustrations. Bibliographies. Index. xii + 270pp. 5¾ x 8. S1131 Paperbound **$2.00**

BRIDGES AND THEIR BUILDERS, David Steinman and Sara Ruth Watson. Engineers, historians, everyone who has ever been fascinated by great spans will find this book an endless source of information and interest. Dr. Steinman, recipient of the Louis Levy medal, was one of the great bridge architects and engineers of all time, and his analysis of the great bridges of history is both authoritative and easily followed. Greek and Roman bridges, medieval bridges, Oriental bridges, modern works such as the Brooklyn Bridge and the Golden Gate Bridge, and many others are described in terms of history, constructional principles, artistry, and function. All in all this book is the most comprehensive and accurate semipopular history of bridges in print in English. New, greatly revised, enlarged edition. 23 photographs, 26 line drawings. Index. xvii + 401pp. 5⅜ x 8. T431 Paperbound **$2.00**

Prices subject to change without notice.

Dover publishes books on art, music, philosophy, literature, languages, history, social sciences, psychology, handcrafts, orientalia, puzzles and entertainments, chess, pets and gardens, books explaining science, intermediate and higher mathematics, mathematical physics, engineering, biological sciences, earth sciences, classics of science, etc. Write to:

Dept. catrr.
Dover Publications, Inc.
180 Varick Street, N.Y. 14, N.Y.